# THE PSYC
# OF SEX

BY

OSWALD SCHWARZ

'One must suffer the laws of things,
not only observe them'

PENGUIN BOOKS

Penguin Books Ltd, Harmondsworth, Middlesex

U.S.A.: Penguin Books Inc., 3300 Clipper Mill Road, Baltimore 11, Md

CANADA: Penguin Books (Canada) Ltd, 178 Norseman Street,
Toronto 18, Ontario

AUSTRALIA: Penguin Books Pty Ltd, 762 Whitehorse Road,
Mitcham, Victoria

—

First published 1949

Reprinted 1951, 1953, 1955, 1956

Made and printed in Great Britain
by Richard Clay & Company, Ltd,
Bungay, Suffolk

IN MEMORIAM

# ALFRED HOWARD EVANS

# CONTENTS



p263 Marriage of the Professional Woman

# FOREWORD

THIS book is written by a medical man, and this fact is responsible for the substance and form of it. There is first of all the method of approach: I have tried to show that the divers sexual activities are successive stages of a continuous development. This is the legitimate way in which not only medicine but the general science of life tries to understand this part of Nature. Secondly, medical science, in particular, has enormously contributed to our knowledge of the functioning of the human body and mind by proving that the abnormal is just a modification of the normal and by discovering the hitherto unknown norm through a careful analysis of the abnormal. The story goes that the ancient Roman patricians made their slaves completely drunk once a year and then taught their adolescent sons the virtue of self-control by making them witness this repulsive spectacle. This indirect method of research we doctors employ in hospital wards and laboratories every day.

In hardly any field has this method yielded more or better results than in that of our knowledge of sex. However careful, direct observation of sexual behaviour could never produce such an intimate and detailed knowledge of all the motives which build up a certain sexual action as does the dissection of abnormal behaviour both in individuals and groups. Besides, no one would submit himself to the laborious and often painful process of psychoanalysis were it not for the hope of being cured in the process.

In this way we have achieved a result infinitely bigger than any special knowledge of sexual behaviour or the cure of any individual case. It has been revealed that the nature of sex, the forms of sexual activities, and the problems of sexual relationship are the same all over the world, and have been the same as far back as history records them. However great the variety of sexual rites and customs among different peoples, love has always and everywhere lifted people up to heaven or driven them to their doom; incest has always been looked upon with the greatest horror; marriage, always the intended end, has been endangered by illicit love and shielded by prostitution; men and women have always endeavoured to free propagation from chance by using contraceptives. There is no sexual perversion now known which has not been the curse of sex life throughout the ages. The struggle between the younger and the older generation for independence, and competition between brothers, have been commemorated in the oldest documents. Compared with these basic facts of life, modes of sexual relationship within the family or community, such as blind obedience to parents, acceptance by wives of the superiority of men, views on pre-marital intercourse or divorce, etc., issue from a rather superficial stratum of our personality. These conventional relationships are regulated by custom and sanctioned by religion, but beneath them dwell and work the immutable arch-instincts which bind men to women or tear them from each other, and these structural elements of man's mind are just as permanent and ubiquitous as those of the physical anatomy.

So too are the conflicts arising from the dualism of human existence and the ensuing fallibility of man. By this term, used here without any theological connotations, I mean that it is given only to the select to attain a perfect balance of body and mind. As a rule, the spirit is willing and the flesh is weak, but when the position is reversed the consequences are just as unfortunate. Customs and other external means may mitigate this original weakness to a certain extent: education in a convent, social taboos, the walls of a harem, or the seclusion of purdah may reduce the risks, protect the body, and cover the face – but the soul and heart of those women remain defenceless if the danger becomes real. Oriental wives, obedient to the laws of their country, may bow submissively to the traditional rights of their husbands, but many of them have always secretly revolted against and frigidly withdrawn from this infringement of their individuality, however pale this concept may be in Eastern thought. On the other hand, in the East and West alike many husbands have responded with impotence to the real or imagined superiority of their wives. And the conflict between mother-in-law and daughter-in-law, so much ridiculed in our comic papers, is, even in traditional China, often concealed only by a thin veneer of a kind of ancestor-worship.

In short, wide medical experience provides ample evidence that the same emotional conflicts produce exactly the same troubles in the sex life of men and women, whatever the colour of their skin or the latitude of their domicile. And if ethnologists dispute these views, it will be up to them to explain how it is that the psychological theories and therapeutic methods discovered by Freud through observations on middle-class people in Vienna can have the same healing effect on patients all over the world.

On these grounds one must feel justified in claiming universal validity for the fundamental tenets of sex psychology as we know them at present. They cut right across all limitations of time and space, racial differences and social stratifications: the perennial psychology.

Finally, the medical standpoint from which this book is written determines its attitude towards its findings. Natural science is content to present facts. Theologians and moral philosophers sift and interpret these facts according to the basic principles and standards of the theology or philosophy they have chosen. Conventional morality disregards facts, or forces them wilfully into the Procrustean bed of prejudice and arbitrary codes of conduct. But medical science respects and honours the genuine rights of facts. It accepts as the desirable aim the state towards which the laws of development point. Physicians are not the masters of Life but its guardians and trustees. *We do not look at civilization, of which morality is only an aspect, as the adversary of Nature, but as Nature raised to the spiritual level.* Therefore, we never state what ought to be, but only what is meant to be or to become, and are confident that nothing that is truly natural can be really immoral. It is my firm belief that *there can be no discord between the four elements of man's life, Religion, Morality, Aesthetics, and Science* – if only uncompromising dogmatism gives way to consideration of essential principles. This thesis, in fact, will be the main theme of this book.

Lastly, a word of warning. Man's life consists of a great number of biological or mental functions tightly interwoven and correlated with many institutions and organizations that make often conflicting demands for supremacy. These organizations and institutions impose their will upon the individual through laws, conventions and religions, ethical and moral codes, through the formulations of science, and the prevailing aesthetic preferences. Each of these institutions makes an imperious and exclusive demand, and man's life is the battle-ground on which they struggle for their supremacy. The complexity of our life arises from the fact that whatever we do takes place simultaneously in all these divers spheres of existence. We must eat, for instance, but as soon as we try to get food we find ourselves caught in the meshes of an economic system, and as only the moon belongs to everybody, we must make money to buy food; here the law steps in, and even when we keep within its confines we find that our efforts to earn money are hampered by special regulations and restrictions imposed by social conventions, professional organizations, or moral and even aesthetic considerations, as some people find making money a 'dirty business'.

Over no part of our life is this struggle of institutions for supremacy fiercer than in the realm of sex. As the sexual is the strongest of all instincts, each of these authorities wants to assert its exclusive rights over it and tries to harness this powerful urge for its own purposes. If a man loves a girl religious doctrines step in their way, moral codes insist on being respected, social consequences must be considered; if they want to live together, legal conditions must be obeyed, sometimes racial and other prejudices must be overcome, and all too often economic factors pile insurmountable obstacles in their path. This state of affairs has led to the deplorable, although inevitable, consequence that any view held, or any statement made about sexual problems is bound to provoke the opposition of the partisans of every school of thought or group of people holding views that conflict with those expressed. There are always pyres lighted, courts assembled, prison doors open, deportation orders ready, to punish the offender. The last two centuries have seen the rapid ascension of science as a claimant to the role of supreme arbiter in all human affairs. But in recent years an ever-growing number of scientists have realized that this pretence and arrogance of science is as unjustified and untenable as were in earlier times the similar claims of the Church. The development of modern medicine, to which psychology has contributed a great deal, proves a strong incentive to such a more conciliatory and comprehending attitude. This is partly because medicine is not a pure science, but is only based on science, and partly because doctors, and particularly psychologists, know too much about the misery brought upon men by one-sidedness and intolerance to want to support it. Hence, it is the main purpose of this book to describe the facts about our sex life which medical experience has so far safely established, and which must form the solid basis - although, as I said above, not the whole material - for any argument, friendly or adverse, about sex problems.

On the other hand, every inquiry into human affairs contains, admittedly in varying degrees, an autobiographical element: the questions a student asks and the answers he receives depend, more than many people are ready to admit, on the personality of the inquirer. This is essentially due to the nature of the subject matter, as Pascal says: 'One writes things which one can only prove by asking the reader to ponder over them himself.' Similarly one often says things which one can only discover by listening-in to oneself. The same applies to the moral aspect of the problem: austerity of view is always suspect of aridity of feeling and scarcity of experience.

## CHAPTER 1

# THE MEANING OF SEX

SEXUAL contact is a form of human association like family ties, friendship, business relationships, membership of a club or political party, or any kind of teamwork; but three characteristics distinguish the sexual relationship from all others, and make it unique. First, in all other relationships the partners remain separate individuals, linked together only by common interest or activity – e.g. a scientific problem, making money, or defending one's country – but the sexual relationship completely transforms the individuality of the man and the woman, welding the 'I' and the 'Thou' into a new entity, the 'We'. Secondly, sexuality embraces all three modes of human existence – Spirit, Mind, and Body – integrating them into one function. And thirdly, the sexual association in its mature and perfect form, which is marriage, is meant to be enduring.

Although the discussion of these three component parts of sexuality will constitute the theme of this book, it will be necessary before going further to discuss the second in some detail in order to make clear the principle which will underlie our whole argument.

The *sexual impulse* is an instinct like hunger and thirst. It is dependent on the proper functioning of the sexual glands, the testicles and ovaries. The function of every instinct is to satisfy a particular need of the organism. Hunger, for example, causes us to supply a certain amount of nutrition which the organism needs at a given time. What need, then, does the sexual instinct satisfy? Postponing the answer for a time, let us first remember that, besides hunger, we know in connexion with the intake of food another sensation, called appetite. Appetite is stimulated by the sight of attractive food, irrespective of its nutritive value or of our need of energy. Our sexual appetite, i.e. our susceptibility to sexual stimuli, has the magic capacity of transforming the world around us in an amazing way, and sometimes with terrific power. About the attractiveness of the body of the opposite sex not much need be said. But even the most indifferent objects can be transformed into stimuli of the greatest sexual value if they are in some way connected with, or reminiscent of, the man or woman we love. A piece of paper, for instance, on which he has written a few words of love, a ribbon she has worn – to the man or woman in love these are full of significance and can become powerful sexual stimuli, whereas to the indifferent eye such things have nothing more than their surface value. Incidentally, this miraculous juggling with values in a state of hormonal intoxication occurs also in the biological sphere: viewed objectively, there is hardly anything uglier than the male genital organ, but for a woman or a homosexual man it possesses an attraction cutting right through all aesthetic prejudices.

What, then, is the purpose of the sexual impulse? Cynics may quickly answer: It is the relief of the peculiar tension one feels in a state of sexual excitement, and the pleasure accompanying it. It is a fact that the satisfaction of several of our bodily needs is usually felt as a relief and is accompanied by a pleasurable sensation. The more dependent on our will the function is, the keener this sensation. There is no such pleasure associated with the activities of our heart or intestines, because they function entirely automatically. Breathing, which is partly a deliberate function, gives a certain amount of pleasure on some occasions – for example, when inhaling deeply the cool morning air. Defaecation, a largely voluntary act, has for some people a certain very definite pleasure distinctly different from the purely physical relief. Small children, for instance, often retain their stool deliberately in order to enjoy all the more this additional pleasure component of evacuation. As the sexual function is entirely a voluntary act and not vital for the maintenance of the individual existence, sexual pleasure is the greatest. Must be, said an otherwise great philosopher of the early nineteenth century, because it is the 'cunning of Nature' to lure men into the burdensome task of continuing the human race. And Freud had the same idea when he called the sexual and other similar pleasures a 'premium' for doing a job. But such theories are, if anything, part of a philosophy of Nature and therefore beyond the realm of science.

Before we continue, a very strange fact may be mentioned in passing. It has been said that civilization came into existence at the moment when a hunter, for the first time, refrained from devouring his prey on the spot, but took it home to cook it, thus postponing the immediate pleasure of stilling his hunger. But during the development of civilization this divorcing of pleasure from need has become almost a characteristic feature of civilization, to the extent that all too often we do things merely for pleasure, disregarding their intrinsic values and purposes. We eat too much, irrespective of the nutritive value of the food. We drink and sleep far more than we need. We have learnt to divorce satisfaction from need, and to create artificial needs in order to enjoy their satisfaction. Similarly, sexual enjoyment has become an end in itself.

What need does the sexual instinct reveal and help to satisfy? That it has something to do with propagation is obvious. It is only the way in which this happens that is problematic, for no psychological analysis has ever revealed a conscious or subconscious impulse to propagate, whether on biological, religious, tribal, or patriotic grounds, and it is most unlikely that even Frenchmen went to bed with their wives resolved to procure some more grenadiers for l'Empereur.

Biology comes to our aid. It is a well-proved biological law that every organ of our body wants to function, to do its job, and if it is prevented from doing it, trouble arises. A large part of a woman's body is organized for gestation, and if a woman is denied this fulfilment of her physical and mental organization she withers. But in motherhood she acquires a new, a spiritual beauty, which by far outshines any damage her body may have suffered – so long as she is a real mother and has for her partner a real man who perceives this transfiguration. Every doctor knows some cases, admittedly exceptional, that strikingly demonstrate how inseparably sexual enjoyment is still linked up with the biological function. Thus I remember a woman who had a full orgasm only twice in her life – on the two occasions when she conceived her children; on all the many other occasions intercourse was a meaningless and therefore joyless affair. Another woman, who had been very satisfactorily married for several years, became completely frigid when she learnt that she could not have children owing to the lack of spermatozoa in her husband's semen.

This is the purpose, at any rate on the biological level, which the sexual instinct serves. If someone argues that this is a very selfish task, he should remember two facts. Firstly, that we can serve a purpose bigger than ourselves if, and only if, we have fulfilled ourselves. And secondly, that there is no such thing as a trans-subjective or altruistic instinct. It is useless to point to the herd instinct, because a human community is totally different from a herd, or to mention altruistic motives for impulsive actions carried out on the spur of the moment, such as jumping after a child in danger of drowning. These forms of behaviour are far more complex than instinctive responses. If an instinct for propagation exists, which is more than doubtful, it could arise only if an individual felt himself completely as part of a species. Such an attitude would belong to a different mode of existence entirely beyond the distinction of egotism or altruism.

There is in men no equivalent to the maternal instinct, because men do not need children for their physical or personal completeness. One cannot overrate the profound symbolical significance of the fact that the woman carries her sexual organs inside her body, whereas the man's are only an appendage to his anatomy. To the man, a child is not essential for his biological perfection, but is important for him in the social sphere. A man wants a child as an heir to his name or business; he often hopes his child will fulfil his ambitions more successfully than he himself was able to do. For these purposes he brings up the child which his wife has borne, and the product of her body becomes an achievement of his mind.

Again on comparatively rare occasions we may discover a peculiar kind of instinct in men, which for want of a better name one could term 'impregnation lust'. Sensitive men sometimes report a faint but unmistakable dissatisfaction on the occasion of an otherwise perfect cohabitation when circumstances have denied them an impregnation of their wives. What they miss is the satisfaction of their desire for the greatest possible fusion with their partners: for the penetration of the semen into all the ramifications of the female genital provides the deepest possible spatial permeation and the ensuing pregnancy seems to be an extension in time of the transitory union of the sexual act.

Just a few words about contraceptives. We are not concerned

here with the question whether the use of contraceptives is impermissible on religious grounds, whether it is an economic necessity, or advisable for health reasons. We are interested only in the way it affects sexual life. The question has been answered already for the small number of women for whom sexual gratification – and that means sexual life itself – is inseparably linked with impregnation. Apart from these exceptions it can be said that in principle the use of contraceptives introduces a considerable element of ethics into our sexual life. It raises a biological function to the level of a human deed. In other words, an unprotected coitus may or may not lead to impregnation, depending in any given case on anatomical and chemical conditions. This leaves the creation of a new human being to chance; a most depressing thought, and a definitely immoral action. By using contraceptives, and dispensing with them only when a child is honestly desired, we replace a haphazard happening by a resolve of our free will. This need not necessarily be planned in cold blood, but may be the expression of a climax of passionate affection – and this means lending dignity to the greatest moment of our lives.

So much for the sexual instinct. The second component part of sexuality, the emotional, is commonly called *love*. Although ordinary men think they know all about this noble emotion, professional men are not so certain. We shall have a good deal to say about these uncertainties in a later chapter, but here it will suffice to sketch the relationship between sexual instinct and love.

There is an ancient Greek myth which describes the real nature of love better than anyone has been able to do since. Originally, so the story goes, the earth was populated by beings half-man, half-woman. Swollen with pride in their completeness – *hybris* is the untranslatable Greek word for it – they rebelled against the gods, until the irate Zeus split each of them in half and scattered the halves over the earth. Ever since, each half has been searching for its other half, and this yearning for completion is what we call love. There is a later, more 'modern' version of the same theme: the Greek god Hermes and the goddess Aphrodite had a son Hermaphroditos. The nymph of the well at Salamis, in love with the beautiful youth, prayed to the gods to be eternally united with him. Thus, the bodies of the boy and the girl were welded into one, but the characteristics of both sexes were preserved. Hence individuals who under pathological conditions possess in addition to their own some sexual characteristics of the other sex are called hermaphrodites.

The word 'relationship' means that two different things have to do with one another but are not of the same kind. The sexual impulse belongs to the biological, love to the personal, sphere of our existence, a difference which, fundamental as it is, is still far from being generally recognized. Unfortunately progress in this respect is still being held up by the fact that two men who knew most about sexuality – Havelock Ellis and Sigmund Freud – held that love can develop from, and revert to, the sexual impulse. In strict contradiction to this theory, it must be pointed out that the sexual impulse satisfies a need of the individual, and is therefore restricted to the individual who feels it, whereas love carries us away from ourselves, over to another being. The urge of the instinct disappears with its satisfaction, whereas the longing of love, knowing no satisfaction, creates a lasting bond. For love is not a static condition; it is an ever-renewed activity, but an activity which is an end in itself and does not strive after, or come to rest through, possessing the other partner. The satisfaction of the physical urge is sharply contrasted with the everlasting yearning of love. A purely physical coitus is almost inevitably followed by exhaustion and the difference or tedium of satiation, whereas lovers awake from their ecstasy refreshed, new-born, looking at each other full of wonderment, as if they had not known each other before. And they have not, really. The sexual impulse is blind: the Male unites with the Female, that is to say, any woman would do for any man, and any man for any woman. It is a process clouded in anonymity. But love makes men see. It opens our eyes to the very being, the intrinsic personal values, of the beloved, and in the sexual act we have deeply probed into the mystery of another soul. Adam 'knew' Eve. Traditional psychology calls love an emotion. No doubt there is a strong emotional element in it, but essentially love is a cognitive act, indeed the only way to grasp the innermost core of personality. The purely physical act tires and exhausts, but physical union born of love enriches and invigorates, and the creative act on the physical plane conditions spiritual creativeness. 'In every creative thought live again thousands of forgotten nights of love, and fill it with majesty and greatness.' (R. M. Rilke.) Christopher Caudwell says almost exactly the same: 'Sexual love ... [is] enriched by all the complex history of emotion and experience shared in common by a thousand generations.' (*Illusion and Reality*.)

Although totally different in nature, sexual impulse and love are dependent on, and complementary to, each other. *In a perfect, fully mature human being only this inseparable fusion of sexual impulse and love exists.* This is the fundamental principle of any psychology of sex. If there be anyone capable of experiencing the purely physical gratification of sex he is thereby stigmatized as sexually subnormal (immature or otherwise). Whether, on the other hand, a purely 'spiritual' love exists – 'Platonic' love is a misnomer – is open to question, although I for one firmly believe it does. By this, I mean that it is possible for a man to fall in love with the spirit of a woman – not with a spirit, accidentally as it were, incarnate in a female body, but the sublime way a woman interprets reality through the medium of her womanhood; in other words, loving her perfect way of being a woman. Dante's love for Beatrice may have been of this kind, whereas the loves of the troubadours strike me as rather emasculate and affected.

Apart from this one rare exception, the above thesis, of the complexity of our sexuality and particularly of the non-existence of a purely physical sexual urge in a fully grown-up man or woman, stands unqualified.

If further proofs were needed, sexual pathology could supply ample evidence. The most common sexual trouble with men is failure to have an erection. This has nothing whatever to do with physical abnormality of the sexual apparatus, but is always due to the fact that subconscious complexes are inhibiting the normal function of the sexual organs. This fact explains why an integrated adult man, to whom this union of body and mind is a living experience, must, by virtue of his knowledge of perfection, inevitably fail if he allows himself to be tempted into a loveless intercourse, a mere gesture devoid of any emotional meaning. For sexuality is the only function which cannot lie; in sexual matters we are forced to be honest, occasionally even against ourselves. And against appearance too. I remember among my patients men who fought in the forlornness of the jungle, and men who fought high up in the loneliness of the skies – and failed hopelessly in bed. In their heart of hearts they were afraid, in spite of their great military exploits. They were no 'men' in the true sense of the word, and their sexual failures gave them away; *this is the essential morality of sex.*

*The spiritual element.* From time immemorial we find sexuality always closely connected with morality. Positivists explain that the purpose of these taboos was to protect society and particularly marriage, and religious sanctions were invoked in order to strengthen the efficiency of these controls. That is certainly one aspect of the problem, but hardly the most important one. Besides this morality which has changed with the changing conventions in the course of history, there exists an essential, intrinsic sexual morality. It issues from the nature of sexuality itself and demonstrates once more the exceptional position of the sexual impulse among all the other impulses in human life. Civilization can be defined as a state in which the 'natural' impulses are somehow kept under control, sometimes to the extent of mutilation. This applies to the instincts of self-preservation, such as hunger, aggression, etc. The sexual instinct, on the other hand, i.e. the blind urge of the male to copulate with the female, is not domesticated by control or mutilation, but it is amalgamated with the emotional and spiritual element and thus incorporated into the whole of human personality. Human 'nature' is Nature permeated by spirit. Human sexuality is not a mere happening, it is a deed for which we are responsible, and if we meekly submit to the physical impulse, we incur guilt. Because it fails the essentially spiritual nature of man, a purely physical intercourse is essentially immoral. Unbridled sexual urge always indicates abnormality. We meet it in three types: the immature, the insane, and the criminal.

There are three ways in which the 'higher', i.e. the psychological-spiritual factors, regulate the instinct. Firstly, conscious control by reason. It works only on a particular occasion, and never for long; we speak in such cases of 'suppression'. If such a control is subconscious and permanent, we call it 'repression' and everybody knows nowadays that this is the cause of a widespread pathological condition called neurosis.

By far the most important is the third form. The most amazing phenomenon in man's sexual life is voluntary celibacy and chastity as practised for instance by Roman Catholic clergy, or by men and women devoted to a supra individual task. Now, whatever may cause this strange state, one thing is certain beyond the slightest shadow of doubt, that it is the result neither of suppression nor of repression. For no one could suppress a live sexual instinct all his life, and to ascribe their chastity to repression and declare these men and women to be simply neurotic is an absurd arrogance of incompetent psychologists. Freud has subsumed this and similar phenomena under the concept of 'sublimation', by which he means that the sexual impulse is transformed into 'higher' mental activities, such as charity, love of art, interest in science, and the like. Freud holds that culture is nothing more than a wholesale sublimation of sex. This concept is a typical product of the materialistic psychology of the eighties, and no psychologist outside the ranks of the Freudian school continues to believe in the existence of such a psychological alchemy. It is not more possible to transform sex into spirit than to change base metals into gold.[1]

This concept of sublimation is based on the equally erroneous concept of sex 'energy'. The term energy is borrowed from physics, where it is legitimately used because the existence of physical energies can be demonstrated and they can be measured. Neither is the case with the so-called sex energy; no one has seen it, no one has measured it, no one can prove that it exists: the whole thing is no more than a figment invented for the sole purpose of supporting untenable theories. It would not be worth while mentioning this theoretical argument if this misconception had not led to most deplorable practical consequences. Thus, for instance, it is still believed, and not only by laymen, that masturbation 'uses up an enormous amount of energy' and that 'it is the misuse of this energy which leads to fatigue and a general feeling of dissatisfaction'. Contrary to this opinion, overwhelming practical experience

1. On the history of the idea of 'sublimation' cf. Kenneth Walker's *Physiology of Sex* (Pelican Books, 1945 ed.), ch. 6, p. 77.

has proved that men after many years of regular masturbation are in full possession of their sexual capacities when they have sufficiently grown up to use them for proper sexual relations.

Equally arbitrary but still more harmful are statements, occasionally made in books on sex education, that 'sex energy possesses the power of being transferred into other channels not directly concerned with sex without losing any strength'; or, 'There is no need for sex energy to be expressed actively ... celibacy and marriage should be regarded as parallel states leading to the same ultimate spiritual development'. Nothing can be further from the truth: a life without sexuality is from any point of view a defective life, however great the achievements of such a person may be in any field of human activities. Such achievements are attained in spite of but certainly not through celibacy, at least within the sphere of common life which we ordinary people lead. And this is still more true of women than of men. By remaining celibate a man gives up some of the fullness of life, but a woman sacrifices an essential part of herself. This is how even the great ones feel. Evangeline Booth, General of the Salvation Army, when 81 years old, speaking of her youth, is reported as saying: 'But my only real love wanted me to give up the Army. So we parted. I have been devoted to millions of hearts instead of to one. I am not sorry, but I do remember.'[1] No one, I think, can fail to sense the force of the struggle still reverberating in the remembering heart.

If we refrain from specious explanations, and confine ourselves to the facts that can be ascertained, we must say that just the reverse process takes place: not because sex is denied its moral outlet does it turn into spirit – as an escape in disguise, as it were – but because a man is wholly filled with religious faith and fervour the sexual urge vanishes. Accepting this view, the story of the temptations of St Anthony appears to belittle his saintliness somewhat, and if a medieval monk in his solitary cell had to cast out the temptations of the flesh through all sorts of physical discomforts, he simply proved that he was not, or not as yet, one of the elect.

Even we, the ordinary rank and file of humanity, experience the same mysterious process on many occasions. No one, for

1. *Reader's Digest*, September 1947.

instance, 'can' give up smoking, however strong his 'willpower', if, and as long as, he doubts the implacable necessity of doing so; but the desire to smoke vanishes at once and spontaneously as soon as he fully realizes he ought to give it up, and really accepts the inevitable. Or, if a doctor finds himself in the privacy of his consulting-room *vis-à-vis* an attractive young woman, his absorption in his work and his professional decency protect him – at any rate under normal conditions – against any temptation, by producing a complete insensitiveness to the alluring qualities of his patient. But if he meets the same woman at a party, when all these controls are removed, things may take quite a different turn.

This last example permits us to formulate the basic structure of our sexuality; love is the driving and directing force, the sexual impulse is the executive organ, and the spiritual element is the controlling power. *The presence, direction, and intensity of the sexual drive are at any given moment the resultant of physical impetus and spiritual control*; purely physical drive on the one hand, and complete asexuality on the other, are the two extremes between which innumerable combinations of these two factors are possible.

*

No doubt many people will raise many objections to many of the above statements. Everybody knows a friend, or the friend of a friend, whose sexual behaviour defies more than one of these principles and the conclusions drawn from them, and will point out that this person is able to perform intercourse whenever, and with any woman, he likes; he scoffs at love and treats things spiritual as outmoded superstitions. There are several answers to this, and, in this case at least, the multiplicity of answers is no proof that none of them is really conclusive.

First of all, it presupposes a great intimacy to get reliable information about the intricacies of a person's sexual life. Secondly, it requires a fair amount of professional knowledge to make proper use of these confessions and observations. But by far the most important answer is the third one, which is based on a theory of human existence: it must be remembered, and never be forgotten, that all the above statements apply only to men and women at the height of their development as persons, fully matured and imbued with the essential morality as previously defined. I call such an individual an '*authentic*' or '*exemplary existence*'.[1] Many fall short of this standard. There are those who develop slowly, and reach maturity comparatively late or, still worse, never at all: they dwell all their lives in the lowlands of promiscuity. But even the many, normal according to medical standards, reach different degrees of 'exemplariness' owing to the different measure of substance, fibre, value in their personality. This has nothing to do with social status, erudition, or sophistication; it springs from the core of humanness, irrespective of the more or less accidental qualities, the glamorous façade which surrounds and often enough obscures the core. More than once I have been surprised, almost startled, when during a professional conversation a very ordinary man, completely unaware of what he was saying, made a philosophical remark or psychological comment very similar to conclusions philosophers and psychologists have arrived at as the result of much laborious thinking. Such observations seem to confirm a theory recently propounded, that science cannot discover anything really new, but only elaborates, with its refined methods of technique, thoughts which are age-old possessions of mankind. The most challenging theories of Freud, for instance, can be found anticipated in old Jewish writings, or in Plato's dialogues, or as the famous Oedipus complex in Greek tragedies. This must by no means minimize Freud's merits, as it was only his discoveries that made us understand the often hidden meanings of these passages. It looks as if there were only a limited number of basic ideas

1. The term 'existence', or 'existential', is used in this book in the traditional sense in which philosophy has used it since the Schoolmen introduced the distinction between essence and existence; it was revived by Kierkegaard and systematically explored by Heidegger and Jaspers. The term denotes the pure being from which our factual life derives. It is difficult to explain in brief, but will be quite clear by its practical use during our analysis. (It must be mentioned that the meaning of the word 'existence' in English usage is the very opposite of its philosophical meaning, inasmuch as it denotes a merely fleeting rudimentary form of 'life'.) On the other hand, it goes without saying that it has nothing whatever to do with the current craze of a modern French literary group calling themselves, God only knows why, 'Existentialists'. The best introduction to the difficult subject is William Barret, *What is Existentialism?* (Partisan Review Series, No. 2, New York, 1947).

which men have thought since they started thinking, and that only the forms in which these are expressed have changed – from myths, prophecies, epics, to scientific doctrines.

To these 'real' men and women comes the perfect sexuality as their natural way of being. To the lower orders of this hierarchy belong the above-mentioned objectors, their friends, and the friends of their friends.

Or, to show this problem from another angle. Our physical sexuality is, so to speak, nothing in its own right, but only a means for expressing our mind, as does blushing, laughing, sweating, or crying. We cannot cry or sweat or blush at will in the absence of the adequate emotions. This is not strictly true of laughter, for a laugh can be forced; but the artificiality and insincerity of such a manufactured laugh is quite unmistakable. The closest analogy to the sexual function is speaking. We have the capacity to speak in order to express ourselves, our thoughts, emotions, intentions, etc. A normal man speaks only if he has something to say, but there are many people who, although they have nothing to say, talk because they like hearing themselves speak, or want to impress other people, or for some other inessential reason. Similarly, to have indiscriminate sexual intercourse is to make the gesture of expressing an emotional relationship when there is none to be expressed: a kind of sexual loquacity. And to be a chatterbox or a busybody is by no means a faculty to be desired, still less to be envied.

One may now ask: But is it of any use to develop doctrines and to turn them into postulates which apply only to the few? It is. But the attempt to prove it confronts us with the most difficult problem of a real science of human existence: the problem of the *Norm.* What are the standards which enable us to pronounce human behaviour normal?

Most of the confusion that obscures the concept of the norm is due to insufficient realization of the fact that there is not only one meaning of this concept, but one for each group of objects to which it is applied. The best-known type of norm is the statistical or norm of the average. If one measures the heights of a sufficient number of men of a given population, or the intelligence of a given group of children, one can say that the statistical average of height or intelligence represents the norm of height or intelligence in these groups, and a man or a child who conforms to this average is normal. On the other hand, the fact that almost everybody has one or several decayed teeth cannot possibly lead to the conclusion that having decayed teeth is normal, for the biological concept of norm is different from the statistical. An organ or an organism is biologically normal when it is fully adapted to its function. But if we now turn to gauging human behaviour, where values and particularly moral values are involved, neither the statistical nor the biological concept of norm is adequate. We cannot be content that people *usually* tell the truth, or that *most* marriages don't break up, or that *many* people go to church on Sundays, but we must insist that it is 'normal' to stick to the truth under any circumstances, to keep one's marriage intact and to remember one's moral code on week-days also. In other words, *the standard for the personal norm, as it is called, is perfection.*[1] And this would hold good even if only one single man lived up to this standard, and although statistics show that in our society, such as it is, not only is the flesh very weak, but the spirit no less.

There is nowadays a tendency among progressive educators, parents as well as teachers, to treat sexual matters in a 'perfectly natural manner'. By 'natural' they mean dealing with sexual subjects not only without embarrassment, if possible, but in the same way as every other school subject, as a solid piece of information which can, and should, be given to every child. And biology has been chosen as the best way of approaching this thorny problem.

Unfortunately this whole design rests on two fallacies. The first one concerns the biological approach. Phrases like 'with animals' or 'in the realm of animals' make no sense whatever, because the variety of sex behaviour amongst animals is as great as the variety of their behaviour in other respects. There are animal couples that die when separated from each other, whereas the female spider kills the male after copulation; some females sacrifice their lives for their young, others devour their offspring immediately after birth; some males part from the females immediately after mating, others stay on for a time,

1. The same idea is expressed in Pascal's words: 'Man can only be properly understood if one looks down on him from the standpoint of God or the Superman.'

others even for good, and others keep a sort of harem. In other words, for any kind of human sex behaviour analogies could be found 'among animals'. But still more important, the sexual institutions – if one may call them so – of the animals bear no resemblance to, much less are identical with, similar institutions among men: the harem of a pasha is no barnyard, a matriarchal tribe is no beehive, a family is no herd, and marriage is more than mating. At the root of these comparisons slumbers the idea that man is an animal plus 'something', whatever that may be. Thus if a man behaves in a manner unworthy of men, we like to say that the animal in him has come to the fore. This is psychologically incorrect, as well as unfair to animals. Animals are not defective men, but every species is perfect in itself. If a man loses or discards the additional 'something' that makes him human he does not become a perfect animal, but remains always an imperfect man.

The sexual activities of all animals are automatically regulated, being strictly confined to the periods of heat. Thereby a proper alternation of feeding and propagating, collecting and spending strength, is guaranteed. With man, such controls no longer exist. In their stead we get the spirit, and with it the freedom of decision over ourselves. If a man divests himself of this freedom, he surrenders himself to the uncontrolled and uncontrollable sexual impulses and becomes lower than an animal.

This comparing or contrasting of men with animals is the wrong way to find out what is 'natural' for men, and recourse to the *Origin of Species* does not lead to the discovery of the Origin of Morals.

The exploding of the second fallacy is all the more important as it helps us to discover another essential characteristic of human sexuality. To introduce children to the 'facts of life' by making them watch animals in their sexual activities, and by explaining to them what the animals are doing, is an error of judgement. By no stretch of imagination is it possible for a child to apply these strange activities or truly horrifying events to his own parents; and the suggestion that he himself was once such a mess of blood and flesh as new-born puppies and calves are all too often does lasting harm to the child's attitude to sex in later years. It is a strange and not sufficiently acknowledged fact that it is impossible – or at any rate extremely difficult – even for a grown-up to visualize his parents as young people, let alone as lovers. A beneficial limitation of our imagination covers and protects these facts, and our sex life cannot be treated in a 'perfectly natural manner', because it is more than a purely 'natural' phenomenon. For human sexuality is shrouded in mystery. By this I do not mean the hypocritical pseudo-morality with which sex has occasionally been treated in the past, but the essential mystery which surrounds our origin: the mystery of origin, companion to the mystery of death, the Unknown from whence we came, and the Unknown to which we go.

And the man and the woman experience the same mystery of creation in every single sexual act: Consciousness ceases, Time stands still, and the two sink into the unfathomable depths of Space – it is a moment of pure Being for the two, and the origin of new life.

Now at last we are sufficiently prepared to answer the question: 'What is the meaning of Sex?' We cannot do it better than in the words of Berdyaev, who writes in his book *The Destiny of Man*: 'The meaning and the purpose of the union between man and woman is to be found not in continuation of the species or in its social import, but in personality, in its striving for the completeness and fullness of life and in its longing for eternity'.

## CHAPTER 2

# SEXUALITY IN THE CHILD

In two books – *Interpretation of Dreams* (1901) and *Three Contributions to the Theory of Sex* (1905) – which have since become landmarks in the development of psychology, Freud contended that, contrary to the commonly held belief, our sex life does not begin with puberty but actually starts very early in childhood. This startling thesis was bitterly opposed by psychologists of all creeds and denominations, until child psychology proper took up the challenge and by a large number of observations and experiments confirmed Freud's findings in principle and in many details. It is controversial whether one is justified in terming these experiences and practices of the child 'sexual', but this is largely a matter of definition. The fact remains that small children experience emotions akin to what grown-ups experience in a state of sexual excitement; some of these childish emotions and practices appear to be component parts which in the course of development gradually build up the mature sexuality.

People trained not only in nursing but also in observing infants know that boys and girls alike *masturbate*, but the significance of these activities is not always the same: the large majority of these children simply manipulate their genitals in a purely playful manner, in much the same way as they play with their fingers and toes. But there is another, much smaller group, comprising boys and girls, in which these manipulations mean much more. Boys by playing with their penis, girls by rocking movements, get themselves into a peculiar state: the body becomes limp, the face flushed, the eyes are glassy. The child is deeply absorbed and cannot be diverted from its action. The process reaches a climax, after which the child relaxes and sinks into a deep sleep: all these are symptoms of true masturbation. Large-scale observations have proved that this kind of masturbation occurs only in infants who feel neglected and unhappy, or cannot sufficiently occupy themselves through lack of toys and nursing personnel, and that they give up this practice spontaneously as soon as these needs are filled. No one who has ever watched such a child could feel the slightest doubt that it passes through a very strong sensual experience which, if perhaps not identical with, is certainly equivalent to, sexual lust and gratification. And the purpose of it? Obviously to comfort the child in a joyless reality and to remove it into a more pleasant world of imagination. This, by the way, is also the function of masturbation at any age: to be a substitute. As will be explained in the next chapter, this function may be twofold: if the real thing is still beyond the reach of the individual such a substitute is legitimate, and masturbation must be considered as a normal sexual action, as e.g. during puberty and early adolescence. In all other circumstances it is definitely abnormal, as it is then a means of escape: an infant properly looked after need not, and does not, masturbate, and a grown-up must not masturbate because it is, or should be, in his power to do the real thing.

Between the second and fourth year children show a peculiar *tenderness* towards persons of their environment: passionate devotion, loving consideration, chivalry, possessiveness, and jealousy are the features of this early love, because love it is that these children feel. They are not very fastidious in the choice of the objects of their affection, which embraces boys and girls alike. This indifference to the sex of the partner is all the more noteworthy because in other associations, e.g. in the selection of playmates, sexual differences play an important part. This fact alone would prove that this affection is of an entirely non-sensuous nature. This early love is just as unreasonable, and the motives given for it are just as arbitrary, as at any other time later in life. A four-and-a-half-year-old boy was very much 'in love' with Mary, the cook of the family; suddenly he switched his affection to Rosie, the parlourmaid from next door, and to his mother's teasing question: 'Don't you like Mary any more?' he cried: 'No, Rosie is much fatter!' [1]

The important conclusion which these facts suggest is that the sensuous and the emotional elements of our mature sexuality

1. This, and all other facts of the child's development quoted in this book, are taken from Charlotte Buehler's researches in the Institute of Child Psychology at Vienna.

(i.e. physical sexuality and erotic) start quite independently of each other early in life. They go on developing along separate lines until the end of puberty, then they converge and are in late adolescence merged into the unity of mature sexuality. It is now fairly generally accepted that perversions are products of a retarded development, and the theses expounded above and in the previous chapter, about the relationship between emotions and sex, were admirably demonstrated by what a patient with slight sadistic tendencies discovered within himself: he has tender, but inadequately sensuous feelings towards his partner and quite separate sadistic tendencies. The tenderness has no dynamic force, and the sadistic drive lacks the personal aim – any woman would do as its object. If 'something' (sc. the pure driving-force) could be taken out of the sadistic (i.e. sexual) drive and fused with the tenderness, his difficulties would be over.

Compared with these two essential elements, a few more acquisitions during the growing period are of a more accidental nature. But they too help to build up the sexuality of the adult. Here should be mentioned first of all the *obscene and the sensational.* Otherwise well-behaved children in their fifth year start to use dirty language, mainly concerned with the anus and its function. It would be too simple to explain this only by the pleasure of doing things which are forbidden. Most children by this time have already developed feelings of shame and disgust, so that the real anal function is felt as repulsive, and it is only in imagination that it acquires a peculiar attraction. The whole behaviour of these children bears out that much more is happening than just being naughty: the shining eyes, general excitement, over-loud laughing, uncontrolled temper – all this shows that they are enjoying a very special lust: obscenity and indecency. Speaking generally, the pleasure in obscenity lies in debasing something valuable or decent, and it is the revolt against values, not artificially enforced but spontaneously accepted, which the children enjoy. If hypocrisy is said to be 'the homage which vice pays to virtue', then one could equally well say that obscenity presupposes a genuine appreciation of decency. Nothing whatever two lovers do is obscene, but the most 'normal' sexual activity is if it is done for the purely sensuous enjoyment. Nor is a nude body obscene, but a half-undressed one is, and still more so the process of denuding – a fact from which every strip-tease dancer profits. And these children enjoy the same pleasure by stripping, as it were, the anus of its proper function.

At the same age children show another strange trait: *cruelty*. Cruelty is a prerogative of man; no animal is cruel. Cruelty does not consist in exercising power or doing harm, but in enjoying it, and such a reflective attitude is wholly beyond the mental capacity of any animal, but characteristic of man. This cruelty in children is entirely confined to the imagination, and often the object of these imagined orgies is dearly loved in real life – such as a baby brother or a pet animal. Furthermore, it seems open to question whether what these children experience is real cruelty or whether it is only the sensational element in the imagined scenes, the dramatic situation, the heroic attitude. For example, four children aged five were indulging in sinister designs as to what they were going to do with their cat. 'We'll put him on the rails so that he gets run over.' – 'We'll gouge his eyes out – no, we'll take a drill and bore them out.' – 'We'll put a brick in his brain and one in his heart – oh, we are so tough!' At the moment when the excitement reached its climax, the cat actually appeared, and the children immediately tried to outdo each other in caressing, stroking, and fondling the animal.

After the acquisition of the two essential and some accidental component parts, the first phase of our sexual development comes to an end, and the whole sexual interest recedes into the background for a few years (period of latency, according to Freud) because the development of some other parts of the personality now takes up all the biological strength and attention of the child.

## CHAPTER 3

# ON PUBERTY

It is generally held that puberty and the awakening of sexuality in the commonly used sense of this word are synonymous. This is incorrect. Puberty is the most important and most dramatic phase of the development of our whole personality, and of all the many changes which the body and mind of the child undergo at this time the sexual change is only a part – admittedly the most conspicuous and alarming, but a part all the same.

In our climate, physical puberty lasts with boys from 14 to 16, with girls from 13 to 15, whereas the psychological development starts earlier (10 to 12) and lasts till 19 to 22. One usually subdivides this period into puberty proper (approximately up to the age of 17) and adolescence. Psychologically, this division is justified by the complete reversal of the children's attitudes towards themselves and the world that marks the transition from the first phase to the second: in puberty this attitude is negative, whereas the adolescent opens up towards life with emphatic joy.

Man's life can be divided into three phases: childhood, maturity, and old age. Between these phases two periods of transition are interposed: puberty and climacteric. (The change of life is a typical phenomenon with women. It has an equivalent in men as well, although its nature and meaning are totally different.) Both are periods of farewell: in puberty we bid farewell to childhood and the quiet protected existence in the parental home; the climacteric, particularly for women, is a parting with the fullness of life and a turning towards the quietude of old age. But whereas a woman who can look back on a harmonious and satisfactory life bids the farewell with composed dignity and reaps the mellow beauty of a sunny autumn, puberty is always a most stormy, essentially disruptive phase. It is safe to say that an uncomfortable climacteric, full of all sorts of physical and mental symptoms, is definitely pathological, but a turbulent puberty bodes well for the emerging personality of the child.

Like the surviving primitive people of our times, the ancient peoples, Jews, Babylonians, Arabs, Mexicans, and others, understood well the meaning of puberty. For them it was not a private affair of the child, or a partly interesting, partly tiresome stage of development. It was, as Frazer said, 'the central mystery of primitive society'. The child left the house of women and became a member of the community of men. A powerful arch-instinct puts puberty beside birth and death, being death and rebirth in one, and considers the beginning of maturation the decisive event in life. The severity and cruelty of the rites of initiation had the purpose of bringing the boy out of himself and leading him through trance and ecstasy into his new existence.

What actually happens during these crucial years is: First, the discovery of the Ego and an objective world beyond it, and an attempt to bring these two together by means of a philosophy of life and a design for living. This implies still another great discovery: the awareness of Time. Being a child is a static way of living, but from puberty onwards life starts to move forward in time. Planning involves and evolves a concept of the future, and the future is actually the first dimension of time which a child discovers, whereas only in contrast to the future does everything else appear to have happened in the 'Past'. This is confirmed by the fact that at this age children start writing diaries. This means they dissociate themselves from their past life and look at it in an objective way – with a 'historical sense'. The discovery of the 'Present', not as a hypothetical point where future and past meet, not only as a grammatical tense, or as a tiresome something which bars the impatient from a splendid future, but as the only time in which we really live, is a prerogative of maturity.

The third, perhaps the most important, discovery is the idea of a supermaterial world, the realm of spiritual ideas and values: the real ethical sphere. 'True' no longer means 'that which is real', as the boy thought at the age of ten; 'right' is not merely that which serves a purpose; 'honour' is no longer the outcome of strength and vigour, but Truth, Right, Honour, etc., are now conceived as objective ideas, completely devoid of any materialistic sense and practical application. Just as ten years ago the child suddenly felt in himself an echo to the demand imposed upon him by his work, and responded to the call by developing the concept of 'duty', so now the adolescent hears the call of these values and responds by developing the higher equivalent of duty: moral responsibility.

I said that the pubescent discovers himself, the World and Time and Values, but in fact he does not discover them; rather, he comes 'aware' of these elements of our existence which have always been there in his life. But now they become meaningful, not only parts of his being but objects of his attention and action. Each time a human being reaches this stage the old story is re-enacted: man parts with the innocence of the paradise of childhood, and his eyes are opened, and he will be like the gods, knowing good and evil. And true enough, this exuberant sense of godlike omniscience and almightiness is the main feature of the adolescent – and makes him so trying to live with.

Although this approach towards the world takes place on the whole front of our personality, sex plays the part of a spearhead: the discovery of the world as no longer a mere surrounding but as something related to me, of which I am an essential part, is concentrated in and effected by the discovery of the Thou and its intimate and essential relatedness to the I; by the realization *that there can be no I in its completeness without a Thou.* Prior to this time, the other was just another I like myself, a playmate: now the other is being perceived as someone radically different, someone I need, and who needs me. This is the service sexuality renders, its contribution to our maturation: the sexual partner is the radical different, and at the same time the indispensable complement; the discovery of the supreme value of this personality opens up our sense of spiritual values; and the union with the one person tears us out of the solitariness of the I into ever larger unions: the We, family, society, mankind. And the physical sexual act is only the manifest part of this universal merging.

The conquest of the last component part, of Time, the transformation of the transient sexual act into the finality of real togetherness, takes approximately another decade. When this has been achieved, the adolescent has become a man and is ripe for marriage.

## CHAPTER 4

# SEXUALITY OF THE PUBESCENT

### (*a*) MASTURBATION

MASTURBATION is probably the most frequent, certainly the most maligned, sexual activity. From tiredness, loss of memory, impotence, right up to paralysis and insanity, besides all degrees of moral depravity runs the inventory of all the ills attributed to masturbation, and many a boy, misguided by these erroneous ideas, fears in despair that every time he could not refrain from masturbation has driven another nail into his coffin. Contrary to these misconceptions, it cannot be emphasized enough that *masturbation never causes any physical or mental harm, either temporary or lasting.*

The misfortunes of masturbation started when it was given a name. 'Masturbation' is a technical term, whereas in most languages the word used in ordinary parlance is 'onanism'. This name is derived from Onan, son of Judah and Bathshua, of whom it is said 'he used to spill the seed on the ground'. This action was interpreted as masturbation, whereas the context makes it quite clear that it was *coitus interruptus.*[1] No more justified is the term 'auto-eroticism', because it covers only an early, immature form of masturbation.

Primarily masturbation is a means of relief from a purely physical sexual urge. This form of masturbation can also be found among animals, mainly dogs and horses, but also among elephants and monkeys in captivity. It is also frequently practised by adults when circumstances prevent them from normal sexual contact, as in prisons, on long voyages, etc.

In a second group, masturbation serves as an instrument for relieving any kind of non-sexual tension. It includes the masturbation by infants, which, as we have seen, relieves the unpleasantness of loneliness. Some people masturbate because

1. Genesis xxxviii: '... he used to spill the seed on the ground, whenever he went into his brother's widow, in order to avoid producing a child of his brother's.' This terminological error was first made by Tissot (1760).

they cannot go to sleep, trying to relieve the restlessness and mental tension which keep them awake through the genital relaxation. I say genital and not sexual because the process is completely non-sexual, the orgasm is dull and without any pleasurable sensation, and the whole thing is felt as a tedious although necessary affair. I knew a student of philosophy who occasionally found himself so hopelessly entangled in the intricacies of a philosophical argument that he could not resist the urge to masturbate, which loosened the intolerable mental tension, although, of course, it did not solve the philosophical problems. During a written examination schoolboys sometimes waste the best part of the allotted time, and having deliberately worked themselves up into a state of frenzy, they relieve this tension by masturbating and then quickly finish their work. Not only children, but a good many grown-ups, reward themselves for some work well done or comfort themselves for some bad luck by the cheap pleasure of masturbation. Thus we see that the most varied emotions, such as pride, anxiety, joy, oppression, etc., may find bodily relief in masturbation as a ready vent. This is undesirable because children should learn as early as possible to put up with stress and strain, and relieve them only in natural ways. But it is not masturbation that is unnatural and harmful, it is that the whole character is wrong when the child takes advantage of this evasion. The most charming and instructive experience of this kind that I ever learnt of was not in my professional capacity: a friend told me that at the age of six he saw in a film the slow-motion picture of an unfolding flower – which caused in him an erection. It could at this age only have been the enjoyment of beauty, of which the child was quite aware, that led to the genital reaction. Many years later the grown-up man repeatedly had the same experience. But now he realized the sexual character of both processes, the botanical and the physiological. The 'abandonment and relaxation' of the unfolding flower translated itself into visions of a voluptuously abandoned woman.

From the time of puberty onwards, when the sexual urge becomes increasingly imperative, the genital function gets ever more closely linked up with and monopolized by sexuality proper, and reaches its own stage of perfection. The endogenous physical urge provokes mental images of a sexual nature which in turn lead to masturbation. Only from this stage onwards is masturbation a real, although rudimentary, sexual act. These mental images are either just visions of women or scenes in which the man may actively participate or only watch them as a spectator. The scenes may be repetitions of past experiences or of adventures seen on the films or read about in novels; the leading heroines are women the boy knows, or women far beyond his reach. In short, these imaginary adventures comprise the possible and the impossible, and it constitutes the main benefit derived from masturbation that there are no limits to the wildest excesses of imagined orgies. One small detail is worth mentioning: young boys never draw into these imaginings girls they are fond of in real life; for they feel that this would mean polluting the chastity of their just-awakening feelings. The real reason is that the fusion of sexuality and emotionality has not yet been achieved, and the objects of their love have not yet become sexual stimuli.

It is obvious that these scenes, thanks to the unrestricted omnipotence of imagination, reveal the innermost tendencies and desires of people. For instance, a boy, aged 15, used to imagine himself dressed in scarlet evening dress, with a long whip in each hand, standing in the centre of a circus ring; several women were running round the circle, obediently moving and turning to the cracking of the whip. Then he masturbated, and went fully satisfied to sleep. What, then, was satisfied, and what produced the tension relieved in the act of masturbation? It was the sense of awakening manliness, in a sexual as well as in a more general meaning, which at this age appropriately manifests itself by seeking power – incidentally a mentality which many a man never outgrows in his life. A student 22 years old dreams that he takes part in a swimming competition; he is last, his mother scolds him harshly and kisses another more successful boy; the dreamer feels violently jealous, and wakes up; he immediately starts masturbating, and, continuing the dream as it were, he thinks: 'Perhaps I shall still become a great man, a great physician, a great hero.' Another example of the same kind: A student, aged 21, remembers how happy he was when he first noticed signs of growing up: a few hairs on his body, erections, etc. It occurred to him that he might accelerate this development through physical exercises. Through the use of his muscles, but mainly through the thought of 'getting on', he had a new, most pleasant, sensuous experience, which one day caused an emission. Soon afterwards he discovered that he could provoke the same sensation by rubbing his penis on the bedsheets, and practised masturbation as 'another kind of physical training'. At the age of 14, during these practices, suddenly images of some of his particularly strong and handsome schoolfellows appeared: he tried to identify himself with these boys, full of admiration for their strong bodies and envy of their achievement. From 15 onwards visions of girls sporadically appeared in his masturbation imaginings, and from 17 onwards the images of boys had completely disappeared. It would be a great error to take these images as indications of a homosexual inclination, because these boys were not partners with whom the boy did something, but ideals with which he identified himself. And this feeling of pride and beauty was the cause of his sexual excitement.

Often all kinds of perverted trends come up in these imaginings and are relieved in masturbation; trends that would never be indulged in real life. In such cases the function of masturbation as a safety-valve becomes quite manifest. And it becomes equally obvious that these people must keep on masturbating all their lives unless psychological treatment relieves them from their obsessions.

Occasionally a man reports that he has a seemingly perfectly normal sexual intercourse with his wife, but cannot resist masturbating shortly, almost immediately afterwards. An analysis reveals that the cohabitation was, so to speak, no more than a kind gesture towards his partner, devoid of desire, excitement, and satisfaction. The real sexual object of such a man is a woman other than his wife, or a man, or a kind of perverse activity: somehow physically stirred up by the just-performed coitus, he conjures up his more congenial images, which cause proper sexual excitement and lead to an adequate genital relief.

These men are fairly honest compared with another type, who roll these two parts of their sexual personality into one, and cheat their partners shamelessly. Such a man, or woman for that matter, indulges during the coitus in his private imaginings, steals in this way his, or her, sexual gratification and degrades what seems to be a coitus to a mere masturbation. Surprisingly many marriages maintain their sordid existence by means of these practices.

Thus prepared, we may now ask how to define masturbation, or what the real idea or essence of masturbation is. Certain it is that to describe it as self-satisfaction misses the point completely, or applies only to those relatively few cases in which masturbation consists only in a purely mechanical genital relief. But in all the other cases a human being makes an imaginary contact with another human being. For this reason masturbation is a real, however abortive, form of sexuality. True, it is only imaginary partnership, and therefore masturbation takes its place half-way between the autosexuality of the child and the heterosexuality of the grown-up. The technical term 'masturbation' is derived from the Latin word 'manus' which means 'hand', probably because the most frequently used method of producing the orgasm is rubbing the genitals with one hand. But it is commonly known that any other means of producing the necessary friction would do as well; among others, also the vagina of a woman, as in the above-mentioned cases of a sham cohabitation. A reliable indication that what seems to be a cohabitation is in reality only masturbation is provided by some sexual rituals, as it were, or conditions, on which some people insist: if, e.g. a husband insists on having the lights turned off, or if too much active participation from his wife disturbs him, if she must not talk or sigh – then it is obvious that all this interferes with his imagination by reminding him unpleasantly of the presence of a real partner and her claims on his attention, and it becomes clear that this man is just masturbating. On the other hand, just as not all that looks like a cohabitation need be one, not all that is technically masturbation need be so essentially: we know by now that not the action but only the intention decides upon the nature of an activity, sexual or otherwise. Hence, if a man and woman strive after a union of their minds and hearts, no matter what they do to effect contact of their bodies also, it is not masturbation, however much it may technically resemble it.

Considering all these divers experiences, one could arrive at a definition of masturbation: masturbation is a sexual activity in which the contact with the person from whom we derive the sexual stimulus exists only in our imagination; the kind of sexual activity in which the contact is effected is immaterial. But this living in an imaginary world instead of the real one stigmatizes *masturbation as the sexuality of the solitary*. This solitariness is an essential feature of youth and consequently masturbation is at this age 'normal', because for biological, psychological, and sociological reasons a youth is not yet in a position to have proper sexual relations. Large-scale statistics covering tens of thousands of men have shown that 85 per cent of all men admitted to having masturbated at some time in their youth. This does not 'prove' that masturbation is normal, because statistical frequency proves nothing in personal matters, but these figures are only a welcome confirmation of the results of the above analysis. If a young man does not overcome this psychic isolation in later years he will not overcome masturbation either. In these cases masturbation is an indication and result of a retarded development, and therefore abnormal. Not a few men never find the way to the other sex, and remain overgrown adolescents all their lives.[1]

All this applies in principle to both sexes. But in some details the development of girls is different from that of boys. We know very little indeed about the frequency of masturbation among girls. The evidence suggests that it appears much less often, and is by no means a regular occurrence. The main difference is that with boys the sexual urge awakes spontaneously together with the beginnings of the function of the testicles. Not so with girls: the woman's sexuality remains dormant until it is awakened by a man. Not by any man, but by the right one, and many a woman grows up, becomes the mother of children, and still remains a Sleeping Beauty. A normal girl whose physical urge has not been brutally stirred up need not and does not masturbate at any time in her life. Masturbation with women is always abnormal. This is not a

1. A special study concerning the age at which masturbation begins gave the following results:

| Age: | under 10 | 10–11 | 12–13 | 14–15 | 16–17 | 18–19 | over 19 |
|---|---|---|---|---|---|---|---|
| Percentage of cases: | 4·3 | 5·1 | 22·5 | **42·0** | 16·7 | 7·2 | 2·2 |

(These figures hold accurately for Central European conditions only.)

pious postulate, but a fact; women say they are not interested in it, it means nothing to them, they truly dislike the idea – because women are on the whole more conscious than men of the real meaning of sex and the significance of any sort of sexual activity, and do not content themselves easily with substitutes.

How complex the symbolism of masturbation can be, and how thoroughly the whole personality expresses itself in this symbolic act, may be illustrated by two examples. A young woman, a novelist, masturbated when she found her work too difficult: she felt masturbation 'as a symbol for failure and sterility of mind and body'. Her sense of inferiority in other respects made her feel during masturbation: 'I am man and woman in one, I can satisfy myself and need no help from the world outside.' And her conflict with her husband, whom she almost despised because of his lack of manliness, found also some relief in masturbation: 'I don't need him.' It was resignation, defiance, and solace that this woman experienced through masturbation, and thus she solved her three main problems in life – in her imagination. For almost the same reasons another woman, who may well be taken as representative of a whole group, could not masturbate at all. She was a very energetic, professionally successful, self-reliant person who for very obvious reasons tried to emphasize her femininity in other respects. She chose sexuality as the proper field for this demonstration and overdid the passivity during intercourse to the extent of complete, ostentatious self-abandonment. Even the activity, however slight, which masturbation requires, seemed abhorrent to her, because it did not fit in with her scheme.

Finally a few words about the attitude an educator versed in psychology should adopt towards masturbation. If someone objects to masturbation or to any other sexual activity on religious or moral grounds, no argument is possible, because no scientist has the right to interfere with anyone's belief or principles. Science states only the facts as they are, and must leave it to the discretion of the individual to take them for his benefit, or leave them at his peril. In the case of masturbation, the situation is comparatively simple: masturbation, as we have seen, changes its character according to the age at which it is practised; during infancy it is abnormal, during puberty it is normal, and it becomes abnormal again after this period. In infancy it can be easily prevented or stopped; with adults it is in almost all cases a neurotic symptom and requires a psychological treatment; and only during puberty may it present an educational problem. But as masturbation does not harm, there is no need to interfere with it forcibly; one may just voice a word of warning against excesses – more to the comfort of one's own conscience than for the benefit of the boy. Nor is abstinence harmful, if, but only if, it is practised on the boy's own volition and not as a result of threats and ensuing subconscious repressions. In these latter cases the absence of masturbation is already the first symptom of a long history of sexual troubles in later life.

### (*b*) Homosexuality of Youth

Masturbation bridges the gulf between the autoeroticism of the child and the heterosexuality of the grown-up, by way of introducing an imaginary partner; it is a normal step in our sexual development and independent of environmental influences, for which reason practically every normal boy masturbates more or less during a certain period of his life.

The homosexuality of youth, the only form of homosexuality with which we are dealing here, is another step in this development, but it is always definitely abnormal, to a very large extent induced by the environment, and therefore practised by only a very small number of boys.

It consists, at any rate in its fully developed form, in mutual masturbation. In some cases these activities are a relief of a genuine physical urge which can no longer be satisfied by solitary masturbation but needs a kind of live partner. In other cases an emotional attachment which tends towards physical manifestation is the prime incentive. Thus in several respects this kind of homosexuality bears some resemblance to grown-up sexuality; it can, from the purely developmental point of view, be considered as a step towards it, but, as I said before, an unnecessary and therefore an abnormal one. In order to understand its nature it must be distinguished from friendship on the one hand and from homosexuality proper on the other.

It is more than friendship, and from homosexuality proper it borrows only the gesture.

*Friendship*, like any other human attitude towards the world, passes through some well-defined stages of development until it reaches its final character. Friendship among children is hardly more than a rather loosely knit grouping of playmates and not before puberty does real friendship develop. Its core is a longing for completion, for support, for a helper in the distress and anxious loneliness in which the growing child finds itself during the difficult period of puberty. The friend is someone we can trust, confide in, someone who understands. The purpose of these friendships is to bring about the consolidation of the personality of each of the two. Characteristically, one is always the more active, the other the more passive partner, one is the leader, the other the led; the younger looks up to the older one, and the older protects his younger friend. The friendship of grown-up men unites equals, the relationship of subordination changes into co-operation, and working together for a common purpose constitutes the unifying factor.

The second element of the emotional life of the pubescent is *erotic*. Since Plato made this concept the centre of his whole philosophy, many times through the ages attempts have been made to define this phenomenon, which is as intangible, elusive, indescribable, as all real emotional arch-phenomena are. Delight in the beauty, charm, strength of the body is at the root of eroticism; but it is not the body as such, not its material beauty but the beauty of a soul expressed in the loveliness of the body. This is the true meaning of the much-misused term 'Platonic love'. It is not a pale, emaciated sentiment, but the vigorous desire to express the spiritual-emotional experience in bodily contact as well. Nearest to it comes what we call 'tenderness'. *Tenderness*, too, wants physical manifestation, such as touching, stroking, embracing, kissing. And what can already be seen from these activities, and can be conclusively proved psychologically, is that these erotic-tender relationships are essentially different from sexual ones. Later on they become a constituent part of mature sexuality, they lie at the bottom of sensuality and stand at its beginning and its end, from the moment a woman puts her arm round the neck of her friend until the lovers fall asleep in each other's arms.

All these three elements, friendship, eroticism, and sensuality, contribute to the mature sexuality; from friendship comes the 'standing-up' for one another, from eroticism the tenderness, and from sensuality springs sexuality proper.

Now, this erotic tenderness forms the core of adolescent homosexuality. In practice we meet with different forms of homosexual relationships according to the different motives that lead to them. Just as we did with masturbation, we find here a primitive form established for the relief of a purely physical urge – mutual masturbation in the strict sense of the term. In a second group we find, again in perfect analogy to what we have learned in the case of masturbation, that originally non-sexual sensations are relieved through genital functions. With homosexuality this sensation is what I should call the 'tension of subordination'. There are analogies to be found in the sexual activities of animals. With male rats, for example, the weaker rat takes on the part of the female; tired cockchafers are treated as females by stronger males; birds of different species but of the same sex, kept in the same cage, copulate in a homosexual manner: in other words, all kinds of differences (physical superiority, racial difference) can be experienced in these cases as 'sexual' differences. In the case of adolescent homosexuality the same tension of subordination is operative, inasmuch as one of the partners is the older or stronger one, the leader, the master. In a third group erotic tenderness is the motive for homosexual activities.[1]

So far so good. But there is still the urgent and intriguing question, what causes a boy to turn his tender affection to another boy, instead of to a girl, as the vast majority of 'normal' boys do. In the first place it must be admitted that some external factors support this choice, such as boarding-school education and all sorts of youth clubs; the Wandervogel movement in pre-Hitler Germany, for instance, was in this respect a worthy forerunner of the Hitler Youth. If during these critical years boys find themselves practically cut off

1. This love, in the truest sense Platonic, can also be experienced by grown-up men towards adolescents without losing its emotional delicacy. Such an experience on the part of an ageing man is described in Thomas Mann's classic novel *Death in Venice* (Penguin Books, 1955) and in Fr Rolfe's *The Desire and Pursuit of the Whole*, one of the most fragrant and delicate love stories ever written.

from the company of girls, it is understandable that their often violently awakening emotions turn to the only sort of objects they can get hold of: other boys. But it is obvious that this seclusion is only a supporting and by no means the real causal factor. The true reason must be looked for elsewhere. It lies, as in all cases of sexual difficulty and aberration, not in the sexual sphere itself but in an abnormality of the whole personality of the boy. Its roots are in that abnormality of which it is but one manifestation. In order to make this quite clear we must once more revert to developmental psychology. Our life is from the beginning a continuous breaking-up of existing contacts and entering into new ones. The new-born leaves the body of his mother and after the umbilical cord has been cut he starts a semi-independent existence; semi-independent only because he still gets his food from his mother's breast. When this bodily link too is severed, the child still lives in the orbit of his mother, often enough tied to her by her notorious apron-strings. When more children arrive he enters into their group, and it is only too well known how difficult it is for many a first-born to be demoted from his unique position to being just one among many. The first real break comes when the child leaves home and goes to school, which means entering the 'world'. Brothers and sisters are separate individuals, but still of the same flesh and blood, but schoolmates are real strangers, although here again strangeness is still mitigated by their being creatures of the same sex. But when after the end of puberty the boy is expected to turn to girls, he finds himself facing utter strangeness, an individual with whom he has nothing in common, but in whom he may dimly sense an unknown danger. To take this final step needs self-reliance, determination, and courage, and some hesitate on the brink. Instead of taking the ditch in one leap, they cautiously step on to a stepping-stone in the midst of the water and take a rest: the stepping-stone is the partner of the same sex, and the rest is adolescent homosexuality. In other words, this kind of homosexuality is the result of timidity, a manifestation of the celebrated inferiority complex, and therefore is abnormal.

Occasionally one comes across a different variety or higher degree of the same trouble: a boy wants to be a girl and, if this desire is strong enough, adopts a female mentality which may lead to all sorts of absurdities in later life, such as homosexuality, dressing as a woman (transvestism), or even the wish to be transformed into a woman by means of operations. In all these cases, with the very rare exception of those with glandular anomalies, this tendency is due to unfortunate experiences on the part of the child attributable to his being a boy. In some such cases the parents have wanted a girl instead of a boy and make the boy feel their disappointment,[1] or, more frequently, the boy suffers from the successful competition of a sister. I remember a young man who gave this explanation for his 'perversion': 'My sister knew everything without learning, and I always tried hard to learn but never knew a thing, and at school the girls were always preferred by the masters.' Thus he formed the resolve to become a girl. What actually stood behind it was not the wish to change his sex, but only his tiresome life, and to get his success by a trick, as he despaired of getting it by normal means. The concept 'girl' was completely desexualized and only meant 'enviable existence'. In other cases it means 'easier competition', as in the following story, which demonstrates the genesis of homosexuality with rare lucidity. A man, now 26 years old, was a frail and timid little boy. He went to a co-educational school in which boys and girls played games separately. He was not very good at games and was mercilessly teased about it by his schoolmates. One day it occurred to him that things might be much better if he played with the girls, which he did. The one piece of luck which this man had at this difficult time in his life was that the headmaster of the school understood the situation at once and tolerated this most unusual arrangement. Thus, the boy went on playing the game of life on the other side of the fence, that is to say, when later on sex awoke in him, he expressed his timidity in sexual terms and became – homosexual.

But the most important and most frequent cause of homosexuality in youth is the desire for support and security. This is the motive of adolescents having affairs with grown-up men, the form of homosexuality most condemned by society. I knew a young man, aged 21, who had several affairs with grown-up

1. The far-reaching results of the stubborn refusal of parents to accept facts as they are is admirably described in Radclyffe Hall's autobiographical novel *The Well of Loneliness*.

men after he had been seduced by a schoolmaster when he was 14. What attracted the boy was maturity as such, and what he wanted was stability, security, and permanency. As time went by it occurred to him that a homosexual relation was mainly based on sex because these men seemed to want only sex; the security they gave him was only incidental for them, whereas he wanted and gave passion above all. It gradually dawned on him that what he wanted could really only be given by a woman. Only a woman could be co-operative in feelings and decisions, and although sex must not be the main thing in marriage, the stability he so urgently needed, and which would so much enhance his efficiency, could derive only from a sexual relationship with a woman. This realization put an end to his 'homosexuality'.

This story needs no comment. The sexuality was hardly more than the price, as it were, which he paid for the security he wanted, and passion was the vehicle through which the proximity of these men, the source of his security, was established. The obvious cause of this whole attitude was the fact that his father had left the family when the boy was still small, and all these men had to take over the paternal function. The most remarkable feature of this development is the correct intuition of the young man that only in a proper man–woman relationship can a lasting bond between two persons be established, and that this notion eventually broke through the thin texture of his pseudo-homosexuality.

The case of girls at this stage of their development is somewhat different. The psychological situation is similar to that of boys, but one cannot speak of homosexuality, since everything remains almost exclusively in the erotic sphere. There are kisses, strokings, and embracings, but no real sexual acts. Emotions, on the other hand, are very prominent and ardent, and frequently we find diaries expressing the most passionate devotion, the object of which is frequently a woman teacher. As far as we know at present, this 'crush' phase is a normal one; nearly all girls pass through it.

Finally, a few words about the attitude educators should adopt towards the problem. As to the victim, the younger boy, it all depends on whether he has already reached the stage of sexual awareness. If not, he remains practically unaffected, and things may sometimes take a rather amusing turn. One day an irate father stormed into my consulting-room bitterly complaining that his boy had been seduced at one of the expensive public schools. When I had an opportunity of talking to the boy himself, he quite frankly admitted the facts, and when I asked him how he felt about it at the time he said: 'Well, sir, I was so bored with all this that I went on eating my apple.' But even at a later stage, the resilience of a healthy mind is so great that most boys forget these experiences and emerge unscathed. But it must be admitted that boys predisposed by their aforementioned debility of character are exposed to risks which under more favourable circumstances they might have avoided. More complicated is the position of the older, the aggressive, partner. Here, too, Nature comes to our assistance in that most boys outgrow their physical inferiority and mental timidity, and therefore drop their sexual anomalies before they leave school and find the way to the other sex. But not all of them do so, and by far the larger proportion of all those young men who parade as homosexuals at college and later in life are nothing but overgrown schoolboys.

True, these practices cannot be tolerated in schools, but vigorous severity is just as out of date as is corporal punishment as a means of education; nor are moral exhortations much good. Experience has proved that it is practically most effective and psychologically least harmful to treat the whole thing as a matter of discipline, as something that cannot be tolerated in a school any more than smoking or talking after lights-out, supported perhaps by an appeal to the sense of responsibility of older boys towards their juniors. Boys who do not respond must have psychological treatment, not because of their homosexuality, but because of the underlying cause, as described above.

One would think that co-education is the obvious way to circumvent the whole problem of the approach to sex, of which homosexuality in youth is only one, although the most conspicuous, manifestation. And it is so in many respects: homosexuality is almost unknown in co-educational schools, and women students in Oxford or Cambridge can at once distinguish by his easy manners a co-educated male student from one coming from a tough boys' school. But there is still another aspect to this question. I remember a boy who when I discussed this problem with him laughingly said: 'But how can one fall in love with a girl who sweats and toils and fears and hopes in class just like oneself?' What he meant was that the close proximity of comradeship lowers the 'tension of difference' which, as we have seen before, is an essential element of sexual sentiment – or another version of the old adage that familiarity breeds contempt. But that this need not always be so has been amply demonstrated during the war, when work done and danger braved together has helped many a boy to meet girls. There is obviously no clear-cut solution to this problem, any more than of any other real problem of life, and even educators and psychologists must have experienced the unfathomable complexity of life by themselves, in order to be protected from the lure of scientific oversimplification.

CHAPTER 5

# ON SEX EDUCATION

WE live in an age of great educational zest and optimism, which is a heritage of the eighteenth-century faith in the almightiness of Reason, supported by the nineteenth-century pride in harnessing Nature and the twentieth-century belief in the necessity and efficiency of planning. Sex education is the latest and, apart from the long-overdue political education, probably the last addition to the curriculum of modern education. It is nowadays widely, although by no means generally, agreed that sex education should be given in schools, and the only question left is how best to do it.

During the many years I have worked as psychological adviser to several preparatory and public schools in this country I have always upheld the principle that education is an activity entirely of its own, based on its own principles and directed by its own rules. Hence psychologists have no right to tell educators what to do and how to do it, but the proper service psychology can, and must, render to educationalists is to supply a proper knowledge of the material they mould, that is, of the child's personality under normal and abnormal circumstances. This psychological background of sex education will be sketched in the following pages. If a certain measure of scepticism is revealed by this analysis it is by no means intended to discourage this educational movement but rather to support it by preventing it from attempting the unattainable.

It has become customary to subdivide the subject of sex-education into 'sex instruction', which means giving the mere facts of sexuality as a biological function, and 'sex education' proper, which aims at incorporating these facts in our life as a whole. This means teaching the young that these facts are never mere facts, but always have a meaning attached to them, giving them values. *True, meaningless facts unrelated to moral values cannot exist in a normal man's sex life*. No one, I think, will dispute this statement, but the kind of morality one teaches and the manner in which this complex subject should be imparted to the children can be the subject of much dispute.

Even the more modest aim of sex instruction is beset with difficulties, the chief of which is proper timing. At what age should information be given? If we are too early, the best efforts are wasted, and if we are too late, we risk making ourselves ridiculous. The child's sexual development is not so strictly connected with age as are other capacities, and sexual precocity, as well as considerable retardation, occurs more frequently than other functional irregularities. The condition for a proper understanding of sex information is a peculiar capacity which, for want of a better word, I should term '*sex awareness*'. By this I mean the awareness that words used, facts related and even actions done, show the iridescent colouring of sex, and are somehow connected with this strange and dimly felt sensation. Before this development stage is reached, not only are our educational efforts wasted, but the children are impregnable to sexual impacts coming from outside. The degree and kind of this imperturbability are different with different children. The following cases may illustrate some extremes:

A fourteen-year-old boy said that he naturally heard all about sex at school from his companions' conversations. The coarseness of their conversation had revolted him, and he was not interested in its substance. He had clearly felt that they were talking about things that would only have a meaning for him later on. An adolescent of 17 had learned masturbation in school at 14, and had practised it because the others did so. The physical enjoyment had not been particularly great, and so he had soon given it up. He felt obscurely, but definitely, that sex would only have a meaning when it was concerned with women, and that that time had not yet come for him. For a year and a half from the age of 14 a young man of 21 had had homosexual relations with one of his masters. At the same time his schoolmates had shown him how to masturbate, and indeed had forced him to do so, but he soon gave it up as he received no pleasure from it. At the age of 21 he suddenly 'discovered' masturbation spontaneously, as if he had never before known anything about it, and thenceforward enjoyed it greatly. Sometimes sexual awareness starts very early in life. Every now and then a patient tells that he had erections at the age of 6 or thereabouts, and that rubbing enhanced the pleasurable sensation. Admittedly these are the exceptions, but they prove quite unexpectedly an all-important principle: most of these men remember quite clearly a sense of doing something wrong; they did not know what this wrong might be, and were much too afraid to ask. They are equally certain that this sense of guilt was quite genuine inasmuch as sex had never been mentioned to them before and some of them were even quite unconscious of the 'sexual' nature of their activities. The principle proved by such experiences is that we have a dim but definite *a priori* notion of the existence and uniqueness of sex, and that playing with the penis is totally different from any other kind of playing. The cause of the sense of guilt is unknown. The only suggestion I could make is that it springs from a notion of the inadequacy and prematurity of this sensation and stimulation; but I have only a few remarks of patients on which to base this conjecture. In most cases such an exceptionally early awakening of sexual interest is an ominous sign of a neurotic disposition of the child.

These examples show that sex instruction, verbal and practical, sinks in only when, and not before, the capacity for digesting and assimilating it has been developed. The most striking example I remember is that of a physician who, as a part symptom of his impotence, complained of his great difficulty in finding his bearing during the act! Professionally, so to speak, he knew, of course, the anatomy and physiology of the female genital, but what he did not know was how to transform this 'knowing' into feeling, understanding, and acting. For only from a purely materialistic, and therefore inadequate, point of view, was this part of his wife's body, in which her femininity concentrated, identical with the vagina of an anatomical specimen. Strictly speaking, his difficulty was not so much due to unawareness as to repression, but both these mental processes belong to the same group. Furthermore, this case throws a bright light on the dubious benefits of purely verbal sex information. And so does the case of a young girl who, ashamed of her ignorance, tried to get some information about the female genital from an illustrated text-book of anatomy. However much she tried she could neither understand nor remember these explanations. Only much later, during her first loving association, did the hitherto dead knowledge turn into living experience. Whether one tries to explain this rather strange reaction as a manifestation of real chastity or as the effect of a pathological repression is immaterial for our purpose.

Consideration of the time factor and the degree of sex awareness provides an interesting comment on other problems of the developing sexuality. There is, for example, the problem of *seduction.* In the early stages of medical psychology, which for all practical purposes consisted only of the early part of Freud's teachings, it was generally assumed that painful sex experiences in childhood caused lasting psychological harm; seduction loomed large among these shocks. This view is now abandoned, since it has been realized that of a great many children who were exposed to the same danger only a few succumb to it. Seduction has a subversive effect only where it finds the ground already prepared through some abnormality in the child's individual balance. The resilience of the normal child to such insults is truly surprising; seduction remains either a meaningless fact or the shock is absorbed without lasting ill-effects.

Educators and psychologists who have practical experience in lecturing to children on sex matters are agreed that the pre-adolescent child should have full knowledge of the anatomy and functioning of the sex organs. In schools where regular sex teaching is practised the accepted scheme seems to be to give three lectures: the first at the end of the first term at a public school (or its equivalent), the second at about sixteen, and the third when the children are leaving school. Teaching sex in class, 'just like any other school subject', has been found a suitable procedure, supported by private talks if necessary. In co-educational schools the classes are attended by both sexes together. Practically all the men and women who do the teaching and the heads of the schools in which the teaching is done are very satisfied with the results. And up to a point they are quite justified, so far as the immediate results go: boys and girls of all ages follow the lectures with keen and sincere interest, a certain embarrassment, inevitable at the beginning, is soon overcome, and relief from conscious and unconscious tensions is unmistakable. But whether the really intended result of these effects can be attained, that is to say whether sex life has been given a sounder basis and has generally been improved, can be seen only one or two generations hence – and this applies to sex education still more than to sex instruction. Let us hope it will be so.[1]

One means of assessing whether sex teaching has at least done no harm is to find out whether or not it has affected the genuine sense of shame. There is a tendency to dismiss shame as an undesirable by-product of civilization or even as the result of an out-dated moralism. In fact, psychological analysis as well as ethnology proves that the sense of shame is one of the arch-possessions of mankind. There is no primitive tribe known which does not show a sense of shame, however rudimentary, and so do small children: during the development of mankind, as well as of the individual, the range of objects which shame protects increases, that is all. Protection is the specific function of shame.

How genuine a sensation shame is can be seen from the indulgence of five-year-olds in the obscene-sensational, described in a previous chapter. What these children insult, as it were, is shame, and not just a regulation; an ought-not and not just a must-not. Only the violation of something fundamental and essential produces this lustful exhilaration, the concupiscence which is the real opposite of shame. Shamelessness is the emotionally indifferent attitude which permits one to do things that otherwise would not have been done, whereas concupiscence is the dynamic sensation which drives us to do things we ought not to do.

It is pretty obvious that shame primarily protects the genitals and their function: not for what they are in themselves in terms of anatomy and physiology but for what is behind them: the mystery of sex. There are so many occasions of disenchantment

1. Here is amusing evidence that the last chance of sex education can be missed. In all universities in the former Imperial Austria and Germany, and in the few in the U.S.A. which I have visited, a student of medicine finishes his studies without – officially – knowing any detail about sex-life in general and even the sex act in particular. He learns about the anatomy and physiology of the sex organs; he learns that children are born and that venereal diseases occasionally spoil the fun; in the lectures on psychiatry he occasionally learns of gruesome sex perversions. But to fill the gap between the bare anatomical facts and the clinical consequences the educational authorities obviously rely on the assistance of the helpful ladies walking the Ringstrasse or Times Square.

that the warning cannot be repeated often enough. Too many parents, for instance, pride themselves on enjoying the unrestricted confidence of their growing children. They do not know how essential an element of growing-up it is to have and to protect something that is entirely one's own, one's innermost secret, the '*jardin secret*' as Baudelaire calls it. This secret is guarded by shame, and as sex is at that age, more perhaps than at any time later, the newest, strangest, and therefore most intimate experience, sex becomes the foremost object of shame. This must be respected and not endangered by 'sex education', however well intended. If mothers attempt to lower the unique mother-daughter relationship to the level of 'friendship' they sacrifice the essential distance between the generations, respect for elders gives way to familiarity and criticism between equals, the mystery is unveiled, nothing more is left to be protected by shame, and these daughters grow up into an existence without depth and roots and secrets.

The claim to progressiveness and modernism is often no more than a cloak for insensitiveness to essential values, and shame is one of the first victims of this moral aberration. The nudist movement, for instance, is, or should be, a deterrent example. As far as it is confined to adults it is just a matter of bad taste, but it becomes a fearful calamity if foolish parents introduce it into home life. It is always a most painful experience to listen to parents priding themselves on how freely and 'naturally' they bring up their children, in that father, mother, sons, and daughters bathe together and walk about naked, firmly believing that they thus transform their suburban garden into the lost paradise.

Shame needs protection in order to protect, not the conventions of civilization, but the most tender elements of human nature. From sex as its origin and core, shame later on protects our whole personality, not in its debased form as vanity, but as a proper sense of self-esteem: we need not be ashamed of our errors and mistakes, but when we have made fools of ourselves.

Closely linked up with the question when to tell a child is the problem what to tell. Here, particularly for the early ages, child psychology is a reliable guide. Children often begin to ask questions very early. When a little girl for the first time sees the organ of her younger brother, it is very natural that she should ask what this strange little thing is. But this is by no means a 'sexual' question, but rather a 'scientific' one. This difference must always be kept in mind. Between four and five most children ask innumerable questions. They are largely 'psychological' questions, which means that the children want to attract the attention of their mother, and have discovered that questions are a suitable means to that end: it is the answering rather than the answer itself which the child seeks. As far as the subject of these questions is concerned, children of this age chiefly want to know where things come from, and thus they ask, *inter alia*, where children come from. This question is quite unspecific, and has nothing to do with sexual curiosity. One may answer it honestly, e.g. saying that the mother carries the baby in her tummy, and need not be afraid of further searching questions on the subject, as children of this age have not yet acquired the capacity for discursive thinking.[1]

Another wave of inquisitiveness swamps the child and its educators at the age of 9 or 10. By this time the child has developed a strong sense of reality; he wants to learn how things are made: stars, watches, babies, etc. Now it is imperative to be honest in our answers, since the child already has a clear feeling for truth and falsehood. A certain amount of comfort for an embarrassed mother may be drawn from the fact, emerging from extensive statistics, that the most difficult detail of sex life, the part taken by the father in the process, is only very rarely inquired into.

On the other hand, a real sexual curiosity shown at this age or even earlier must always arouse suspicion of some neurotic tendencies.

So far we are on safe ground. In later years only one definite task of sex information can be pointed out. Adolescent boys, at any rate, should be informed about certain matters, such as

1. Besides, they forget very quickly information which has emotional implications they are not yet ready to grasp. Pearl Buck, the novelist, recounts how she adopted a baby girl and informed the child about this fact when it was still quite young. A few years later, when she was visiting the child at school, the girl pointed to a friend of hers, saying pityingly: 'This poor dear, she's adopted', obviously entirely oblivious of the fact that she herself was in the same position. This remarkable educational success of Mrs Buck's was greatly assisted by the beneficial forgetfulness of children.

the prevention of venereal diseases, the use of contraceptives, etc., since they can thus be saved from much unnecessary harm. Even there the problem of timing remains. A friend of mine, also a doctor, was invited by the headmaster of the school in Vienna which his son attended to give the boys a talk on these matters before they left school. When he asked his son what he thought his friends would be most interested in, the boy replied with a superior smile: 'I wonder what you could tell us that we don't already know!' But still it is better to tell these things twice than not at all.

*

Should one go further and explain not only the biological elements of sex but also the whole complex of love-life? This is a question which psychology, theoretical or practical, is incompetent to answer expertly. And I dare say the educationalists are in very much the same position. Sexuality, in the full sense in which we use the term in these pages, is so much part of our whole life that nothing short of a consistent philosophy of life would enable us to formulate principles about sex life as part of this whole. And such a philosophy embodies necessarily the views held by its individual creator, as no period in the past has lacked a generally accepted body of beliefs so completely as does ours.[1] Under these circumstances it would be the most natural thing that parents should assume this heavy burden and should lead their growing children at least to the gates of this land of promise. But how few parents are able and willing to accept this task! Those who do are the fortunate ones, and still more fortunate are their children. All depends on tact, experience, and the kind of relationship between parents and children, and that hour in which a son confides his innermost anxieties to his father, and the father confesses his most secret memories to his child, may become a blessing for life – to both of them. But this living continuity of tradition and purpose, this handing over of personal experience and belief to the younger man who should now carry on the race, is not what

1. Cf. the excellent analysis in E. G. Lee's *Mass Man and Religion* (Hutchinson, 1947) and the amazing figures in 'Puzzled People', *Mass Observation* (Gollancz, 1947).

the modern advocates of sex education have in mind. They mean organized teaching in schools in accordance with the mental climate of an age which tends everywhere to replace individual initiative by planned collectivism. This being so, I fail to see the difference between 'sex instruction' and 'sex education', as the latter is now nothing more than instruction, only in a far more complex subject.

If one reads the fast-growing literature on sex education one must appreciate how ambitious the programme is.[1] Its advocates stress that ethics, aesthetics, religion, must come under consideration, and sex education must fit sex into the whole pattern of our life. Can this be done? How? By whom? And would the result be worth the effort? The answers to these questions go far beyond the narrow confines of sex education and touch the roots of education as a whole. As far as sex education goes, I see two main difficulties. First, sexuality is more than pure biology and less than pure spirituality, but a unique combination of both. Can this complex matter be taught with full fairness to either of its elements? I cannot help feeling that the ethics of sex are being too closely connected with religion.[2] This is particularly disadvantageous when talking to adolescents, because, as everybody knows, boys of this group are hypercritical and in revolt, sometimes violent, against everything metaphysical; and sex is often enough consciously or unconsciously used by them to manifest this emancipation. It is then important to purify the language used from any unctuous piety: words like 'nice' girl and 'clean' living should be carefully avoided if for no other reason than because the implication is too obvious that any sex activity that does not comply with the speaker's view must be a 'dirty' business. Nor is it very helpful to call sex activity a 'God-given function' because bright boys may quickly discover that this attribute applies to business acumen just as well, without the fact having

1. A very instructive survey can be found in E. F. Griffith's *The Road to Maturity* (Methuen & Co., Ltd., reprinted 1947) and *Experiments in Sex Education*, published by the Federation of Progressive Societies and Individuals (London, 1935). Very interesting are the observations of W. B. Curry in his recent book *Education for Sanity* (Heinemann, 1947).

2. How formidable problems arise that way can be learned from Weatherhead's excellent book *Mastery of Sex*.

any visible influence on our private or public way of conducting business. This problem is important enough to justify going into a few more details. The genesis of religious feeling is still obscure, but child psychology has already furnished enough facts to sketch its development on broad lines. The concept of God awakens spontaneously very early in life. The five-year-old, soon after he has discovered that all things are 'made', jumps very quickly to the conclusion that a final Maker must exist, which is God. This is the first, the intellectual, root of religion. Many years later, between 16 and 18, the other, the emotional, element is added. A well-educated ten-year-old child treats the religion that he is taught as a matter of course, as part of the routine of life, no more and no less. Not before puberty do religious problems awaken, again quite spontaneously, this time as an urgent need with a strong emotional tinge. Bewildered and exhausted by the physical and mental changes which this stage of his development brings about, helpless against these strange powers, despairing of being helped by grown-ups, the child in his agony turns to a mightier Helper. This is the true birthday of religious feelings.

The most potent cause of this inner turmoil is the awakening of sexuality. Here the evolution is strongest and strangest, the helpfulness of adults most deficient, and yet help most needed: thus we see that sexuality leads the adolescent to God – and not the other way round. Furthermore, in his erotic sentiment the adolescent seeks also another human being on whom he may lean, who becomes his complement, to whom he can surrender himself and find peace. The same need leads him to God as the supreme support, and once more to a very large extent failure in the erotic relationship provides a strong stimulus for establishing the divine contact. Finally we meet here, in the spontaneous development of the religious sentiment, an awakening of religious 'awareness', a turning-point as crucial as a similar one that occurs in the sexual field. Before this point, words are just words, and actions just actions, whereas afterwards words and actions recede behind the lived experience pregnant with meaning.[1]

1. This exposition is based on Charlotte Buehler's standard work *Kindheit and Jugend*, l.c. My own experience with 320 public-school boys conforms completely with her findings.

The spontaneous growth of his religious notions does not permit the adolescent to go beyond the concept of God as supreme Maker and Helper, and from his religious instruction he may add the idea of him as a Law-giver; in principle this is an anthropomorphic view. The spiritual element of religion, the Holy, the concept of God not as guardian but as incarnation of moral values, a Being to whom one not only turns in adversity but with whom one communes in felicity – all this is far beyond the power of comprehension at this age. Reading through the literature on sex education one is left wondering how far all these psychological facts are taken into due consideration. To admonish an adolescent to 'preserve himself for marriage' neglects the fact that the adolescent is just tentatively developing the concept of himself, or any human being, as a moral value; of human relationships he knows only comradeship, and sex is a new experience which he is quite incapable of incorporating into his life. Marriage can be for an adolescent nothing else than one of the many things which may come after the school certificate, and the moral essence of marriage may not be conceived of until five to ten years later – if at all. Thus the above advice leaves the young in the dark as to what they are to preserve and for what. Generally speaking, basing sex education on religion and putting it under the sanction of God means hardly more than replacing the home and school authorities by a higher authority which, for reasons hardly comprehensible to the youth, wants him to battle against the most powerful of his instincts. I am far from saying that this form of education is wrong or without some merits, but I am still further from believing that it attains the aims which it intends. But what is one to do? If one studies a text-book of child psychology one must be filled with awe of the wise and inexorable laws of Nature which see to it that faculties awake in a child at the very moment when they are needed, as we have shown regarding awareness and a sense of values. Thus, if only the substance of a child's mind is sound and has not been spoilt by undue and arbitrary interference, a second kind of sex awareness appears at the end of puberty which spontaneously opens up a youth's mind to the essential values and the essential morality of sex – if only ...!

But far more puzzling is a second problem. There is nothing

that cannot be taught up to a point, but there is nothing that can be taught beyond this point. In other words, no function of real life can be properly imparted by teaching or mastered by learning alone – least of all the art of sex. In this respect I fully subscribe to the classic tenet of Macmurray's philosophy that living is primarily action. And therefore it can be learnt only in action.

There is actually a school subject – literature – the proper appreciation of which presents similar difficulties, and from experience gained in teaching literature the methods and prospects of teaching sex may benefit a good deal. Are there many men or women who gratefully remember their lessons in literature? Are there not many more whose appreciation of the classics was not only not awakened but definitely spoilt for ever by those lessons? This result is not, or not entirely, due to the ineptitude of the teachers, but much more to the fact that these treasures are forced on children at an age when they are not yet capable of grasping beauty in an abstract way. It is most fortunate to find this view corroborated by one of the most eminent of our literary critics. Desmond MacCarthy, commenting on a performance of *Henry IV* by boys at Harrow, wrote these memorable words: 'Than this there could be no better way of getting the young to care about Shakespeare; the right entrance to the garden of Literature and Art is through the gate of excitement and pleasure. Once at home in it, the botanist and herbalist may be of some use, but if editors and professors introduce them, that garden may well seem to the young a cemetery where the labels are obviously more important than the flowers.' I remember the greatest actor of our time blaming the decline of the art of acting on to the schools of dramatic art. In the past, he said, a young man had to defy the prejudice of his family and the conventions of society and learn his *métier* the hard way, on the road. To-day he gets a certificate from one of these schools and seeks safe employment in a theatre just like any other employee in a commercial firm.

Similarly the art of Love must be learned the hard way. Educators who recommend learning it from books and personal talks and leaving the practice of it for marriage court disaster for their charges. No experienced psychologist will easily forget the lament of deceived young wives, who find these experiments 'degrading', 'distasteful', and who refuse to be 'guinea-pigs'. Not many may have the humour and charm of the girl-friend of one of my students: when, a bit uncertain of himself, he tried to explain to her the 'problems' of love and sex, she cut short his oration by exclaiming impatiently: 'I don't want to be taught geography – I want to be taken to these places!'

The adolescent feels inchoately but powerfully that he must measure his strength against the vicissitudes of life, that he must discover life 'through a process of finding out, through error and through trial, through fantasy and illusion, through falsehood and his own foolishness, through being mistaken and wrong and an idiot and egotistical, and aspiring and hopeful and believing and confused, and pretty much what everyone of us is, and goes through, and finds out about, and becomes'. In these powerful words Thomas Wolfe, in my view one of the greatest American novelists, describes the development of the hero of his posthumous novel *The Web and the Rock*. And that is the way a man discovers and masters sex. By all means let us give our young men and women sex education as best we can, but we must not deceive ourselves and them that this is all that is needed; we must tell them that these principles must be practised step by step up the steep grade to perfection.

Life is not there to be learnt theoretically, but to be conquered in the school of hard experience, and he who understands and appreciates life's fullness and complexity will realize that it is just in life's inscrutability that its real worth lies. Sex is life's greatest mystery, a riddle which can be solved only by those who will dare all. And a mystery that someone else unveils for us is always a disappointment.

## Appendix

I think it may be a welcome addition to and confirmation of the principles expounded in the previous chapters to relate in some detail the story of a young man, which really sounds as if arbitrarily composed in order to illustrate all the difficulties which can stand in the way of a man's sexual development.

F. G., 28 years old, consulted me because of sexual difficulties in his marriage: he came from a typical lower-middle-class family. Father was a rather shadowy figure, mother was the dominant but by no means domineering element in the family. She created a strictly moral atmosphere, not so much by teaching and preaching as by her way of living. There was also a sister much older than the patient. The patient was a delicate boy, teased and laughed at by his schoolmates, rather shy and very lonely, in his views 'so different from all the other boys'. At the age of 12 he 'noticed' one day that the boys in the swimming-pool walked about quite openly in the nude, and this was a tremendous discovery, because he learnt that something that was strictly taboo at home was not only permissible but apparently the most natural thing on earth. From then on he enjoyed being seen naked by the other boys, not out of personal vanity or any indecent motive but simply to enjoy this newly-found freedom. Shortly afterwards he went a step further: he and two other boys had a hide-out in a wood. There they went one day and undressed, all three; the boy had an erection for the first time in his life, but not, as he had quite definitely explained, through the sight of the naked bodies but because he felt that this time he was doing something wrong: because this time the undressing was no longer inherent in the situation, as it was in the swimming-pool, but done for its own sake. The erection was due to his sense of exuberance in his moral emancipation.

Subsequently the boy went to a public school, and here a further element was added to his development. He felt a strong attraction to older boys because he wanted, and enjoyed if he got it, their protection – nothing else; and when these boys misinterpreted the situation by trying on him all manner of sexual manipulations, he recoiled with anger and disgust. From 16 onwards the desire for protection receded and was gradually replaced by tender feelings towards younger boys and a desire to protect them, although he was much too shy to put this into practice; whereas his relationship towards the older boys had been an affectionate giving and receiving, it was now just giving. And, most significantly, with older boys and men he developed a sense of 'straightforward friendship', which means a proper man-to-man relationship.

At the age of 18 he went to a university. Here in this free atmosphere his sexual development entered its second stage. He met girls, discovered their attractiveness and, having outgrown a good deal of his shyness and diffidence, he started to make love to them. But more than anything else he wanted them to make love to him, because his own thrill and satisfaction was the only thing he desired. But he felt all this was rather crude, and at the back of his mind was the idea that everything would be different one day when he was in love. At this time the homosexual trend reached its climax: the patient felt strong emotional attachments to two men of his own age. With one of them it came to one incident of mutual masturbation, which disgusted the patient so profoundly that from then on he controlled his longing for physical relief completely. And this was the end of his homosexual career. Simultaneously he felt an irresistible desire for proper cohabitation with women. But those he got hold of at the time and on the spot (West Africa) were so distasteful that it hardly came to a proper attempt. A few months ago he met his future wife. She was quite different from all the women he had ever met, he fell in love with her (for the first time in his life), was strongly physically attracted to her, and soon got married. So far he has not yet been able to consummate the marriage properly.

Strange as this story may appear, it is typical, and remarkable only because it shows better than others of its kind how logically and consistently the developmental laws work out their course, knitting into their pattern all the impediments we may put in their way: through the maternal influence and a certain degree of physical weakness the boy found it difficult to fit into the rough community of his schoolmates, and security through protection became the all-important factor in his life. He sought this protection where he could find it – from older boys. As soon as the progress of his self-confidence allowed it, he turned this urge for passive protection into a desire for active protection, and again chose the only available object, younger boys. We remember that young children often relieve all sorts of non-sexual emotions through the sexual channel, and so did this 'late developer', because that is what the man actually is. This giving protection soon became mixed up with affection and later with sexual desires; this was the genesis and essence of his 'homosexuality'. That the whole thing was very much against his real nature is convincingly proved by the strong aversion he felt on the few occasions of homosexual practice. This phase of his development the patient formulated with amazing insight: 'From 19 onwards all would have gone well had I not been under the influence of the idea that sex is wrong. Thus my impulses have been bottled up and were bound to break forth to the second best, which was men.'

But at this time his normal nature broke through all the fences and the young man turned to women. Again he complied instinctively with the rules of development and at first wanted nothing but physical gratification, and when the momentum of his development carried him towards the normal goal, intercourse, another big obstacle reared up in front of him. I cannot better describe it than in the patient's own words: 'My feelings towards women and my wishes as to how they should treat me were inconsistent with how I imagined my mother reacting to my father's approach.' And this is the crucial point: naturally enough he knew nothing about sexual development and the stages this development has to go through, and when he compared his immature sexuality with the mature sexuality of his parents it was only natural that he found his own lamentably wanting. Thus he broke down just when the goal was almost within his reach, and ended up in a psychologist's consulting-room – hardly a desirable result of moral education. There is one detail I want to stress particularly: soon after he had established his first contact with women the boy felt that this was only a preliminary stage and that, as he put it: 'Everything will be different one day when I am in love.' This I think is a remarkable proof of how strongly a dim sense of essential morality worked, even in this otherwise emotionally retarded boy. Unfortunately this 'ought' of essential morality was in the later stages almost completely silenced by the 'must not' of conventional morality.

His mother caused the harm quite unintentionally, just by the emanation of her strong moral attitude, and the lack of sexual instruction consisted only in not warning the boy that he would have to go through all these preliminary stages. Professional sex educators omit this warning deliberately; in fact this is an almost essential point of their sex education, as far as one can learn from their writings. In my opinion, based on experience of many cases like the above-mentioned, this means asking the impossible. These young boys cannot properly understand what they should preserve themselves for, or how they can face this supreme task of marriage completely unprepared. Is it not reasonable to teach children first to read and write before expecting them to write perfect poetry? I am quite prepared to admit that a perfectly normal young man could achieve this sexual maturity in one leap. (Incidentally, isn't it the very idea of maturation that it is a process of gradual transition from stage to stage?) But even the slightly weaker ones need preparation and assistance, and who would dare to say with confidence how many of the boys and girls who sit in a classroom listening to a lecture on sex education are perfectly normal?

## CHAPTER 6

# TOWARDS MATURITY

### (*a*) ON PROSTITUTION

THE existence of prostitution is neither an essentially moral nor a purely social-economic problem; in fact it comprises both these elements of our existence, and some others. It is a fact much too little known, or at any rate recognized, that prostitution has existed ever since, and everywhere that, men have lived in a community. The fame of the Greek hetaerae and of the Japanese geishas, and the fact that barren women in South Sea islands are expelled into the woods at the service of any man, testify to the antiquity and ubiquity of this institution.

Prostitution belongs essentially to civilization, as the shadow belongs to the light, and only because the shadow deepens as the light brightens is prostitution – or so at least it seems – much more widely spread nowadays than it was in the past. In a previous chapter (page 17) I have described one aspect of the mentality of civilized man as the capacity to postpone the immediate satisfaction of a physical urge. During the growth of civilization this virtue has been turned into the fateful technique separating the component elements of life's complex wholeness; form from content, values from facts, pleasure from need, soul from body, profit from labour, business from morals. *Prostitution begins when sexual gratification is separated from personal union.* These few examples, which could easily be added to, show that prostitution is nothing more or less than the manifestation in the sexual field of the basic dualism of the civilized mentality. An additional reason why prostitution is found less frequently in primitive societies than in higher ones probably lies in the fact that economic difficulties grow with the degree of civilization and prevent young people from marrying when they become sexually mature. Thus the attempt to fight this social evil by legal means on the sexual front alone must prove as certain a failure as did the experiment of prohibition in the United States some seventeen years ago, or the attempt to stop dope traffic by customs regulation, or to end wars by old-fashioned diplomatic antics.

Nothing short of a spiritual revolution would be sufficient to rectify the sexual as well as some other effects of our way of living. A purely economic revolution would not do, as the experience of Russia proved in the early years of the Soviets. The new régime tried to combat prostitution as one of the evils typical of capitalistic economy, and succeeded beyond belief – but for a very unexpected reason: an important item in the programme of the social reorganization was the abolition of the institution of marriage as part of the complete atomization of society; this resulted at once in a hitherto unheard-of lowering of sexual morality to the level of extreme promiscuity. Consequently professional prostitution became unnecessary, because the whole of Russia turned – as Lenin himself described it to Clara Zetkin – into a gigantic brothel.

According to common opinion, a prostitute is a woman who accepts monetary reward for an essentially unsaleable commodity. And if one does not limit this bargain to the taking just of money, but applies the term, as one is perfectly justified in doing from a psychological point of view, to any woman who puts a price on something essentially priceless, the full magnitude of the problem clearly emerges. For it is not only the girl who sells her poor attraction on a dark street-corner who prostitutes herself, but also the American millionairess who marries the European heir to an aristocratic title, and all the legion of women in between these extremes who use their favours as something to bargain with.

It is interesting to recall that the acceptance of a reward in money or kind was not always considered the characteristic of prostitution. According to ancient Roman law, for instance, a prostitute was a woman who offered herself *passim et sine delectu* (everywhere and without pleasure). Observe how much more human than ours this concept is, because it stresses just that lack of emotional participation which lowers the sexual act to a mere genital function and thus constitutes the essential, as distinct from the conventional, immorality of prostitution. Incidentally, the men who frequent prostitutes make themselves guilty of the same offence, because those who pay a price are equal partners with those who accept it. That this has not yet been sufficiently acknowledged, and the odium of prostitution reserved for the woman only, is probably due to the fact that moral codes have always been made by men.

Now, what sort of women volunteer for the sorry trade of prostitution? Careful investigations have proved that the genuine prostitute is not only morally, but also mentally, defective. She lacks a sense of the cardinal value, the value of the human person, and consequently of all values derived from it, including the value of community and work. She is lazy, vain, irresponsible, prodigal, unsettled, etc. But one thing she never is: oversexed. And it is part of her general infantilism that she uses the genital function as a means of obtaining non-sexual aims, just as children do. The existence of the 'timeless prostitute type', as Lombroso termed it, has often been confirmed. The German psychiatrist Schneider, assisted by a surprisingly large number of kind people, made the experiment of placing a sufficient number of these girls in private houses as domestics, companions, and the like. After one year 85 per cent had run away, preferring their sordid previous existence to any sort of social comfort which had to be paid for by work. Besides these genuine prostitutes, who never had a personality, we find another very large group of women who throw their personality away at the bidding of a neurotic impulse. And the most essential and precious part of a woman's personality, her femininity, goes overboard first. Her sense of inferiority devalues this most valuable and vulnerable part of herself, and makes such a woman throw away her body in despair, or use it as a means of self-justification, or offer it gratuitously to any man who asks for it. Some of these women do it in a kind of missionary spirit, looking at their beauty as common property, which everybody has a right to enjoy – and there are sometimes lovely characters among these unfortunates. From this disposition it is only a small step to the so-called 'temple prostitution' as practised in ancient Babylon, Armenia, Greece, and India. It is a strange paradox that what from a psychological point of view must be condemned as essentially immoral could be put to the service of religious ceremony. Priestesses offer themselves to the priests or worshippers as part of the holy service. Another strange example of how closely the highest in human existence is linked with the lowest. In this context must also be mentioned the *jus primae noctis*, or the *droit du seigneur*, a custom which gave the king or feudal lord the right to spend with the young bride the first night after her marriage to one of his subjects. Relevant also is the custom among exotic peoples for a host to offer his wife or daughters to the guest, or for friends to interchange their wives temporarily, as proof of their devotion to each other. These customs have been observed in places as remote and far away from each other as ancient Peru, North America, and Polynesia. They have been practised among Eskimos and in medieval Europe. Various explanations have been propounded for them, but I think the true one lies in the same mental immaturity as causes masturbation in young children: non-sexual emotions (sense of power, hospitality, friendship) are expressed in the sexual function. All these sexual associations have in common the fact that on the part of the woman no personal contact, no emotional incentive exists, and that she does, or suffers, the whole thing from extra-sexual motives. However different, unselfish, or conventionally moral this self-surrender may be, it is a form of sexual activity which in principle, in its essential character, must be defined as prostitution.

Compared with these two types of prostitutes, only a small third group is driven on to the streets by economic distress. These women can be easily recognized by the amateurishness with which they conduct their business; but one must assume that they too suffer from a defect in their personality which permits them to choose this easy way out of their difficulties.

What, now, are the characteristics of a sexual association with a prostitute? They are mainly three: First of all, *Anonymity*: these girls have no face that can be recognized, no name that will be remembered, just a body; they have no emotions, just technique; no individuality, just a trade. Secondly, the relation to *Time*: the association with a prostitute is restricted to the moment when it takes place. It has no extension in time and is wholly unrelated to the future. The fragment of time he spends with a prostitute is completely cut out of a man's life, as a time gap in which nothing significant happened. The third feature is lack of *Significance*, a corollary or result of the previous two: a minute before the man did not know that this woman existed, a minute afterwards he has forgotten that she existed, no trace is left, unchanged he turns away. All these three characteristics indicate that something has happened below the level of specifically human existence, and that those who took part in it lived and acted on this low level, the woman as well as the man.

If we now inquire what kind of men frequent prostitutes, we can distinguish three groups of customers.

The most interesting, practically most important, and from several points of view the most controversial group are the adolescents.

We must remember that the two component parts of our sexuality, the physical and the emotional, develop for a long time on separate lines which only slowly converge. The physical urge finds its first relief in wet dreams and in the primitive form of masturbation. Later on, during adolescence, this urge is no longer purely endogenous, but is aroused by the female body. The prostitute, who, as we have seen, is a body without a soul, caters for this desire. Moreover, an entirely impersonal contact makes it possible for the beginner to learn the technique of the difficult art of love-making. And as the concept of prostitutes includes women of widely varying personal and social standards, the young man may learn not only the elements of sexual 'reading and writing', as it were, but also all the subtleties and refinements of virtuosity.[1]

To this an objection may be raised. In the first chapter of this book I stated with great emphasis that physical sexuality is, or should be, only the expression of a personal relation. This is true, but it must also be remembered that this psychophysical fusion is the characteristic of mature exemplary sexuality. And here we are dealing with adolescents laboriously groping towards maturity. It may even be admitted that the ideally normal young man finds the way to his personal partner in one great sweep of love and sensuality, but this ideal postulate is in real life swamped by the flood of exceptions. That may be deplor-

1. Some of these girls seem to be less willing to accept their 'mission' than they are conscious of their rights as women. One day a man who was already partly advanced in the treatment of his impotence related rather perplexedly this experience. In order to test his progress, he picked up a prostitute, explained his situation, and asked for her assistance – which she refused haughtily, pointing out that she was not a schoolmarm and that she wanted real men. Even she!

able, but deploring never alters facts. We face here a psychological situation very similar to the homosexuality of youth; intercourse with prostitutes is a step in development, although not an inevitable one; it is a half-way solution to a problem which many – and by no means only the abnormal – young men find too difficult to solve in one leap.

But there is still another aspect of our problem. One may ask what is there to be learned. Is there not the instinct of copulation and procreation which guides the first steps of young people on this slippery path? I think the people most competent to answer this question are the many young wives whose marriages are in danger of being wrecked by the total ignorance and incompetence of their 'innocent' husbands. True there is a sexual instinct, but we must never forget that nothing in human life is accomplished by instinct alone, and that the sexual instinctive urge in particular is closely interwoven into the vast complex of 'human relationships' from which it receives guidance and protection. Furthermore, it is one of the defects of civilization that the unity of personal life is being disrupted, and the dislocated instinct either goes astray or must be redirected by the intellect: this new, and in a way artificial, combination of instinct and intellect is what I call 'technique'.[1]

The service prostitutes render to the adolescent, and through him to society, is to teach him the technique of sex life and to offer themselves as a training ground. The impersonal character of this kind of association is essential for this purpose, because any emotional contact would interfere with the unconcernedness with anything but the mere action. And this practical

1. It may be worth pointing out that by civilization I do not mean the equivalent of a Mayfair mentality in capitals or big towns. It is a form of existence permeating and moulding every detail of life. I had the opportunity of watching two generations growing up in a village high up in the Austrian mountains, and saw the people there wrestling with all the problems and conflicts dealt with psychopathology. An official body of research workers recently investigated Miami County, U.S.A., and found that from 10 to 20 per cent of the residents ought to see a psychiatrist. One elementary schoolchild in five was 'seriously maladjusted'; by the time they reached the sixth grade their neurosis was showing. Neuroses were much more common among the poor and ill-educated than among the well-educated. Almost any county in Ohio is considered representative of similar communities in the U.S.A. as a whole.

training is indispensable for the satisfactory performance of the complex act of making love. Nothing is more frustrating to the expression of emotion than the incongruity between the wealth of emotions one wants to express and the inadequate command of the means of expression – as every creative or reproducing artist knows. Of course it is not this educational benefit which the young man seeks, but physical relief and pleasure, and one may attribute it to the cunning of Nature that, however unwittingly, he gets so much more.

The second group of the prostitute's customers is composed of neurotics. They are, biologically at least, grown-ups. But fear, the central phenomenon of the neurotic mentality, holds them back from entering into a proper, personal, complete relationship with women. Contact and union mean to them surrender and captivity. They mistake giving themselves for giving themselves up or away. Merging with another person means to them losing their own personality. They consider emotions as bait that may lure them into a trap, and they sense danger where we expect happiness. No wonder that these men try to avoid risks and turn to women who offer an association of guaranteed safety. Here again the prostitute comes to their aid: the anonymity and transitoriness of the relation and its indifference to success and failure provide the sense of security which these men need above all.

The third and by far the largest group patronizing prostitutes is composed of what one may call the ordinary 'man in the street'. Whereas the adolescent has not yet achieved sexual maturity, and the neurotic is too afraid to attain it, this type of man never does become mature. The poor substance, the primitive and coarse nature of the personality of these men bar them from ever reaching the fusion of mind and body which constitutes the perfect adult sexuality. The body seeks its gratification, the mind wants pleasure, and the spirit weeps. Once more the prostitute supplies all that is required, and this type of man is the genuine consumer of her wares. The counterpart of these primitives are the over-sophisticated men. I said before that the term 'prostitute' must not be confined to the girls who make a precarious living from their trade, but that the mentality of prostituting oneself, for whatever purpose, pervades our whole society. This verdict applies to men as well in various ways, and I mean not so much that they prostitute themselves, which often enough they do, as their whole way of living. These socialites who rush from one party to another are incapable of grasping, and therefore establishing, real human relationships, and seek only ephemeral and impersonal contacts, and their sexual contacts are often of the same kind and order.

If one ponders over the psychology of prostitutes and of the men who frequent them, one may come to think that God, or Providence, or whoever may be responsible for this sort of thing, has created this type of defective woman for the express purpose of being a match for the three types of defective men.[1]

### (*b*) The Affair

No doubt marriage is the perfect and highest form of sexual relationship, partly because marriage is the most complete association which includes all the component parts of sexual contacts, partly because marriage is the goal of man's sexual development. This will be convincingly proved in the progress of our analysis. But there is no justification for condemning all non-marital relationships, that is love-making for the sake of love, as impermissible or immoral because they are only partial fulfilments and stages of the development towards marriage. Leaving all moral considerations aside, would not such a rigorism dishonour all the famous lovers whose memory history has preserved, as well as all the lovely characters poets have created? But even from a strictly scientific point of view, such an attitude is untenable, although the same error of judgement

1. The only man who has a legitimate and objective interest in the trade of prostitution is the Inspector of Taxes. Although socially ostracized, the prostitutes have to pay income-tax in several European countries. In this country only the procedure is different. The girls have to present themselves at the police station once a month, are charged under an Act of 1839 with 'soliciting to the annoyance of passengers', and fined forty shillings each time. A prostitute interviewed by the author of the article in the *New Statesman and Nation* (May 1947) from which I quote said: 'It's fair enough, really. It's only forty shillings. I have got to live, haven't I? They can't fine me forty bob if they don't let me earn it; they don't mind where it comes from as long as they get their money.' Saddening proofs, all these facts, that even the impersonal authority of the State knows how to combine propriety with profit.

has been committed on other occasions. There is the idea, for example, that animals are imperfect and inferior to men because they are 'only' stages of a development towards the human species. Recently this fanatical Darwinism has had to give way to the better understanding that each species is complete in itself and perfect in its own right. And the same arrogance appears in the concept of history as a progressive development in which all the greatness of past periods served only as preparation for the glorious days in which we happen to live.

Contrary to this narrow-minded and prejudiced mode of assessing the merits of a phenomenon according to arbitrary standards, we must try to discover the nature of any phenomenon and to assess its virtue, biological as well as moral, by the way and the extent to which it fulfils its own nature and serves its own essential purposes.

*

The next form of sexual relationship which we have to examine according to this methodical principle is the 'affair'.

In common parlance the term 'affair' is used with a slightly derogatory inflection, but for want of a better word I use it here as a kind of technical term for a very serious matter. *I mean by it a sexual, extra-matrimonial relationship with a person with whom one is in love.* Sexual development through childhood and adolescence is a gradual and orderly preparation of the body and mind for marriage as the form of mature sexuality. By commerce with prostitutes the young man has won his first laurels and suffered his first defeats, and now in the affair he discovers something entirely new: the emotional contact, the experience of 'belonging' to another person. The playmate of a group of children, later the customer of a prostitute, becomes now a real 'partner'. A primarily personal-emotional contact seeks its expression in the physical sphere also. The affair is the last station before the youth embarks on the long and perilous journey into married life. It is a kind of dress rehearsal for the permanent union.

It is interesting to watch how the three characteristics of the association with prostitutes – anonymity, timelessness, and lack of significance – change in this new form of relationship. The *anonymity* is lifted, the girl has now a name: perhaps only a Christian name, or even a pet name, but all the same a name which identifies her as a person, an unexchangeable individual being.

But far more important is the factor of *Time*. The affair has a duration, although a limited one. It is quite essential that every affair has a predestined end. The whole structure of the affair, as well as every detail of it, is determined by the fact that right from the outset it carries in itself the germ of its end. True, there are affairs which are terminated only by the death of one of the partners, but in such a case the death has occurred before the affair has outlived its own span of life. Another more frequent reason for such a protracted affair is fear of marriage, mostly on the part of the man, who gets stuck in this preliminary form of relationship for fear of the definite one: hence such an affair is more a living corpse than a live relationship. I do not forget, of course, that often enough external circumstances prevent people from getting properly married, but these cases are of no psychological interest, because most of the obstacles could be surmounted with some effort and goodwill. An affair does not tend to 'grow' into marriage, and in cases in which this seems to happen one might better say that it has deteriorated into one: because such a perpetuation is alien to its very nature, and consequently more often than not proves a grievous mistake, because the two people concerned match each other only in those respects which make a short relationship most happy but a lasting one completely unbearable. How much grief would be spared if lovers were always conscious that they have entered only into a transitory relationship, that they are permitted to walk together only for a short stretch of life, and will be torn asunder by the inexorable law of their association.

The reasons for the death of an affair are as diverse as for the death of men. Most die of old age, some by external accidents, some of boredom; the soul, and the reason for being, of an affair is love, however immature and imperfect, and love, or better the emotional element in it, must die, and with its soul dies the affair too. There is not much to be said about many of these cases, but there are some whose expiration is of a distinctly tragic nature. A Chinese proverb says: 'Enjoy yourself, it is later than you think.' If this is true of anything, it is true of an affair: quite unexpectedly something has gone wrong between the two, they believe it is still high noon, they cling together and won't have it that the sun is already setting on the horizon, and an episode of their lives has come to an end.

In contrast to an association with a prostitute, the affair has *significance.* Man is essentially alone and lonely, and from this isolation he cannot be saved by someone else but only by himself through the fact that he loves, that he belongs to another human being. This opening-up of ourselves is the great liberating function of love, and the affair is the first experience of this miracle and the first revelation of its effect: by belonging to someone else we belong to the world at large, far from losing individuality we find it for the first time. For 'whosoever will save his life shall lose it'.

This 'belonging to' is distinctly different from any other relationship because it embraces the whole personality – not only the mind but the body as well. Therefore sexuality is an essential, indispensable constituent of an affair, and the genital function is the instrument and symbol of the dovetailing of the two personalities. Nevertheless the affair is in all respects an incomplete relationship, therefore coitus as the complete physical relationship is not yet essential, and often enough in an affair sexual practices of a kind that in a perfect relationship are only preliminary and preparatory to the coitus are all that is intended and achieved. Because of this essential incompleteness the woman partner in an affair is always a '*demi-vierge*', as Prévost in a once sensational novel calls his heroine, whether or not this may be anatomically quite correct in a given case.

The sexual union in an affair is an end in itself and is not meant to transcend itself by producing a child, because a child is a symbol of permanency which, as we know, is contrary to the nature of an affair. There are many practical reasons why such a couple dreads and tries to avoid having a child, but apart from them the only finally valid reason for this reluctance is the inadequacy of their relationship for the production of a child.

The affair is by one dimension richer than all the previously discussed forms of sexuality: in its social aspect. Here the incompleteness of an affair is most clearly revealed and is the reason for the insoluble conflict inherent in this relationship. The appropriate domain of the affair is privacy, but on many occasions it is dragged into the open or the public intrudes into its intimacy. The couple want to realize their togetherness by sharing life with each other – and that is where the trouble starts: for the affair is only a part-time occupation, commanding only the interest of leisure hours, and almost inevitably the man and the woman share only the sunny side of life. And all these limitations are at the expense of the woman. She must accept it that her friend's work comes first, that the essential parts of his life are more or less kept from her, and that factually and symbolically she is relegated to a side-street. Again, if he takes her out, new conflicts may arise: many of the qualities which make her lovable and attractive as a lover lose their value in public and quite unessential ones come to the fore: her manners, how she dresses, her tastes. In marriage the whole of the personality matters, in an affair only parts and aspects of it.

Having an affair marks a quite essential step in our development – and not only in the sexual field. We must always bear in mind that sexuality is only one part of our life among several others. On the other hand the sexual function is part of the functioning of our whole personality, it is dependent on and determined by that whole for good or evil. Hence, a weak personality will have a weak sexuality, an immature person an immature sexuality, an exemplary person will have an exemplary sex life. A second consequence of this basic fact is that our sexual development follows closely the development of all the other functions of our personality.

A child's growing into the world is, according to Charlotte Buehler, at first tentative and provisional. The second decade of our life is a period of 'trial and error' in which we try to establish ourselves in positions which are specific and are, at least by intention, final: this is true of our occupation, social status, and sex relationship. And here we meet a very strange fact: we spend many years in preparing ourselves mentally and technically for a career – twelve to fifteen years, for instance, in the medical profession; we go through an often very strenuous social training: but we are expected, without the slightest instruction, training, or experience, to know how to treat a woman and to find at the first attempt the one with whom we could live for ever! This is rather odd. There is only one other activity into which men stumble completely untrained – politics; and the results hardly recommend the method.

Women are total strangers to men, living in a world totally different from ours, as we shall see presently, and this is their virtue and their danger. Their emotions and reactions, arising from a different background, are different from men's, and different women show these differences in different ways. In his morally, perhaps highly valued, but practically calamitous innocence and ignorance, how can a young man know how to treat these precious and complex creatures adequately and successfully? He does not know. Nor does he know what tremendous importance, often enough decisive for the rest of her life, her first sexual experience has for a woman.

He does not know that disillusionment breeds contempt, and that contempt is the next-door neighbour to hate.[1] Lost in the immensity of his task, he simply carries on, and tramples down all the sweetness, fragrance, and tenderness that have been so carefully preserved for and so lovingly offered to him – a bull in the bedroom, no less destructive than in a china shop. Of course, I do not suggest by any means that having affairs is the panacea for this wrecking of marriages, but it is the only means to protect them against this particular danger; there will always be a few talented men who will not need instruction and practice, and on the other hand there are vast numbers of people incapable of learning anyway, but in between these extremes are the many who can be saved. If the purists and other people who claim to have a say in these matters knew the tragedies which take place behind the curtains of the bridal

1. The French novelists do know this. One, whose name I have unfortunately forgotten, invented this delicious scene: a man was very much in love with a young actress, without any success. One day she rang him up: would he take her to the country for the week-end? He did, and his surprise and joy reached a climax when he discovered that he was obviously the first man in her life. All went well, and on Monday morning when they prepared to go back to town, she gave him the explanation for his puzzling adventure: 'I am engaged to be married to a man who, I suppose, is your greatest friend. I know that women can sometimes never forgive a man for any mistake on the first occasion – and I asked your help in order to protect my fiancé from this risk.' A bit cynical, no doubt, but what psychology!

chamber, they would with less complacency trust the omnipotence of instincts which, incidentally, they have done their very best to nip in the bud.

Trial and error! This implies association with several women, particularly if one takes into account that affairs are short-lived. Thus the idea arose that man is promiscuous or polygamous by nature. And not only for this reason, but also because many grown-up men pretend to need change, saying that they cannot confine themselves to one woman only, that any woman loses her sexual attraction after some time, and so forth. The fact that these men feel that way cannot be denied, but it does not prove that these reactions are natural and therefore normal. On the contrary, they are abnormal in every respect. It is true that the purely physical attraction of a sexual partner gets less and less, particularly if the sensation of novelty which is always an important element of the stimulus has worn thin. But this applies only to the purely physical urge, and this physical urge never exists as such in a grown-up person, but is, as we have seen before, always embedded in an emotional contact – love – which keeps it alive and renewed. But love also lasts only for a limited space of time; that is why affairs, too, are doomed to come to an end. And only the closeness of marriage guarantees a lasting emotional and physical attraction – if it is a real marriage. Hence, if a grown-up man knows only the passing stir and satisfaction of the physical urge, he must need change and variety, and proves thereby his immaturity.

Very different, on the other hand, is the position of a growing youth. He needs no more change and variety of women than a man at any age, but he needs variegated experience of women; in other words, what he wants is not just pleasure nor women as objects, but rather as means to attain his own perfection for the benefit of his future marriage. He does not reject permanency as incompatible with his instinctive needs, but he is not yet mature enough to attain it. For these reasons a transitory relationship is the only one a young man can accomplish, and is at the same time an experience he essentially needs in order to develop.

*

All these facts seem to prove conclusively that a sexual relationship of the kind we called an 'affair' is an essential step in our psychological development towards sexual maturity. It will now be quite interesting to inquire whether such premarital sexual relationships have existed in previous civilizations, and what part they have played in the sexual development of mankind. In order to put the results of this ethnological research into proper perspective a few critical remarks will be useful, the more so as we shall have recourse to ethnology on several occasions in the subsequent chapters. Every technically conceivable form of sexual relationship has been found at some time somewhere among some peoples, and had they not been factually observed they should have been postulated, because everything possible must also be real. Hence for any hypothesis about the nature or origin of the human sex relationship the customs of one or several peoples could be cited as proofs. But most of these various forms are no more than freaks, trials, and errors of Nature, and it is easy to point out the main trend of development. About the origin of this trend arguments are possible, as the most 'primitive' races or tribes still living have a history of several hundred thousand years behind them. They stand accidentally at the beginning of our known history, but certainly not at the beginning of the human race, and their modes of behaviour need by no means have been the first to exist. One may even doubt whether there has been much of a development during the pittance of a few thousand years of our history, because the moral codes and modes of sexual relationship among these primitive people show all the features of our own. Moreover, it would not be easy to disprove the contention that what there is of development in historical times has rather a downward trend.

This makes untenable the idea, much cherished by the giants of ethnology like Bachofen, Morgan, and Lubbock, that in the beginning was the darkness of promiscuity upon the face of the deep and that the moral genius of Western humanity has gradually produced from this chaos the heights of mid nineteenth-century prudery. The importance of this problem may justify a quotation from E. Westermarck's *History of Human Marriage*: 'Even if some of the statements are right, and the intercourse between the sexes among a few people is, or has been, promiscuous, it would be a mistake to infer that these utterly exceptional cases represent a stage of human development which mankind, as a whole, has gone through. Further, nothing would entitle us to consider this promiscuity as a survival of the primitive life of man, or even as a mark of a very rude state of society. It is by no means among the lowest peoples that sexual relations most nearly approach to promiscuity.' On the other hand, some of the lowest races on earth, as for example the Veddahs (Ceylon), are truly monagomous people and hold that 'death alone separates husband and wife'.

The same applies to premarital intercourse. There are numerous peoples among whom premarital intercourse is very rare and unchastity in women is considered a disgrace. With the aborigines in New South Wales, for example, the two sexes are kept strictly apart. But among many other races the unmarried girl may have sexual intercourse with young men – provided she takes only one lover at a time and is careful not to have a child. With the Maoris it is a generally accepted custom for the children of a chieftain to have affairs with ordinary subjects of their father. After such an affair has come to an end these partners drop back to their previous social status and marry members of their own class. If the daughter of a chief happens to have a child by such a liaison, this love-child, as it is called, is brought up as a full member of the family, with all rights except the right of succession. In countries as far distant from each other as South America and Lapland, or among the hill tribes in North Arakan and many others, chastity is a disadvantage rather than an asset, as far as the chances of the girl's getting married are concerned, because it casts a slur on her sexual desirability. Oddly enough, and affording a strong hint at the uniformity of mankind, the same custom still exists among the Austrian mountain people, incidentally the stronghold of Central European Catholicism. But the identity goes even further, for in the South Seas it must be a man of the same tribe, while in Austria only a man of the same village is eligible, presumably because the chances of later marriage are thus the greatest. It may be worth pointing out how even these peoples instinctively feel the essential difference between an affair and marriage: to have an affair the man and woman must be of the same tribe, whereas among the same peoples the law of exogamy (marriage outside the tribe) is sacred. Whether outraged morality or a proprietary feeling or jealousy is the motive, the punishment of a seducer among these more or less primitive peoples is savagely cruel, often enough including death, whereas in our temperate emotional climate the value of a wife's virtue can be assessed in hard cash, according to the damages awarded by the divorce courts to the insulted husband.

Thus we find free premarital intercourse, affairs in our sense, as a widespread form of sex relationship among peoples whose sexual morality we have no right to put on a lower level than ours. This is all the more noteworthy as neither social, economic, nor any other barriers to early marriage exist among them.

There is a last problem which claims consideration: the problem of chastity or, as it more often seems to be, hostility to sex. Why has there always been a taboo on sexual activity and enjoyment, and why have these only been permitted with restrictions and safeguards? Although this is one of the few cardinal problems of our existence, a satisfactory answer has, at any rate to my knowledge, not yet been given.

There is, first, the fact that marriage has at all times and everywhere been considered the natural state into which young people must enter as soon as it is permitted by their physical development. The Hebrew proverb: 'He who has no wife is no man' sums up the genuine feeling of mankind. And the Chinese, the most family-conscious people, even went so far as to believe that the spirits of all boys and girls who died in infancy would be married to each other. But this insistence on marriage was, as I said, more the expression of a true conception of human nature than a sexual consideration. Sex seems not to have played a great part in it. Occasionally, of course, it does, as for instance in the very strange advice St Paul gave to the unmarried and widows: 'But if they have not continency, let them marry, for it is better to marry than to burn.' (1 Corinthians vii. 9.) This institutional morality prevails up to the present day, although it debases marriage to a means to a poor end, making it the lesser of two evils, a choice, incidentally, on which not every married man would agree.

A second source of the high esteem in which chastity has been held since time immemorial is the idea of the uncleanness of sex. This idea is deeply rooted in magic and superstition. For example, it was supposed that the blood from the female genitals was poisonous. I have on a previous occasion mentioned the custom of offering young girls to kings, priests, or foreigners for defloration. The original idea was that the bridegrooms of these women should be protected by other men, who drew the poison on themselves, kings and priests being immune, and about the foreigners no one bothered. All over the world and through all ages the idea has spread that he who wants to devote himself to the service of the gods must observe celibacy, men and women alike; and there is great wisdom in that, not because of the sinfulness of sex, but because of the weakness of men, which debases even the purest. The sex relationship, unlike any other, involves the whole personality, and men are liable to confuse this claim for wholeness with servitude. There are a few exceptions to this universal rule, as for instance the Jews and Lutherans; the reason I think is that in these two religions the priest is devoid of any mystical significance and does not mediate between man and the divine.

But this idea of the impurity of sex or its tendency to distract men from higher pursuits, the undying lure of the paradisal apple, is by no means confined to the religious sphere. Four hundred years before Jesus insisted on the necessity of deserting one's family to follow him, Plato had already exhorted his disciples, almost in the same words, to cast away all human bonds in order to be ready for the service of the spirit. This is undoubtedly true of those exalted religions to which these great leaders called men, but the very reverse is true on the lower levels on which we spend our daily life. There is no greater fallacy than the assertion that love and marriage debar men from great achievements. On the contrary, the peace of body and mind, as well as the tremendous uplift, emotional lucidity and spiritual awareness which a happy love life provides, are the prerequisites of greatness. That there are exceptions to this rule, as to any other, is not to be wondered at.

One is almost led to the conclusion that it is fear that made men surround love and sex with all sorts of vetoes and regulations. How disgraceful is the word 'illicit' love; why does one need a licence to enjoy the greatest happiness an otherwise rather parsimonious Fate has granted men? There has been for some time a strong trend operating in Anglo-Saxon countries, on both sides of the Atlantic, towards liberation from the puritanical restriction of the natural love life, and, as always happens in such periods, the movement has been accompanied by too much immodesty and ostentation. I remember a professor of sociology from one of the famous American universities who visited Vienna. We became friends, and one day he surprised me with his discovery of the high standard of sexual morality in Vienna: he had counted – how truly American! – the lovers in public places in Vienna, and found their numbers amazingly small compared with those of the courting couples sprawling over the lawns of the Royal Parks in London, or the petting parties in cars lining the highways in the States. Almost apologetically I explained to him that the Viennese do that sort of thing indoors – they have already learned to be discreet.

The following figures taken from an article in *The Lancet* (1 February 1947) give an idea of the actual solution of this 'problem'. In 1938–43 the average number of women who bore extra-maritally conceived children was for each year almost exactly 80,000 (1 in 3 of all first maternities). It may be safely estimated that 1 in 10 of all women have sex relationships outside marriage. In 1938 40 per cent of all girls marrying under the age of 20 were already pregnant; 30 per cent of those aged 20; and 20 per cent of those aged 21. These figures, impressive as they are – and it may be noted that they include two pre-war years – represent only those affairs in which something has gone wrong, that is to say, only a small fraction of those which actually have existed. Better sex instruction might have saved a good many of the 480,000 unfortunate, because unwanted, children from being brought into this world. But I do not believe that an intensive effort at sex education would have prevented in the past, or will redress in the future, this surge towards freedom and naturalness, so palpably part of the general trend of history.

Nor is the ban on affairs justified as a measure for the protection of marriage. An affair is no menace to marriage – on the contrary it works, as I have tried to show, as its safeguard. But on the other hand, many a marriage has proved a failure because getting married was the only way a young couple knew of consummating their ardent, although only passing, love. Thus they wrecked it all – their love, their marriage, and their lives, for singleness of mind and finality of purpose is the privilege only of the mature.

If we ask again what attitude the educator should take towards the problems presented by the stages of development we have discussed in the last two chapters, the answer is: None – unless advice is explicitly asked for. The reason for this caution is, besides those already mentioned, the uselessness of such advice. If a young man asks whether he should go to a prostitute one should discourage him: for a normal adolescent would not ask. He would either do what he felt himself driven to, or his moral outlook would stop him even contemplating such a course. Those who do ask are not yet sufficiently grown up to take this step, and to recommend it would only increase their confusion. Such a young man should see a professional psychologist, because it is important, but not always easy, to decide whether his hesitation is the result of real moral restraint, is caused only by a slightly retarded development, or is the first visible symptom of neurotic repressions. At this stage any psychological difficulties can easily be put right, but if neglected they may lead to more serious troubles later on. It goes without saying that between these two extreme types a great many others confront us with the not so easy task of judiciously combining encouragement with warning.

All this applies just as well to the problem of starting an affair with a woman, although here the occasions on which advice is sought are still fewer. A considerable proportion of the patients who consult psychologists are, at least in years, grown-up men who have found it impossible to start a proper sexual life, or whose more or less forced attempts have led only to failures. All these men are neurotics who meet with difficulties in other walks of life also, but their sexual troubles are the most conspicuous and alarming.

They need, of course, systematic psychological treatment, which, if circumstances are not too unpropitious, has a very good chance of success. During such treatment there always comes a phase in which educational guidance is an important part of the reconstruction of the personality. And over and over again the patient must be warned that any attempt to force the issue is doomed to failure, that not every woman he happens to meet is an easy prey or just a guinea-pig, that Nature must be given a chance of recovering and asserting herself. The doctor must never give the signal 'go ahead', but almost always he, and the patient, are surprised by a sudden and unexpected success. Psychologists are gardeners who know the virtue of patience, and so must the true educator. But both psychologist and educator must be even more, and here is an earnest warning: no one has the right, or must be permitted, to take part in sexual education who has not a proper sexual life himself! One must have experienced oneself what one wants others to experience; no one can properly assess the sweetness of grapes which have all his life been beyond his reach, and ignorance, resentment, frustration, and piety are the worst of counsellors.

*

In the preceding chapters I have tried to present a kind of slow-motion picture of the sexual development. All its stages – infantile sexuality, masturbation, homosexuality, commerce with prostitutes, and affairs – may appear to have been unduly drawn out, but this was necessary in order to study their features in a close-up. That they are real stages of an intelligible process has, I hope, been demonstrated, but whether they are also necessary steps in practice is impossible to say. This would be a matter of statistics, and the only people who would be in a position to collect sufficient data are psychologists, but they, by the very nature of their work, meet only those people whose development has gone wrong. It would certainly be ideal if a young man and a young woman discovered through their love the mystery of physical union, which then would be no more a mere technique, but a real manifestation of life. But this book, written by a medical man, is not about ideals or for paragons of perfection, but about and for Mary and John. No doubt many men can take all the hurdles in one great jump, and land safely and successfully in the bridal chamber, but for the majority a more pedestrian pace may be a safer way to this goal. Besides, and this seems a very important qualification, much depends on what one means by success. There may be many who can play a simple tune on the piano with one finger or two, but real music needs all the fingers of both hands. It always strikes me as odd that we willingly spend so much time, effort, and money in order to learn to play an instrument, or, for that matter, to earn our livelihood; but that we trust so confidently to our 'instincts' to master the most difficult art of loving – and Nature is not always willing to justify these expectations.

The greatest difficulty in dispassionately discussing the problem of sex education, as well as in carrying it out properly, is the fact that it is so inextricably involved in the religious, ethical, social, even the political views of the educator. And these are premises about which no argument is possible, barely permissible. But two principles stand out above the controversy of opinions:

> If the atmosphere of the home provides for a proper development of the child's whole personality no special sex education is needed.
>
> Those who stress the sinfulness, immorality, and dangerousness of sexuality do their very best to stifle the sexual as well as the personal development of their charges right from the start.

And here, at last, is a piece of comfort for those frightened by the magnitude of the task that may confront them. As I have said before, one's educational capacities are not often put to the test. I myself, as the father of two grown-up sons, as one-time teacher and trusted friend of a very large number of university students, and last but not least as a professional man, can remember only a very few such inquiries from what I should call normal young men. And I am not quite certain whether I have even in these few cases said the right things. But what I wanted to say to educators on many occasions was: 'Come on, gentlemen, let us forget all the pomposity and learnedness, and let us truthfully admit that the affair carries its justification in itself: it embodies all the blissful happiness of being in love, and the glory of being young, and its sentimental souvenirs and faded memories feed the nostalgic pleasures of our autumn.' I once read a lovely saying: 'We all believe that our first love will be the last, and that the last was the first true one.' How very true psychologically, but how comforting to know, at least in retrospect, that we were wrong on both occasions.

But ... there is still another aspect of this problem: nothing that has been said in this chapter must be interpreted as an apologia for any sort of naturalism, because we know already that such a condition never exists in human behaviour. Always the instincts are permeated and modified by the spirit, and this union finds expression in the 'forms' of life: style, customs, institutions, conventions, etc. The most complete institutionalization of our life was achieved during the ages in which the Church ruled supreme. The Renaissance and the Reformation were the first revolts against this bondage. Another height was reached during the period of absolutism in the seventeenth century. The French Revolution broke the fetters in the political field, whereas in the field of private and social morals institutionalism and conventionalism lingered on until the second half of the last century; then the two great wars swept away the last vestiges. Whether one calls this 'progress' and 'conquest of freedom', or 'decay of style in living', depends on temperament, taste, or the philosophy of history one has adopted. But now man stands alone, unsupported by faith or belief, and burdened with the full responsibility for his actions. One may question whether he discharges this responsibility with success.

But in the sexual field we have obtained true freedom, there can be no doubt about it. It is a well-known but apparently not sufficiently appreciated fact that in periods of greatest moral formalism, e.g. in the seventeenth and eighteenth centuries, sexual morality was at its lowest level. It was as if men and women used sexuality as a safety-valve to release the high emotional tension caused by oppression in all the other walks of life. In our time this pressure has been removed in general, and in the sexual field particularly, all the crippling restrictions have been lifted, the false romanticism and sentimentality have gone, together with crinolines, corsets, and *billets doux*. Men and women have become human and 'know' each other. Admittedly this new-gained freedom is being savagely misused, but this cannot obscure the fact that it is real freedom and not only libertinage. The discarded bonds of tribal taboos, religious prohibitions, and traditional customs are now replaced by what I have tried to describe as essential morality – protected by tact and decency, and essentially embraced by the unchallengeable and unchangeable institution of marriage.

CHAPTER 7

# ON LOVE

ASKED what love is most people will say: an emotion, though on reflexion some may hesitate, pondering what kind of emotion it may be. Commonly shared as this notion is, it is incorrect. It would be foolish to deny, of course, that there is a strong emotional element in love, but it is only a part of it, and not even an essential one. To emotions applies what I have said earlier about instincts: they are signals informing us about happenings in the depths of our existence, with the one difference that instincts belong to the biological sphere whereas emotions are connected with events on the personal level. Contentment, for instance, informs our conscious mind that a task has been done; whether objectively well done or not is less important than that the tension inherent in the nature of tasks or duties is being relieved. Happiness, that so often and so badly discussed and ill-defined emotion, is nothing but contentment on a higher level and spread over the whole of our existence. It indicates that we are in a state of harmony with our material, human, and spiritual environment. Fear and all kindred emotions, such as sense of inferiority or insecurity, indicate that we are maladjusted, ill-prepared for a particular task or a particular situation. And anguish stands to fear as happiness to contentment: it springs from a sense of complete annihilation. When we find ourselves *vis-à-vis de rien* the bottom is knocked out of our existence, and the future is cut off without hope.

Then what precisely is the state of our being that reveals itself in the emotion of love? The answer can be put very briefly: *Love is the very opposite of anguish. To be in love means to be anchored in the safest anchorage, that is, in complete union with another human being.* It means the opening up of unlimited horizons, the extension of our existence far beyond the boundaries of our personality, means richness and fullness through fulfilment. The intensity of the emotion of loving, frequently called passion, is proportionate to the degree of self-surrender.

An apparently far-fetched analogy may serve to highlight this quite fundamental concept. Religion is considered by most people a matter of 'feeling' or emotion. In fact, emotions have just as much or as little to do with the religious experience as they have with the experience of love between man and woman. The essence of the religious experience is striving after union with the divine, and the emotion of religious ecstasy indicates that this union has been achieved. Human love and religious experience are not identical by any means, but the intentions and emotions forming them are closely analogous. This is the only reason and justification for the use of the expression 'Love of God'. And as sexuality is the supreme manifestation of the closest possible union with another being, and as sexual terms are the only ones in which human language can express such a union, mystics in their attempts to describe their ectasies use sexual words, well knowing how pitifully inadequate they are. This fact has misled some quick-witted but careless psychologists into the absurd, almost obscene, contention that religious ecstasy is 'nothing but' a sexual experience.

This concept of love, seemingly so simple but in fact highly complex, as the intended and achieved existential union of man and woman, has a long history. At its beginning looms the heroic figure of Plato, who laid down its pattern as he did for so many other aspects of European thought. It has since been repeated by a host of thinkers who have expressed the same ideas, only altering his philosophical language into terms current in the historical periods in which they have lived.

In the *Symposium* Plato contends that erotic passion is the realization of and delight in beauty, that is to say the Idea of Beauty as such is the supreme reality of which all beautiful intramundane things are only derivatives. This realization tends towards a complete fusion of the Self with the Supreme and Universal and has complete unity with it as its aim – 'Love is the ascent from non-being to being'. This holistic concept considers individuality as a 'misfortune', a 'grievous error' from which fusion with or return to the whole brings the only salvation – and love is the way to it.[1] All the characteristics which in the course of history have been considered essential for the state of being in love were already known to Plato. First among them is the sense of destiny, the inescapable power that throws the lovers into each other's arms. Plato finds an explanation in the already mentioned myth of the hermaphrodites: 'But if one of them has met *his true* half, then they are loath to be apart from each other, even for the shortest time; and those who are now reunited for life cannot even tell what they really want from each other.' Then, there is complete fusion through ecstasy and enthusiasm. And finally, the inevitable catastrophe, death overtakes all true lovers: having attained their supreme aim, fusion with the All, they have forfeited any possibility of returning to their previous existence as separate individuals.

Christianity introduced an entirely different concept of love, called Agape. It is not the flaming passion, which annihilates the individuality of the lover in the ecstatic fusion with the absolute, but a communion between two equal individuals, as exemplified in the 'marriage' of Christ to the Church. This opposition of Eros and Agape is the theme which in many variations and with considerable monotony runs through the history of European speculation about love.

For our purpose it is not necessary to discuss this history at length, but one or two interesting facts may be mentioned. The general trend has been to water down metaphysics to psychology. What in antiquity was thought of as the influence of external powers is nowadays explained as the working of our subconscious mind. The irresistible power of passionate love was originally attributed to the wrath or malice of the gods. During the Middle Ages it was represented as the effect of love potions which the lovers voluntarily or unknowingly drank. In modern times we take it for granted as one of the many capacities of the human mind, or at worst as the effect of pathological complexes. Romance has been reduced to the status of an almost morbid excitement.

It is interesting too to observe that love, as we understand it, which is almost the sole preoccupation of our literature and

1. Hegel, the greatest modern representative of the holistic philosophy, means precisely this when he speaks of individuality as 'essential malady'.

our day-dreams, is a comparatively recent experience. It was almost unknown in antiquity and is not understood in the East. The naturalistic part of it, the purely sensuous desire and delight, were of course known, but were looked upon as frenzy or madness. But the above statement needs a qualification of a general character. It is a law of history that every human faculty and consequently every possible form of its expression has been realized at all times throughout history. Only the proportion changes from one period to another; that is to say, what is the rule at one period is in another the rare exception. Thus only a few instances of romantic love were known in antiquity, such as the love of Hero and Leander, Dido and Aeneas, Sappho and Phaon. In fact, the ignorance of ancient and Eastern peoples of passionate love is not surprising, because the concept of individuality, the condition of this kind of love, was at that time unknown. 'Eros' meant only being in love with an Idea. And although the concept of the uniqueness of the individual soul is the central tenet of Christianity, Agape, the Christian love, meant only the communion of two individuals without passion.

In the twelfth century something new and quite unexpected happened: two ardent, passionate lovers, Abelard and Héloise, stepped on to the stage of history, and shortly afterwards the first great epic of love, the *Romance of Tristram and Iseult*, was written. It presents, as Denis de Rougemont points out in his brilliant analysis, the two main characteristics of modern love: the conflict of *cortesia*, which is courtly love, with feudal law (a version of the conflict of Eros and Agape) and secondly the union of love and death. From a psychological point of view it is most interesting that the poems betrays the characteristics of a period transition: the ancient idea of a blind fate that overtakes the lovers is symbolized by the love potion which Tristram drinks. More important, the lovers do not yet love one another, but Love itself, the 'being in love'; all Iseult needs is her passionate dream, and her lover is needed only to keep the flame alight (Rougemont). This idea is a Platonic heritage.

For the evolution of the modern idea of love a further element had to be added. It was provided at the Renaissance, by the discovery of individuality in its own right, as it were, free of all religious implications. Thus the scene was set for the appearance of the first modern love poetry: Petrarch's sonnets to Laura in the first half of the fourteenth century. 'The language of love has at last become the language of the heart', as Rougemont puts it. Abelard and Héloise were followed by Paolo Malatesta and Francesca da Rimini, and, most celebrated of all lovers, Romeo and Juliet; they were the protagonists of an endless procession of real lovers, and imaginary ones created by the imagination of countless poets; love was secularized, and nowadays the tragedies of love become news items in daily papers.

It is indeed strange that professional psychology, medical no more than academic, has contributed hardly anything to our knowledge of the intimate or essential nature of love. Curiously enough this task has been left to the philosophers, people whom we should have expected to be least qualified to deal with it, and they have done extremely well. To put the point in a nutshell: all modern theories of love are Platonism in psychological disguise. The idea of beauty and perfection has been brought down from metaphysical heights and transformed into the concept of the essential value of the individual, who is no longer the mere embodiment of a lofty idea, but the creator of his own value and worth. Max Scheler, whose views are representative of modern phenomenological philosophy, sees the essence of love as the capacity to grasp the gist, the central value of a personality, in a single perception. This value is not calculated, is not an estimate obtained by counting up the good qualities of a given person and balancing them against the bad ones. Love disregards manifest qualities and sees right through them down to the true essential value. Furthermore, love divines all the talents, the still dormant potentialities, of the beloved, brings them to life, and thus increases his value.

The same view is held by Vladimir Solovyev, the great Russian philosopher: 'We know in mind and through mind the divine image which every human being contains, but through love it is known in the concrete and in life. Through love we assert the unconditional significance of a personality. But to assert that an individual possesses this significance in his particularity and separateness is absurd and blasphemous: the ideal content and the empirical person are only two separate aspects of the selfsame person, and only through steadfast faith and the insight of love can we know that the ideal content is not merely subjective but is the Truth which shines through the actual phenomenon.' This is the Christian version of the holistic philosophy. But Solovyev elaborates, indeed makes central in his teaching, another theory which German philosophy has only lightly touched. He says that love as the effectual abrogation of egoism is a valid justification and salvation of individuality. 'The meaning of love, speaking generally, is the justification and deliverance of individuality through sacrifice of egoism.' And finally, 'Only false spirituality and an impotent moralism could wish to replace sex love by any other kind of love, because only sex love creates the homogeneity, equality, and reciprocity between two persons which alone exclude egoism. The authentic man in the fullness of his ideal personality can only exist in complete fusion of man and woman.'

Besides the ancient Greek, the modern German, and the Christian Russian, I want to call still another witness, the Spaniard José Ortega y Gasset, a man of truly European stature.[1] In his essay *On Love* he writes: 'Love is a flood which wells up from the depths of our personality. It is not a static thus-being, but moves up towards the beloved. Love is an emotional action, a warm, affirmative participation with the other being for its own sake. In the depth of his being the lover feels himself unconditionally united with the object of his love; it is a "vital, ontologic altogetherness". Love is yearning for the perfect. The sweetness of love consists in that the lover becomes in a "metaphysical sense" transparent and finds his final satisfaction in the amalgamation with the beloved. In this "state of Grace" life loses all its ponderousness, and with the magnanimity of a great lord the lover smiles at all his fellow men.'

Last but not least we will not forget the great panegyric upon love found in the thirteenth chapter of the first Corinthians: 'Love never faileth.' 'For we know in part, and we prophesy in

1. Max Scheler, *Wesen und Formen der Sympathiegefühle* (Bonn, 1929); Denis de Rougemont, *L'Amour et l'Occident* (Paris, 1939) (English translation: *Passion and Society* (London, 1941); Vladimir Solovyev, *The Meaning of Love* (London, 1945); José Ortega y Gasset, *Uber Liebe* (Stuttgart, 1932).

part: but when that which is perfect is come, that which is in part shall be done away.' This brief survey bears out what I said before. All those great thinkers say the same, echoing the words of Plato, and what they say amounts to this: *Love is not an emotion or a desire, but a cognitive act in which we grasp the very essence of another person;* a '*connaissance du cœur*' as Pascal calls it. But we do not know this person in an abstract or detached way, as we know scientific facts; we move towards him and merge into him. It is a 'vital', an 'ontological', or, as I should put it in a modern term, an 'existential' knowing and merging. This difficult concept needs an explanation which I will try to give in some detail, though it will be only an approximation.

The lover lives in a world of his own, wherein only that which is lovable exists and matters. It is like entering a country in which only its own currency is valid, and no other. This does not mean that the lover disregards or passively accepts other values – they are simply non-existent for him, just as a real scientist is oblivious to the economic rewards of his discoveries, or the profiteer to aesthetic values. By comparison with the centre of the personality, on which the lover's gaze is fixed, peripheral qualities and faculties lose their significance. That a woman possesses fair hair, a lovely voice, and a splendid figure, that she plays the piano well and is widely read, is very important, as one may rather crudely say, for her commercial value, but not for her lover; these attributes are not assets in the exclusive world of love. On the other hand, qualities that may be unpleasant from the common point of view do not deter the lover, because for him they have no more existence than the attractive ones. Therefore, if a man says he loves a woman 'because' of what she is or can do, he may appreciate her in many ways, but he does not love her in the true sense of the word. But he certainly does love her if he desires her 'in spite of' her weaknesses and the criticism of others. It is quite safe to say that the more irrational and incomprehensible love is the truer it is. There is no greater fallacy than the adage that love is blind; the grain of truth in the saying is that love is blind for everything outside the realm of love, but it opens the eyes for everything that is love-worthy.

It cannot be emphasized strongly enough that this miraculous capacity which love bestows on the lovers consists in the power to discover in the object of love virtues which it actually possesses but which are invisible to the uninspired; they are not invented by the lover, who decorates the beloved with illusory values: love is no self-deception. How imminent the danger of this misconception is can be learned from Stendhal. In his famous book *De l'Amour* he expounds exactly this idea. It is cleverly suggested in his simile of 'crystallization'. With all his theorizing and grumbling, Stendhal might have been a modern psychotherapist used to observing only the shadowy side of life and denouncing virtue as a camouflaged vice. In fact he was only an unloving man, who blamed love for his own ineptitude. The lover is like a water-diviner in whose hands the magic twig rotates when ordinary walking-sticks remain unaffected in the hands of many people, although they too were standing on a spot under which water flows.

The trend of thought opens up a magnificent vista. Faith is the result or the psychological expression of a complete union with the object of faith, be it God or a human being or an idea. To have faith, to believe, is a unique way of grasping this object and can neither be compared with nor assisted by any other kind of approach to reality. It is for instance completely incompatible with the approach, and therefore with the result, of reason. These two faculties operate on entirely different levels, and to say that the ascendancy of Reason during the last three centuries has destroyed Faith is a complete misrepresentation of history. Both these faculties can harmoniously stand side by side, as the great thinkers and scientists of the sixteenth and seventeenth centuries have convincingly proved. Faith 'moves mountains', which Reason never can do, whereas Reason discovers details and laws incomprehensible to Faith. 'Facts' and scientific discoveries can neither invalidate Faith nor 'prove' it. For the student of history the search after the historicity of a person or the authenticity of writings is of the greatest importance, but the believer does not care about such irrelevancies, because he knows he is in possession of, not the objective, but the absolute truth.

History shows that the faculty for religious faith is on the decline, and with it the belief in the brotherhood of man in the spiritual, not in the economic-equalitarian sense. But the implicit and unqualified faith of lovers in each other is in our disenchanted and impoverished world the last legacy of man's nobler pass. Thus, as I said earlier, the virtues of the beloved cannot arouse or explain love, nor can her vices destroy it. For the lover believes unhesitatingly in his beloved woman's way of being, her views and her achievements, and if 'experts' find fault with some of these, all the worse for the experts, because he, her lover, knows himself in possession of the '*vérités du cœur*', as Pascal calls them. The fact that the beloved exists is for him a miracle, newly revealed every new day – and miracles are 'natural' occurrences in the world of Faith and Love. Cardinal Newman said: 'A thousand difficulties do not make a doubt, as I see it.' And every true lover sees it too.

Love always begins suddenly. It need not always be the *coup de foudre*, the dramatic 'love at first sight', but even if a love seems to grow gradually from inconspicuous beginnings, even if one seems to start loving a person one has known for some time – even then, the beginning is sudden. It is a true illumination or conversion of much the same kind as happened once on the road to Damascus and has been experienced countless times since. In a moment the beloved person is suddenly 'there', in a way totally different from that in which she has been there all the time, changed beyond recognition, transfigured in the truest sense of the word. She is no longer this woman whom I have met and talked to so many times, but the 'one' – the only one – whom I now love. And I am changed too, down to the core of myself. Now, as never before, we 'know' each other, and entranced we enter the world of love. In this exclusive world are domiciled those whom one calls 'erotic beings' or 'exemplary lovers'. For them there is no return into the cold world of everyday life, nor can they breathe the rarefied air of their new abode for long, and death is the inevitable fate. That is why all the great lovers whose memory history has preserved die an unnatural death, as we call it; but it is most natural to them.

They know it, and with seeing eyes they go to their doom, because their love is more to them than their lives. This is their tragic fate. This passionate union also contains another element: Guilt. It is hard to see why, but it is a fact that all the great lovers incurred guilt: Hero was a priestess, Iseult was the wife of King Mark, Abelard was a cleric, the Veronese lovers had betrayed their loyalty to their warring families, Francesca was to be engaged to her lover's brother, and Mariana Alcoforada was a nun. Tragic guilt is the price of heroic passion.

The great loves of lesser people pass quickly through this, for them only initial, stage of fascination. As they have not climbed to the summits of passion, the lovers find their way back to earth, and the demonic power of passion changes into the constructive warmth of mutual belongings. Not only does this productive devotion bring to life all dormant potentialities of the beloved, but it also transforms in much the same way the lover himself; it is a mutual building-up of the two personalities right to the limits which their natures permit them to reach. This kind of love does not extinguish or enslave the personality, but enriches and liberates it. It is the strongest, perhaps the sole, stimulus and way to become, in the truest sense, ourselves. Fusion, the first stage of fascination, becomes in the second stage a union of two independent personalities. Rabindranath Tagore has described incomparably this process of parting and reuniting: the lover says to his partner: 'Free me from the enchantment and give me back the courage to offer you once more my liberated heart.' (I quote from memory, and render only the sense, and not the wording.) This dialectical process, by the way, seems to be characteristic of all kinds of spiritual experience shared by the great religious leaders, saints, and artists. If I may quote Caudwell once more: '[The lyric poet] is exhibiting the paradox of art – man withdrawing from his fellows into the world of art, only to enter more closely into communion with humanity.'

In most languages the word 'love' is used to describe all kinds of sympathetic relationships to things and persons, from ice-cream to the divine. This suggests that there is only one kind of love, which can be directed to various objects, such as food, books, one's country, women, God, etc., just as one turns a searchlight whose beam picks up an object from the darkness. This concept is psychologically quite untenable. This sympathetic turning to different objects is in each case a different action, its inner structure varies according to the differing nature of its several objects. Food one likes, one 'incorporates' it, which is a sort of 'fusion' on the material plane. Boys collect all kinds of things that usually are of no value or use to them, simply in order to 'possess' them. A lover of books also wants to possess them, but beyond and above this material desire for ownership he makes them his own, incorporates their content into his spiritual body. The attitude of a scientist towards the object of his researches and of a philosopher towards the problems of his thinking come very close to the idea of love. The devotion is already very similar to the self-surrender and sacrificial self-negation of a true lover. Many of the greatest men have testified to this. Nietzsche, for instance, said that 'Only from love springs the profoundest insight', and Hegel said that 'Only through loving one becomes one with the object' and 'One really knows only what one loves'. The Swiss historian I. v. Müller said, 'Ideas are born in the arms of a wise friend'. The discoveries made through this loving approach are not the property of those who made them. They belong to the world into which they are born, and the concept of plagiarism is a psychological absurdity, is valid only in a commercially-minded world. The closer we approach to the higher regions the more the possibility of 'possessing' the beloved object recedes and another element becomes dominant: reciprocity and response. In the love of a woman, the fullest realization of the idea of love, this reciprocity is essential, as has been shown earlier. The concept of possession destroys this reciprocity because possession is a unilateral action; one may possess the body of a woman during the fleeting moment of physical intercourse, but what love desires is not the factual woman one holds in one's arms, but only her personality, her soul, which is intangible and elusive. Sex love, let it be said over and over again, means insatiable participation in the existence of the beloved. Love is not a state which can be reached and in which our longing comes to rest: love is perpetual striving, unending uncertainty and insecurity, an everlasting act of creation.[1] This element of

1. An Indian myth presents this principle in a charming way: Anangarange, the God of Love, intervened in a matrimonial dispute between Shiva and his wife and was burned to death by the irate husband. When Shiva's wife interceded for him, Shiva brought him back to life, but only so far, that he remained without a material body and became materialized only through and during the embrace of two lovers. That is why he is called Anangarange, which means 'Shape of the shapeless'.

response becomes decisive and dominant in what is commonly called the Love of God. The religious act is by intention an aspiration for a merging with God, and the prayer in which this act is realized is intercourse with God, an existential dialogue, which requires a response. Strangely enough, the English language is the only one which expresses this basic fact, in that it speaks of prayer being 'answered', whereas all other peoples content themselves with having their prayer 'received' and 'acknowledged'. This fact, that prayer is answered, definitely established through a phenomenological analysis of religious experience, proves by itself that any concept or definition of religion other than communion with a personal God goes hopelessly wrong, because one cannot commune with or receive an answer from a moral principle or a pantheistic deity. But whether it is really permissible to speak of the 'love' of God is another question – it is a 'spiritual' love, perhaps, but love in its strict sense and fullness must involve physical contact as well. Sexual love alone fulfils this condition, and all other forms of 'love' are defective forms or, better, just metaphors. There is, finally, yet another form of contact, for which I have no other name than 'belonging to' – the indefinable but very real experience of being part of a whole: family, nation, humanity, or of all things inanimate and living. Through this union St Francis understood the tongues of the birds; the artisan 'understands' the intimate nature of the material in which he works; artists, scientists, philosophers 'understand' the call of an idea which wants to be embodied in thoughts, words, bronze, or stone. The essential definition of a genius, I think, is that he is a man who not only knows the laws of things, but experiences them in himself with self-evident certainty. This experience of pure being transcends even love.

Just in passing it may be pointed out that love, being what it is, cannot be measured; there are no yardsticks for this job, and consequently to call one love 'great' and another 'small', or to say that one has loved one woman 'more' than another, makes no sense. To these situations applies the principle I have just explained at some length: one does not love different people with the same love because the process of fusion and its result depend on both parts fused. One loves a personality with a 'big' love – if this inaccurate term may be used for a moment – and a small personality with a 'small' one, but it is a full love in either case. One may object that sometimes a great love is wasted on an unworthy object; this is undoubtedly true, but it is due to an error of judgement in overrating the love-worthiness of this person. But does this possibility not contradict our previous contention of the unerring certainty of love? It does, but not in principle, and only occasionally in practice, owing to the fallibility of men: external as well as internal circumstances, such as purely physical attraction, or fascination by some outstanding qualities which in themselves have nothing to do with love, may lead a loving heart astray, or may be mistaken for love. Not love errs, but only the lover may err. A small person can love with only a 'small' love which – however 'great' in relation to his stature – may be inadequate to the task of grasping the real value of the personality of the beloved.

I have said that our modern concept of love was born in the twelfth century in that the naturalistic aspect was then replaced or supplanted by romanticism. Love became so intimately linked up with suffering that suffering has ever since been considered an essential ingredient of the experience of love. It is difficult to see why. It is, of course, easy to invent a theory, particularly if one has a religious background, about the function of pain and suffering in man's life as a test of faith or as a warning of physical decay or spiritual lassitude – a way of thinking, incidentally, which modern science has also adopted on the basis of a rather arbitrary teleology – but none of these arguments carries conviction to anyone who was not already convinced of their worth. Therefore, I cannot do more here than to point to some facets of this problem.

Loving is a creative act, as we have seen, and therefore it holds all the bliss and all the suffering every productive man knows so well. Hardly ever, if at all, is the created work an adequate presentation of its idea. Similarly love is a yearning which cannot be satiated because it is an everlasting desire. This sense of inadequacy, this despair of one's ability, is the cause, or at least one cause, of the suffering which seems to be inherent in true love. For this we have the testimony of a few women who ought to know. Thus Mademoiselle de Lespinasse wrote to a friend: 'I love you as one ought to love – in despair.' And Mariana Alcoforado, the famous Portuguese nun and one of the greatest of lovers, wrote to her lover: 'I thank you from the bottom of my heart for the despair into which you have thrown me. Farewell; love me and make me suffer still more.' But there is still another aspect of this problem: not, as theologians and philosophers maintain, the purpose of suffering, but its actual effect, is a great opening-up of our spiritual and emotional sensitiveness, an unlocking of hitherto inaccessible spheres of life. In Kierkegaard's words: 'Despair is one of the maladies of which it can be said that it is the greatest misfortune not to have known it', because 'the awareness of the spirit can never be achieved but through despair'. This has, of course, nothing whatever to do with 'sublimation' in the Freudian sense: it is simply not true that frustrated sex creates love, or that repressed love changes into spirituality. Love and despair, joy and pain, are co-ordinated experiences, and both of them enhance our personality – if there is a personality capable of being enhanced, and not a lack of personality which only makes for bitterness and resentment.

Still another facet of the problem of suffering is the time-honoured conflict between love and any sort of 'ought', such as duty, loyalty, work, and the like.

In fact, it is a sham problem, derived from a rationalistic or materialistic and therefore defective psychology of the concept of 'decision'. One can make a decision only if the two things between which one has to decide have something, and if possible something measurable, in common. One can decide whether this or that business is more profitable. If one wants to buy a warm coat one can decide whether this or that one is preferable; but every woman knows only too well how difficult it is to decide whether this or that hat is more becoming. Decisions become more and more difficult to make, in fact they become almost fictitious, the higher up we move in the scale of values. And eventually we must recognize that decisions cannot be made between personal, and still less between spiritual, values, because the bearers or embodiments of such values are incomparable. *Essential problems of life permit of no solutions.* In the process of living, solutions of such ambiguous situations, or better, answers to such anxious questions, well up from the depths of our existence; we realize in a flash of revelation what is essential for us; one of the alternatives that a moment before still seemed important has paled into insignificance, all uncertainty has gone – and we 'know'. The genius of the English language, by the way, alone among the great European languages shows the difference between a rational 'decision' and a 'resolution' of a conflict: in English – although not only in England – one 'makes' a decision, but one 'takes' a resolve. That means, if I understand the psychological implications correctly, that we make decision on reasonable grounds consciously, whereas a resolve grows in the depth of our being, and we only take the finished product up into our conscious mind. The resolve is a manifestation of what is essential for an individual, wherefore we experience it as an indisputable necessity and are ready to assume supreme responsibility for it. I call the realization of a resolve a deed, as distinctly different from a mere action. Every deed is a true creation.

It must be apparent from these few remarks taken together with what I have said about the nature of love that the conflict between love and duty is an artefact, worrying only people who have never loved or understood that duty is more than a compulsion from without. Love does not enclose us in the solitariness of emotional bondage. On the contrary it opens us up, and the lover wants to embrace not only the one woman, but the whole of life, and work is only one manifestation of this abundant vigour. True, great lovers as well as humble ones find themselves often enough face to face with this dilemma between love and work, and although the resolve is taken almost in the very moment of the awareness of the necessity to choose, they accept this inescapable necessity in pain and sorrow – because they are human. They all wish the cup might pass, but are willing to drink it if this cannot be. It is well known that sometimes love, sometimes duty, prevails, not because love is in one case stronger or greater than in another, but because one man is a lover in the whole structure of his personality and in every fibre of this structure, whereas with those whose personality is epitomized in their concept of duty, the scales of decision are weighed down by this centre of gravity. It must be admitted that sometimes a long and painful struggle precedes the resolve if the conflicting forces are almost equal, and the consequences would be grave. In other cases people cannot wait until their real Self has asserted itself in a spontaneous resolve, or they make quick decisions out of despair. And in all too many cases the personality of a man is so undistinguished and indistinct that reason must come to its aid, and decisions must be made on plainly practical grounds. But all these people live more or less far below the standards and status of exemplariness. The following example illustrates in a unique way the psychology of decision, and not less strikingly the difference between mother love and sex love: a young woman whose marriage was dissolved wants to marry another man, but her child may be a hindrance. She knows that her love for this man means life and future for her, but with a lucid and unquestionable certainty, without any sense of conflict or need of any decision, she knows that her place is with her child. Not – and this is the most original and fascinating point – because the child is 'her flesh and blood'; on the contrary she feels that a child is, and must be made, fully independent of his mother, whereas her love has made this man part of herself. From the independence of the child arises a compelling duty, whereas the oneness with the man entails no right in itself or for her. Thus there are no conflicting forces within her, and her mind is at peace.

There is an objection which I should like to forestall. All the great spiritual leaders have made it a condition for their followers to sever all bonds with their families. This demand for a complete abrogation of their this-worldly personality seems to be another version of the conflict of love and duty. In fact it is not, but it is a unique situation, because the measure of spirituality to which these disciples were called raised them above the level of ordinary life. The saint is not 'the' perfect man, for perfection consists in the totality of personality and not in extreme one-sidedness. Selflessness as the condition of saintliness and the desire for submergence in the Absolute are the very opposites of individuality, which is the condition of being man – and most particularly for love, which amalgamates spirit, mind – and body. Because it comprises all the three elements of human existence sex love is the prototype of love, and all the other forms of love are at best approximations to it and at worst just metaphors for it.

The bodily expression of love is sexuality. How much this is so is proved, if proof were needed, in cases of what I called spiritual love between the sexes. Even there, where any thought of sexual contact would be abhorred, a definite desire, infinitely tender, arises in the man to be near the woman, to touch her hand, hardly anything more. This is the tribute of the spirit to matter. In a fully developed association of a man and a woman the body repays this tribute with regal munificence. When the lovers awake from the complete fusion experienced in the state of ecstacy, they face one another as an I and a Thou in a state of tension which the meeting of two independent individuals essentially creates. This tension is relieved by physical intercourse: here again the separateness of the two disappears in a state of pure togetherness, in the blissful merging of the orgasm. There is no sweeter gratitude than in a satisfied woman's tired smile, no greater contentment than a man's with this creative achievement of his virility, no deeper beatitude than the unconsciousness of their sleep. Once more they awake into the world of reality, transfigured, true lovers now. Nothing reveals more evidently the fundamental difference in satisfaction between a purely physical urge and a loving sexual union than the fact that the former ends in satiation, often in disgust, whereas from a loving coitus love draws renewed strength. Love needs sexuality to keep alive and dries up without the well of vitality. The orgasm is the seal set on this union, condition and price of its sincerity and completeness. For the stakes are high in this game: nothing less than the whole personality of the lover is demanded, and no substitute such as money, honour, social position, and the like is accepted. Only if this condition is fulfilled can a full, relieving, and invigorating orgasm be obtained. *Sexual enjoyment means ultimate truthfulness: thus the body becomes the guardian of the essential morality of sex.*

There is no agreement about the answer to the question whether love – real love, that is – is essentially everlasting or whether it can, or even must, come to an end. Every *essential* attitude towards people, things, principles, purposes, ideas, implies a promise, unspoken but binding, that it will last, and has the character of finality. This is due to the consistency of an exemplary personality so that this fidelity is in the last resort fidelity to ourselves. That this promise is so rarely kept is due not only to the fallibility of men, which causes them to fall short of the demands of essentiality, but also to the fact that all our relationships have only a limited span of life and must come to an end. The sincere and often enough ardent desire that they may last struggling against this predestined end causes painful conflicts. This principle of final loyalty applies above all to love. Every love is meant to last for ever. Against this stands the common experience that most loves, however sincerely loved, come to an end. Have they all been rather superficial affairs? This is impossible to prove, and still harder to believe. But what one can do is to see whether there are any elements in the nature of love, or of the lovers, which make love liable to death or even necessitate its end. And indeed there are three main reasons of this kind.

I have said before that one of the main features of love is the complete disregard of all the surface qualities of the beloved person. This is fully true of the first stage of love, the stage of fascination. But in the bustle of everyday life it is difficult to maintain this superior indifference amid the petty annoyances which surround us. Even then these incompatibilities and ensuing frictions may cause only slight erosions on the surface, not affecting the core of love. There is only one form of love supremely impervious to anything factual: mother love. Right or wrong, a mother's child is her child. In no other relationship can a woman be capable of such implicit love.

Another danger which proves fatal even to the sincerest love is the essential unworthiness of the beloved, if it dawns on the lover late, gradually and irrefutably. 'How can one love a man whom one pities?' was the bitter realization with which a young woman liquidated her mistake. The same final judgement a much older woman pronounced after her lover had left her: 'I shall cease to hate him only when I have forgiven him for being so much my inferior.'

But there is a still more fundamental reason why love may die. The essential function of love is to open us up, to bring all the potentialities of the two lovers to fruition. This creative function of love must come to an end when the creative strength of one lover or the capacity of the other to lend himself as material for the creation has been exhausted. 'We can no longer be anything to each other' is the bitterest of all farewells. Love needs mutuality. Unreciprocated love is an insane torture like Tantalus' insatiable longing. With Sisyphean everlasting labours the lover tries to conquer or to retain the object of his love, and if he fails love grows into obsession and hatred, or dies a languid or violent death, often involving the innocent partner in its own doom.

On some, admittedly very rare, occasions this parting of two lovers is a farewell to more than just one particular woman. It is rather cheap to comfort a distressed lover with the platitude that time heals all ills and that, unlike Paris, no woman is 'worth a candle'. For some men she is. I believe that every exemplary human being ought to have something in his life he cannot do without, which he needs more than the air he breathes, whose loss tears the bottom out of his existence, deprives his whole life of sense and purpose. In other words, it is the belief in the existence of the Absolute. Of course, such a statement lends itself readily to every kind of misuse and can easily be made an excuse for softness and cowardice. But in a case such as I have in mind the incapacity to live on, the rejection of any compromise, is one of the greatest proofs, if not the supreme proof, of greatness and perfection. Once in a lifetime one may come across a man of whom it is tragically true to say: 'He died of a broken heart.'

The final cause of the transitoriness of every love is that love, however thoroughly loved, is not yet the whole, does not yet fulfil and exhaust the whole range of human sexual relationship. Marriage alone accomplishes this. Love only provides the conditions for marriage, and marriage absorbs love in the totality of the relationship of man and woman, and thus endows it with permanency.

*

But is this all? Is this cluster of words, this welter of sentences, really an adequate description of the love which we once hoped for, have lived, and which we ruefully remember? Certainly not. But when, transfixed in the state of fascination, we really experience love, we are not disposed to searching self-analysis, and when we are back from that strange land our memories are like the shreds of a lovely dream in the cold paleness of dawn. Life eludes all fixation in words; science deals only with what has been: and all the psychology of love is but an epitaph.

## CHAPTER 8

# DIFFERENTIAL PSYCHOLOGY OF THE SEXES

### (*a*) Introductory Remarks

Scientists are reputed to be men who wonder where no one else would find anything to wonder at. Thus the difference between the male and female, which one would have supposed to be one of the best-known things from the days of creation, became, not so long ago, an object of scientific wonder. As we shall see presently, the scientists' speculations have not been wholly successful, perhaps because they were not quite voluntarily undertaken. The problem was rather forced on us in the second half of the last century through the intrusion of women into fields of activity which from time immemorial had been considered the safest provinces of men. Thus the rather paradoxical situation arose that men became interested in establishing the scientific differences between the sexes at the very moment when women were most anxious to deny them. The defensive character of these scientific investigations has left an unmistakable imprint on their results. The struggle was for the recognition of the 'equality' of women, and expert witnesses were called for the prosecution and for the defence. But these experts were caught unawares and had to get busy finding out the facts about which they were expected to testify.

Although the problem of the equality or inequality of the sexes was brought to a head mainly by economic and partly by ideological factors (e.g. the democratic ideal of equal rights[1]) it is worth mentioning that it springs from a much deeper source. Man is obsessed with a tendency to valuation: we cannot accept differences between things just as facts, but instantly attribute to them values, that is to say, we take them as indications of superiority or inferiority. Whether this is an innate

1. The first documents were the *Declaration des Droits des Femmes* during the French Revolution (1789), and shortly afterwards Mary Wollstonecraft's *Vindication of the Rights of Woman* (1792).

trait of mankind or the effect of a basically commercial way of thinking, or the manifestation of a 'universal inferiority complex' may be left undecided. Nowhere is this tendency more harmful than in matters of human intercourse, and particularly in the relationship of the sexes. Here Havelock Ellis has spoken the last word in his conception of 'compensatory unlikeness', which means: however different men and women may be, they have a common task, and are therefore designed for and complementary to each other.

Incidentally the whole problem was solved long ago for those at the bottom and those at the top of the social ladder. For ages, women were allowed, if not forced, to do the same jobs as men on the land, in the factories, and on the thrones of many countries – and in all these occupations they did superlatively well. Thus the whole problem exists at present mainly for the middle classes, and probably arose, therefore, with the social rise of this class in the latter half of the last century. By and large, the battle has been won, at least in most countries where the Roman Church has not had sufficient power to retard or prevent its success.[1]

Looking almost anxiously for a reliable guide through the maze of conflicting opinions we may, and must, entrust ourselves to biology. Not because biology is the final arbiter – a view held only by a certain philosophy of Nature, to which one may or may not adhere – but because the problem presents itself in its simplest form on the biological level, and certain facts can there be ascertained with a satisfactory degree of certainty.

1. But fierce rearguard actions are still to be fought. As late as 1856 R. W. Emerson could report: 'The right of the husband to sell his wife has been retained down to our times' (quoted by V. Klein). And even in our time a similar idea is sanctioned by the law in this country: only recently, for instance, a man sued his wife for divorce, claiming £200 damages. The judge, granting a divorce decree, called the wife a 'perfectly brazen hussy' and went on to say that the claim would have been very modest if Mrs X had been a good wife, but under the circumstances he found £40 quite adequate! In another case a judge reduced a claim of £1,000 to £75, saying with regard to the wife: 'She is of no great value. She was extravagant and proved extremely lazy and incompetent.' Conversely a judge awarded £1,000 to a husband because his wife was 'an asset of the greatest possible business value'. Another judge said: 'There is nothing so difficult to assess as the value of an unfaithful wife.' Difficult indeed!

Again the story begins with the Greek myth of the originally hermaphrodite nature of men. I refer to it so often because it seems a fascinating proof of the fact that our scientific discoveries, at any rate those about the nature of men, are only rediscoveries of arch-thoughts of mankind expressed in myths, legends, and superstitions. Modern biology has in a way verified the Greek theory by discovery that man starts his embryonic development as a true hermaphrodite. Although the future sex of the individual is decided from the moment of conception, it takes several weeks of foetal life before the first slight signs of sex differentiation can be detected. And even then the sexual characteristics of both sexes exist side by side in the one embryo. Eventually the sex predestined for a given individual prevails over the other, development continues from then onwards only in this direction, and the contra-sexual characteristics degenerate. But in embryos in which this prevalence is not sufficiently strong, sexual traits of the suppressed sex may grow more or less. Thus, at least theoretically, all sorts of combinations of maleness and femaleness are possible in a given organism, right up to the extreme example of a grown-up individual being half male and half female. Even the fully grown normal individual possesses all the contra-sexual characteristics, but in a rudimentary or typically modified form. Commonly known instances are the rudimentary breasts of men and the clitoris of women, which is a rudimentary penis.

The fact that the sex of the embryo is determined from the beginning of its existence disposes of the idea that at one time during the individual development a neutral form exists, which can afterwards be made into a male or female. Nevertheless, clinical observation as well as laboratory experiments has proved that the female body is the more elementary form, in a sense closer to the fictitious neutral form; for all observations prove conclusively that in the latter part of childhood the awakening function of the testicles develops the male form out of the female: thus the male is biologically a derivative of the female. Incidentally, this is one of the very few instances in which the intuition of the Bible was corrected by modern science.

Here we may pause a moment and recall what I said earlier

about our propensity to fasten values on facts. If one wants to interpret the biological facts just related in terms of values it is a matter of taste – not necessarily a good one – to say that the female is the genuine article and the male is 'only' a derivative; or that as the male is the product of great differentiation, it is therefore the 'higher' type. The same applies to all the manifold biological differences of the sexes, e.g. the traits which Havelock Ellis tabulates as characteristics of the female sex: greater affectability, great disvulnerability, less variational tendency, biological conservatism and infantibility; any or all of them can be judged as assets or as liabilities, according to one's preconceived ideas and lack of scientific conscience. The obvious truth is that it is impermissible to judge biological facts by non-biological standards, and the genuine standard is whether a trait is adapted to the needs of its bearer.

What, then, is the aid biology offers in assessing the psychological characteristics of either sex? There is no clear-cut answer yet. The only two, to my mind safely established, general points are: first, most psychologists and biologists, among them first-rank men, believe that there is a psychological bisexuality corresponding to the physical. In other words, every normal human being is in various degrees a psychological hermaphrodite, combining male and female psychological traits. C. G. Jung's concept of 'animus' and 'anima' is probably the best-known example. Contrary to this view it must be stated with all due emphasis and vigour that not one single proof of this theory has ever been put forward by anyone in any way. This theory assumes too close a correlation of body and mind, based on psychoanalytical findings whose interpretation is very much open to argument, and on a too facile distribution of character traits between the sexes. It is known that women are fond of flowers, wherefore a man who likes flowers is sometimes denounced as possessing a feminine streak, and conversely a woman is masculine if she happens to have business acumen. Even homosexuality provides no evidence in support of this theory, though the claim is still often made that it does. The classic formula 'a woman's soul in a man's body' is lamentably inadequate to explain the complexity of this strange phenomenon. The results of psychotherapy make it more than problematic whether this sexual aberration is rooted in any constitutional abnormality.

The second point is this: just as the anatomy of men and women is in its basic structure the same, both sexes possess the same basic psychological structure. In other words, men and women alike possess all the qualities which build up the human personality, and the description of qualities as typically male or female is more or less arbitrary and unwarranted. But owing to the wholly different existence of the two sexes, each quality acquires a specifically different colouring in men and women. For example no one will still pretend that courage is an exclusive male prerogative. Women too have courage, but of a different kind, corresponding to the different situations in which a woman has to prove her courage; roughly speaking women's courage is of a more defensive nature than that of men. Still less can it be argued that a man's possession or lack of a quality commonly held to be characteristic of women, is an indication that this man has an abnormally strong feminine element in himself: a man showing a lack of courage does not behave 'like a woman' but only like a cowardly man. But even this distinction can no longer be taken as genuine and immutable, as the many women fighting in the Russian front line or in underground movements all over Europe have sufficiently proved.[1]

This introduces still another factor: the historic-sociological influences that have affected the development of psychological differences between the sexes. The unbelievable changes women have undergone during the last few generations are largely due to the rapid changes of our social order from the industrial revolution to the world wars.

This sociological approach 'is based on the assumption that notwithstanding the conditions of his physical and intellectual equipment, man is to a large extent a product of his surroundings and that ... the margin within which his nature is alterable is still wide enough to be of essential interest and to call for special investigation'. (V. Klein.) The problem as such is by

1. 'The core of strength in this French life which refused to accept defeat came chiefly from the women – from those powerful middle-aged women of France.' (Christopher Sykes, cit. in Tom Harrisson's article in *New Statesman and Nation*, 1 January 1947.)

no means new, but just a variant of the argument of Darwin *v.* Lamarck, or the nature–nurture co-operation. The main decision every psychotherapist has to make is how much of a patient's character is genuine and how much is abnormal. Curiously enough a great medical psychologist, Alfred Adler, thought to solve the problem by completely denying it. According to him every character trait is the product of a successful or insufficient social adjustment, and in particular the difference of sexual characteristics resolves itself into a bid for superiority expressed in 'sexual jargon'. The Vaertings paralleled this extremist view in historical terms. They believe they have proved that the qualities of the ruling sex have always been termed masculine or feminine according to which sex was ruling in a given social order: a quality that would be called masculine in a patriarchal state would be considered typically feminine in a matriarchal state: in each case with the same inference of superiority. In other words, the terms 'feminine' and 'masculine' have no real sexual reference and are 'nothing but' social characteristics. But the death-blow to all attempts to establish a differential psychology of the sexes seems to have been dealt by Margaret Mead. In her famous book, *Sex and Temperament in Three Primitive Societies*, she states that in one society all traits generally considered feminine can be found in both men and women, and so in another society can all the 'masculine' traits.

This tendency to 'debunk' is characteristic of the scientific mood of the nineteenth century, and whenever one can preface a statement with the fateful words, 'nothing but', one can be sure that one is dealing with a typical product of that age: man is 'nothing but' a higher animal, colours are 'nothing but' waves, culture is 'nothing but' a superstructure of economic factors, or the sublimation of frustrated libido, etc.

Coming back to reason one must admit that 'eternally immutable' types, 'Man' and 'Woman' do exist as the hard core that adjusts itself to changing circumstances. At present we are in the peculiar position of knowing almost more about the causes and results of adaptation than about the hard core, the intrinsic nature of Man and Woman.

For however identical the basic structure, and however great the social plasticity of human nature may be, it cannot be denied that the male personality radically differs from the female. It is easy to see that it must be so, because each sex has an existence radically different from the other. This existential difference is represented in the biological sphere, palpable and most conspicuous, by the different sexual functions: fertilization and gestation. Hence, an enumeration of so many male and so many female traits and abilities is a pretty hopeless affair; only by analysing the whole structure can we hope to get any further. This will now be attempted for each sex separately.

### (*b*) Psychology of Women

Viola Klein[1] in her studious and cautious analysis of modern scientific research about the feminine character arrives at the conclusion that 'the impression one gains from the variety of descriptions is definite only on one point: namely, the existence of a concept of femininity as the embodiment of certain distinctive psychological traits. What, however, is considered essential to this concept depends to a large extent on personal bias and valuation, and on the socio-historical vantage point of the observer'. The number and variety of traits that have been singled out by various observers are indeed bewildering, although their list does not differ greatly, if at all, from one that common opinion would provide: passivity, emotionality, lack of abstract interests, greater intensity of personal relationships, receptivity, submissiveness, tact, practical realism, sexuality, vanity, inclination to envy and jealousy, weaker moral sense, timidity, shyness, prudishness, compassion, coquetry, playfulness, fondness for children, chastity, modesty, hypocrisy, etc., etc.

For the limited scope of our analysis we need not be interested in the historical or the sociological genesis of one or another personality trait, because what matters for us is the feminine character only in the society in which we live. Further-

1. V. Klein, *The Feminine Character* (London, 1946). Cf. Richard Curle, *Women* (London, 1947). (An unsystematic collection of observations and *aperçus*, some good, some not so good.) Amram Scheinfeld, *Women and Men* (London, 1947) (on the safe ground of biology and less safe superstructure of psychology; impressive wealth of facts).

more, one may doubt whether the effect of external circumstances on the character of women is as drastic as sociologists would have it. That is to say, they need not change the emotional temperament of women, but only make them behave in new ways – against their innate nature, which may remain unchanged beneath the social veneer. The feminine temperament may be more a function of an astounding pliability or resilience of nature. An analogy will illustrate this point. The fact that religious sects, however large, or hygienically minded cranks, however fanatic, live on a purely vegetarian diet, does not alter the fact, proved by the anatomical and physiological structure of our digestive tract, that the nature of man is and always will be to live on a mixed diet. The difference in looks and behaviour of our mothers and our daughters is impressive enough, but a more intimate knowledge of our young women proves abundantly that many of them have preserved all the essential features of the 'eternal femininity' which we cherish. Sometimes one cannot help feeling that, freed from the artificiality of an outmoded decorum, these women live their femininity more than ever in its genuine beauty. And let us remember: not the average but the *élite* represents the human norm.

If we try to isolate the *essential character of femininity* we must start from the undeniable fact that the difference of the sexes is rooted in the difference of their sexual function. Once more biology proves the most reliable guide, because every essential female personality trait must be connected with and derived from the sexual function. In other words, we are not out to pick up a limited number of isolated traits, but we must try to grasp the totality of the feminine 'existence'.

There is a conflict inherent in woman's existence. She has a brain and a womb; like an ellipse she has, as it were, two centres compared with the one centre of the man's existence, which may be likened to a circle. For the woman her sexual function is essential, whereas it is only accidental to the man. There is, among others, a curious biological proof of this fact: the famous American biologist Loeb has proved that eggs of sea-urchins can be fertilized by putting them in a salt solution of special composition. Thus, it may be that in a perhaps not too distant future we men may be replaced, at least for the purposes of propagation, by a slightly more complex chemical solution. Perhaps we may leave it to sociologists to figure out the effects of this biological progress on the female character.

In her propagating function the woman is receiving, conserving, and creating. To produce a child is, as I have said before, not merely to re-create something that was already there, thus only transforming the face of the earth. It is creation in the truest sense, enriching the world materially. This function is the matrix from which the feminine character springs, and only a trait that is derived, however indirectly, from this function can be regarded as essential. Everything else, however characteristic it may seem, is accidental, subject to fashion, like wearing the hair long or short. It is rather fortunate that we are in a position to demonstrate the biological basis of an exquisite female trait: motherhood. The Italian biologist Ceni transplanted a group of incretory glands from a hen into the abdomen of a cock. For twenty days he behaved like a hen, looking after the chicks with all the motherly care of a hen. Afterwards he returned to his original status and behaved like a cock. In parenthesis it may be mentioned that among several peoples in different parts of the world a strange custom exists known as *la couvade*. It requires the father, after the birth of a child, to retire to bed, and to receive the good wishes and presents of friends. A satisfactory explanation of this custom is not yet known, but it may have something to do with uncertainty about the part played by the two sexes in the production of a child. As late as the fourth century B.C. the Greeks believed that only the father is responsible for procreation, and even the authority of Hippocrates could not prevail against this peculiar doctrine. On the other hand, it has been said that it is one of the greatest – if not the greatest – achievements of the human mind to have discovered that the father has anything to do with the birth of a child, because it is really an astounding achievement of reason to establish the connexion between the fleeting moment of cohabitation and the result, shown so many months afterwards. So difficult does it seem to be to accept the idea of co-operation between the sexes.

The existence of woman is akin to the existence of matter:

static, solid, fecund.[1] Hence, woman's personality knows no 'development' towards a higher stage but only 'expansion', i.e. the growth of something that does not change materially. This integration of woman's personality, this inner oneness I once heard a woman describe very aptly in this way: 'About women,' she said, 'I am almost always right, but rarely with men. One gets to know a woman in one single grasp, but a man only bit by bit until one reaches his true self. A woman is always her same self, her vision is never blurred by circumstances.' The importance of this distinction will be shown presently when we discuss the sexual aspect of the problem. The woman does not live 'outside' things, making contact with them when they 'approach' her; she is immediately, intimately, essentially 'one' with everything existing – people, animals, nature. This state of oneness is the form of existence of primitive races and children, it is the basis of religious mysteries, hypnosis, the mother-child relationship and human gregariousness, and is the essence of the experience in the sexual act. This oneness, this being 'in' and not only 'with' things, enables women to 'know' things, understand things inanimate and living, by what one usually calls intuition, certainly not by reason or intellect, but by partaking in their existence. Hence women are so often sure when much more intelligent men hesitate, are right in a simple and humble way where far superior men go helplessly astray. 'I know no distrust', a woman once said to me, 'because I either wholly accept a person or wholly reject.' All over the world this feminine faculty of 'knowing' the Unknown has in ancient times filled men with awe, made them sense something mysterious in women, and venerate them as priestesses and seeresses. In legends it is always a woman, usually a chaste virgin, who redeems a man; it never happens the other way round. This high esteem in which women are held and not the compensation for women's inferiority was the real origin of chivalry. Later on, coarser ages less susceptible to mystery but more ridden

1. This has been realized by men approaching the subject from the most different angles: Aristotle identifies female sexuality with arch-matter (*hylé*), the Swiss ethnologist Bachofen, who rediscovered matriarchy, explains it as 'a state of abandonment to exclusive materiality'; Frobenius sees in matriarchy 'a culture of realism and violent anti-spiritualism'.

by zealotry and fear burned women as witches at the stake instead of putting them on a pedestal. This happened as late as 150 years ago, and to-day thoroughly disenchanted women are even refused equal pay for equal work.

There is another paradox worth mentioning. This oneness with Nature, this intuitive grasp of the nature and law of things, I have previously described as the essence of genius – and curiously enough, it is generally agreed that women have never produced a real genius. This is true only of the masculine concept of genius. Man catches, as it were, abstract ideas, as a receiving set catches electric waves, transforms, re-creates, reincarnates them, and brings them within the range of our minds. Women dig the ore of truth out of the depths of our existence and bring it within the grasp of our senses. It is like revealed truth as opposed to laboriously discovered scientific truth. The masculine type of genius is the rare exception among men, whereas the feminine version is the property of every woman.

Even the greatness of women is a feminine kind of greatness. I can think of no better examples than some of the great women monarchs. The two great Russian empresses – Elizabeth I, whom the Prussian King Frederick II called a crowned whore (a *bon mot* for which he had to pay with the Seven Years' War), and her successor Catherine II – secured their thrones and successes through the sexual side of femininity. The Austrian Empress Maria Theresa took all her numerous peoples maternally to her conveniently large bosom. And Queen Victoria ran her Empire as a family estate.

'The fundamental reason that women do not achieve so greatly as men do', Professor Marjory Nicholson of Columbia University discloses with unusual 'feminine' charm and almost 'masculine' sense of irony, 'is that women have no wives! Until such time as science or economics corrects this blunder of nature, we shall remain, I fear, the inferior sex.' A view so original that one cannot help regretting that it is not true.

Under the guidance of the two above-mentioned principles – that women by virtue of being human must possess all human qualities, although in a feminine version, and that every genuinely feminine trait must be a derivation of the feminine form of existence – it will be easy to find our way through the maze of psychological traits held to be characteristic of women.

For example the much lamented lack of logic in women can be justly deplored if one has in view only a logic of typically masculine conception. This kind of logic consists of a set of rules about arranging thoughts in a consistent sequence which necessarily leads from a premise to a conclusion, irrespective of what the thoughts are about. The feminine logic, on the other hand, is a material logic based on the intrinsic laws of things as they 'are' but not as they are thought of. It is not an abstract, technical logic capable of general application, but a material logic varying with the varying nature of things to which it is applied, or better from which it springs in any given case. The same is true of the alleged immorality of women: they have no sense of and no use for the abstract, codified morality made by and for men; but what I have called 'essential' morality, i.e. the unwritten laws that are the real laws of things, are enshrined in every woman's heart. To these laws she sticks rigidly and uncompromisingly. And the difference between the male and the female approach to sex is essentially a difference between the natural and the artificial morality. We shall have some more to say about this later on.

The same principle applies to the sense of duty which women are alleged to have and to apply to an exasperating degree of pedantry. Duty, as men know it, is a rule arbitrarily imposed from without, compelling us to do a task to which no inner incentive constrains us. Duty as women conceive it is of a very different nature. To understand this we must have recourse to child psychology. In every nursery a scene like this takes place: a child between the ages of 3½ and 5 is absorbed in his play; the mother asks him to do something else, e.g. to go for a walk, but the child answers, 'Wait a moment, I must finish this first'. These words, 'I must finish this first', actually means '*It* must be' – or 'it *wants* to be' – finished first. In other words, the child has discovered for the first time a kind of demand which the work itself imposes on him, and to which he willingly submits. What was, a few minutes before, only play-work, has now become a 'task' which takes command over the child. This moment, by the way, represents the birth of the ethical sense. This 'material' duty is the only one a woman knows. Its demand is irrefutable because it comes from the depths of her existence, which is her oneness with things.

If women have to act, they need not balance one motive against another, need no decisions, no premeditations, no planning. They act on the spur of the moment, secure in their knowledge of the essence and the demands of a situation with which they are one. I once heard a woman say: 'I do not think problems out, I live them.'

This oneness is also the source of female sympathy and commiseration, which is not feeling 'with' the suffering of another person but feeling the same suffering as the other person through a process of identification, or, still better, a state of identity. For women are not 'with', i.e. by the side of their fellow-beings, human or animals or things, but just parts of an all-embracing whole. For the same reason women cannot live alone, they must belong to someone or something; this togetherness is their way of existing, and taken away from these contacts they wither like love-birds, isolated they feel senseless and silly. Artificial contacts, like those provided by any sort of occupation or organization, may, but need not, be a temporary solace. They are certainly no remedy for this loneliness.

The woman has dignity, the man has honour. Honour is an artificial value, created by society, its content is different in different societies, and its obligations need be accepted only by those in a particular social set, just as one must accept the rules of a club to which one wants to belong. Honour can be forfeited by some actions or regained by others – e.g. in certain circles by duelling. Dignity, on the other hand, is a material, inalienable and indestructible element of a woman's existence, a function of the weightiness of a personality. A woman may keep her dignity intact in spite of everything she does, and in situations where a man would have irretrievably lost his honour; and this spark of dignity still gleams through the débris of an otherwise shattered personality. This was brought home to me in my early student days: I shall never forget how at a gay party a girl of rich experience but poor rewards rebuked an offensive remark of one of our companions just by the slight raising of an eyebrow: even she knew when to protect her womanly dignity, in spite of all she had seen, heard, and endured.

Lastly, the time-honoured problem of activity and passivity. It represents the basic misconception of the man–woman relationship. Again our analysis starts in the biological sphere. No doubt in the sexual act the female is the receptive part: the penis penetrates the vagina, and the spermatozoon bores into the ovum. The woman's is also the suffering part, every step in the sexual path is linked with pain, physical and mental alike. On the other hand, the male part is the more mobile. But the cardinal mistake is to identify receiving and suffering with passivity and mobility with activity. Every woman knows what an amount of activity is needed to relax, to let oneself go, and still more to surrender and abandon oneself; only one who has never suffered can believe that suffering is merely to be passive, a victim of superior power. Receiving is one part of female activity.[1] But there is another, still more important, part. Man courts the woman. Often enough the woman takes the initiative by exciting the man's desire, stirring him up out of his indifference, getting him to parade his attractions. But – she does so in order to accept or reject him. In the latter event the disappointed male, misunderstanding the fun of the game, derisively calls her a coquette. The salient point is that the whole display of 'activity' on the part of the man is a necessary, but not decisive, condition for achieving the aim so much desired by both partners, but the final outcome depends on the woman's choice. This consent, this choice, is the essential function of female activity. The essential activity in sex life common to both sexes is the readiness for the coming of the miracle. It is not a passive, indifferent waiting or an overacting eagerness, but an inner opened-upness, confident of being ready when the time is ripe. The adequate emotional matrix of this readiness is, perhaps, a state of tenderness from which actual sexuality springs.

But the difference in the kind of 'activity' due to the different form of existence of men and women leads to a conflict, as painful as it is difficult to avoid, which for want of a better word one may call the conflict of time-lag. As we know, the

1. Aristotle said: 'Male we call that which begets into another one; female that which begets into itself.' The active element contained in the function of 'begetting into itself' is clearly recognized by this great philosopher.

woman's emotional and physical sexuality must be awakened by the demanding desire of the man. Once awakened, it fills the woman's whole being and tends towards permanence. But as every action consumes itself in the process of the acting, the man's emotions cool off and the woman is left behind. The fact that many more women than men are deserted is due not to the so-called polygamic instincts or the immorality of men, but to this conflict of time-lag. True, there are women who take the initiative themselves, and are consequently called 'masculine'. But one may just as well – to my mind much better – say that they are quicker than their would-be partners to take up the challenge of a situation and to make their choice before it has been explicitly offered to them. And last but not least, the time-lag operates also during the sexual act, so that many a woman is left behind, i.e. cheated of her satisfaction because her partner has got his much more quickly than she could obtain hers.

There is still another aspect of this problem. The cultural conditions in a country and period, particularly the relationship of the sexes, are determined by the women. Ever since, in the seventeenth century, the influence of women became a historico-political factor, the invisible influence has been growing ever stronger. They have worked quietly in the background, not minding whether historians called one period or another masculine. Particularly in this country, things have been changing rapidly in recent years, and it is likely that the Glorious and the Industrial Revolutions may be followed by an Amorous revolution, which posterity will remember with no less gratitude.

Last but not least, we must not forget that a normal sexual union requires the same amount of surrendering and abandonment on the part of the man. And sex pathology shows that the incapacity, or rather the unwillingness, of men to surrender or abandon themselves is the root of all sexual trouble. Less fundamental but very amazing difficulties arise if women do not know, or refuse to know, that many men like their active co-operation during coitus as encouraging and gratifying evidence of their vivid participation. These women, or most of them, remain in statuesque passivity, believing out of pure vanity or neurotic frustration that their sheer presence must suffice to arouse their partner to any degree of sexual frenzy. Their sense of inferiority makes them feel that any sign of their own excitement is below their dignity. Still more serious is it if a woman, taking this talk about passivity too seriously, exaggerates it into complete non-co-operation and indifference, and produces the pathological condition called frigidity – a torment to herself and an annoyance to her partner.

Nevertheless, there is a paradoxical, if not fateful, cleavage in woman's nature. She is driven to stimulate and provoke the man – but she depends on his reaction. She has been given the power to choose – but only if choice is offered to her: in other words, she is dependent on men, the more so as sexuality is the core of her existence, and her sexual life is satisfactory only if it is perfect. This essential conflict makes it very difficult for women to keep their inner balance, and it is not surprising that many of them slip into sexual neurosis.

So much for the genuine feminine character. A second group of feminine character traits is due to what one may call '*feminine infantibility*'. This does not mean 'the physiological imbecility of women', which Möbius invented, but simply refers to the fact that biologically the woman's body is nearer to the bodily form of the child than is the physique of man. And so is her mind, in some respects. A good deal of what one calls typically feminine, in a rather deprecatory tone, comes under this heading – playfulness, irresponsibility, moodiness, lack of foresight, hatred of irony, poor sense of direction, unpunctuality – and everything that is epitomized in that dreaded spectre of the road, the woman driver.

And here may be the right place to remember what I said at the beginning of this analysis about *the essential conflict in woman's existence* – that she has a brain as well as a womb. It would be most unfair to attribute this conflict to social circumstances alone; it is something much bigger, a case of dual loyalty, so to speak. The fact that an ever-increasing number of women boldly face this conflict does not minimize the problem, but increases our respect for those women. That a woman could at the same time serve her husband as a wife, her children as a mother, her womanhood through her attractiveness, her patients as a practising doctor and her country as a member of parliament, commands admiration. And the fact that not a few women fulfil their duties as wives and mothers, besides being leading scientists, unmasks as a facile excuse the contention of many a bachelor that his work has kept him from marrying, and debunks as a fallacy the theory of the incompatibility of work and love. But – credit is also due to the men who bravely shoulder the by no means easy task of being husbands to such women and thus contribute to their success.

But the success of these women and their marriages is the exception, and in the broad stratum of ordinary society a woman top-heavy in the truest sense of the word is badly handicapped. Again, not only in their social contacts, where the average man feels still more ill at ease in the presence of an intelligent woman than of an intelligent man; but because intellectuality is essentially difficult to harmonize with the feminine existence. We shall later on see why.[1]

This problem is interesting enough to be illustrated by an example. A. B., aged 36, single, and just recovering from an unhappy love affair, tells her story:[2]

From her earliest years onwards she was always looked upon as a prodigy. She was not impressed by this reputation and actually only learned of it much later; nor did she see the difference between herself and others, but noticed only that people thought there were many such differences. At school she was not popular, although she so much wished she could be. In dancing lessons she was 'unpalatable' to the boys because they said she was – mentally – too 'heavy'.

She thought she was much cleverer as a child than later, 'clever from my heart'. Even now she is more capable of producing clever thoughts spontaneously – 'out of the depths of my body' – than

1. In order to avoid a possible misunderstanding it may be pointed out that intellectuality is not the same as being intelligent. Intelligence is a capacity which in varying degrees every human being possesses, men and women alike; and the question whether men in general are more, or less, intelligent than women is open to argument although, to my mind, rather pointless. Intellectuality, on the other hand, denotes a mode of approaching the world through the intellect rather than through any other faculty such as emotions or intuition. This is a – dubious – prerogative of men.

2. In this as in all the other case histories, the initials, all personal data and all other details irrelevant to the problem to be illustrated are carefully altered. Thus, the stock phrase prefacing many novels could almost be said to apply here too: 'All characters are fictitious and no reference to any living person is intended.'

understanding what intelligent people say. She was closer to the essence of things, rather than intelligent; she never was particularly good at school and still detests difficult books. Her eminent logicality was not an intellectual one but sprang from an immanent sense of what is essential and therefore necessary. Intelligent men felt she was too unpleasantly logical, too 'knowing'. The logic of women, she thinks, is there from the beginning, but men must train themselves to become logical. Often she was called a blue-stocking, most unjustly, because very unlike a blue-stocking she knew things and not only of them. Eventually she accepted her reputation and set out to make use of her quite considerable intelligence. She first studied philosophy at the university and then took up 'intelligent', i.e. 'masculine', jobs. She succeeded only too well in all of them, but gave them up after some years because this sort of life was too much contrary to her nature. She knew perfectly well that she owed her success to her feminine instinct and not to her intelligence; she considered herself a bluff and would have given anything to find out her own 'trick'. She felt – how very 'feminine' – that she had come into the world almost accomplished and has not changed much since; she has acquired more knowledge but has not really developed.[1]

Her existential uncertainty of herself – through being found unpalatable and too heavy because of the femininity she really possessed, and being criticized for her intelligence which was not her real strength – must have badly affected her sexuality. Men were for her a thoroughly strange, incomprehensible phenomenon; she did not know how to behave, was aggressive and timid and ruined every opportunity almost before it arose. But when, at long last, she had overcome most of these inhibitions and gave herself to a man with the full impact of her long-restrained passion, she was – although in a different way – too heavy and suffered her final defeat.

Just another aspect of this intrinsic conflict in woman's nature is the problem of women and men working together. In order to expound it properly it will be necessary to project it on a wider background. In everyday life we never meet people as individuals but always in a particular function. It is not Mr A who meets Mr B in a consulting-room, but I meet in

1. The ancient Greeks believed most significantly that Pallas Athene, the Goddess of Wisdom, emerged in full armour from the head of her father Zeus.

my capacity as a 'doctor' someone else as a 'patient'; in the way the 'employer' meets the 'employee', the 'customer' the 'shopgirl', etc. Even the relationship of parent and child is to a large degree such a functional relationship. Only these impersonal, purely functional contacts make social life possible. Sometimes it is very difficult, indeed impossible, to forget that it is after all a living person and not just a functionary with whom we have to deal, and the interaction of these two relationships, the personal with the functional, is all too often the cause of serious troubles. To speak of 'forgetting' the sex of one's partner is not quite correct, because to this situation applies on a smaller scale what I have said before about the asexuality of saints: a man need not push the femininity of his secretary aside with a more or less conscious or even subconscious effort, but she 'is' not a woman in this situation – just as the customer is always right only as a 'customer' and often very much wrong as a private individual. A woman may be most charming as a woman, but unbearable in her function as a 'wife', and in this functional relationship all her personal attractions pale into nothingness; they 'are' non-existent.

Of all our impulses, sympathies, and aversions, the sexual urge is the most difficult to domesticate or functionalize. It is difficult for a woman to erect such a partition between brain and womb, and not easier for her partner to forget the woman in her function.[1] Very much, of course, depends on the situation. As I said before, in all professional situations this separation is necessary. But on every other occasion I cannot help feeling that it is unfair, if not slightly insulting, in a conversation with a woman, e.g. to pay attention only to the subject of the conversation. At any rate one deprives oneself of the greatest benefit if one neglects the particular feminine approach to the subject in question, because another man can only supply an additional amount of knowledge, which I could just as well

1. A most interesting contribution to the problem can be seen in the explanation Desmond MacCarthy gives for the fact that in Shakespeare's plays boys impersonated women: 'The effect of that convention was by diminishing personal interest to direct the attention of the spectator towards the character impersonated rather than upon the impersonator.... And it may be of some significance that the decline of poetic drama, to which that technique was so admirably suited, begins when women begin to take women's parts.'

have found out by myself, or approaches a subject from an aspect which in principle could also have been mine, whereas a woman, if she is only true to herself, tells me something essentially new; she does not just add something to my knowledge, but she enriches my personality, as a messenger from the world to which we men have no other access. That is how every real woman feels, too, and those who do not, or pretend not to, always have reasons for repressing or disowning their real selves.

Many a man may feel that all this is very abstract and highly overrated, because the women he meets in his everyday life, in offices and at parties, are very ordinary creatures, not at all mysterious or problematic. This is a delusion due to the short-sightedness of these men or, perhaps, to wishful thinking. In fact, we face here another aspect of the bifocal existence of the woman: the discrepancy between the femininity and the general personality of a woman. Often enough a tremendously strong femininity lives in an otherwise quite simple and inconspicuous woman, a fact which many a man must realize on occasions, to his surprise and at his peril. But also the reverse is true, that a great personality may harbour a savage femaleness which breaks through quite unexpectedly, and makes such a woman act in a manner seemingly quite incongruous with one's idea of her. A woman may forgive many things, but she is implacable when she feels that the female in her is slighted: if, for instance, a man does not notice or deliberately ignores the fact that she desires him sexually, or wears a new hat. There is one such occasion which is usually quite incomprehensible to a man: a woman sometimes attempts to put an end to a quarrel or to bring about a reconciliation after an estrangement by a sexual reunion, and if her partner refuses sulkily he forfeits more than he thinks. Or if a wife has betrayed her husband, she may, out of love or for the sake of peace, be quite willing to make every sort of amends, but she would indignantly refuse to admit that she had done wrong, because she would feel it as disloyalty to her female instinct to admit that it had led her astray. Such experiences, disconcerting and unforgettable for any man who has been through them, expose as an often dangerous illusion the frequently heard thesis that a woman is first human and only then a woman.

In the same line of thought lies the answer to the question over which so much ink has been spilled: whether a proper friendship can exist between a man and a woman. Generally speaking, friendship is a relationship half-way between the personal and the functional. Hence friendship between the sexes does exist in practice, but in theory it cannot. Or we may say that women do not believe in it; many men do, but one should be sorry for them. In actual fact, what one usually calls friendship between men and women is a relationship which either has been prevented from becoming a love, or what is left over after love has died – in both cases a rather sad business. Every relationship with a woman grows and develops until it reaches a cross-road: either to take its natural course by becoming a love relationship or to be deflected into a friendship, companionship, or the like. What one calls companionship belongs to the same category. It is often a very pleasant and, within its limits, gratifying relationship, but essentially it is a frustrated affair. The appreciation of the sexual qualities of both partners is deliberately suppressed, either tacitly on both sides or regretfully on only one – for a purpose.

The component parts so far discussed – the essential feminine character, the character traits due to the woman's infantibility, and the behaviour patterns caused by the bio-psychological duality of woman's nature – are enclosed by still another layer: *the sociological reactions of women.* Through various circumstances women have been pushed into a world which since the dawn of history has been a man-made world, and, like all newcomers, they feel uncertain of themselves, insecure, inferior, and therefore in a perpetual state of aggressive defence. Every textbook of medical psychology shows what deep and far-reaching alterations of a person's character can be caused by such an Inferiority Complex, and the picture of the feminine character drawn by modern sociologists is true to this pattern. But with due respect to the extension of our knowledge we owe to this line of research, it must be pointed out that every psychologist knows that these reactive traits are only distortions of some parts of the original personality, and that such an original personality exists.

But there is an effect of the social impact on the modern woman which is more closely connected with the nature of femininity. I have mentioned on a previous occasion that it is a probably genuine trend of men to interpret differences in terms of values. And now we must face the fact that the so highly commercialized mentality of our age conceives of achievement, or the measure of achievement, as the most important value of our existence. We no longer live our lives as ends in themselves, but look upon them as a means to an end, which is achieving something. Another manifestation of this pseudo-moral, in fact purely commercial, attitude is the belief that nothing must come naturally to us but everything, pleasure and all, must be merited.[1] This is a thoroughly masculine approach to life, because man is a do-er. And it is thoroughly uncongenial to women, because they are be-ers. To my mind this is the fundamental reason for the uneasiness of women in our present society. The woman's way of living is to 'be', to live life in its full and true vitality, creator and master of the art of living. This is her congenial 'achievement'. This is the grain of truth in the overworked talk about the 'mysteriousness' of women; for pure being, unmitigated by spirit, is incomprehensible to men, and therefore frightening.[2] This problem becomes particularly acute in our generation, even among a great many of the younger women. Still brought up for a leisurely manner of life, they discover with dismay that the art of living is out of fashion and has deteriorated into a stereotyped routine; not trained for any special work, they ask in bewilderment: 'What shall we do to make life worth living?' – a question to which in this case there is no answer, and which is, by the way, always an unfailing symptom of the beginning of the decay of a civilization.

1. As a corollary to this principle may be mentioned how deeply the originally religious concept of Guilt and Punishment has affected our outlook on life. Psychologically speaking, it is an undue extension of the trend to give meaning to facts. Many people cannot accept happenings, particularly unpleasant ones, as just what they are, but interpret them as punishment for some, however unwittingly incurred, guilt. Even those who ridicule the original concept of guilt and punishment as superstition, still 'touch wood'. In other words, we have lost the innocence of plain living.

2. I know this peculiar sensation from watching the big cats in zoological gardens, those big lumps of living matter, from looking into their large yellow eyes behind which lurks the vast emptiness of pure being.

*Feminine Sexuality*

The male sexuality awakes spontaneously, the female remains dormant until it is awakened – by an enchanted prince, as every woman hopes. As soon as the testicles start to function and swamp the body with their hormones, they produce in the boy the peculiar tension which is the basis of the sexual urge; this tension is localized in the genitals and requires a genital relief. Girls feel at this age only a vague, indefinable sensation which involves their whole personality and manifests itself in a longing for tenderness without aim or object. Thus we see that right from the beginning sexuality is a biological function in the male, whereas in the female it is a mainly psychological phenomenon. The difference in origin is the clue to the understanding of the difference in nature and significance of sexuality in men and women: man's sexuality is self-sufficient, whereas the woman's is dependent on a partner; man's is an action, woman's is a state.

For the man the sexual relationship is only one among several others with persons or things; an important, perhaps the most important, one, but always comparable with others. For the woman, her sexuality is part of herself, of her being. Therefore, most important of all the differences, the woman is so thoroughly embedded in her sexuality, and her sexuality is so much an element of her existence, that a particular act loses much of its importance for her; for the man sexuality consists in isolated sexual actions. This answers the much discussed question whether the woman is more 'sexual' than the man – or rather it reveals this question as originating from a confusion in terms. It is due to the ambiguous meaning of the term 'sexual', which sometimes denotes the biological differences between the sexes (being a woman or a man), sometimes the particular sexual function, emotion, or action. Keeping these two meanings apart, one sees at once that women are not more lustful, voluptuous, or concupiscent than men, as the question infers, but that their happiness and misery, success and defeat in life depend on how much they are able or permitted to manifest, unfold, fulfil their womanhood. This basically different meaning of sex for women and men causes a pathetic but inevitable misunderstanding between the sexes and untold calamities. In startling contrast to the existential importance of sexuality for women, the sexual activity, i.e. cohabitation, weighs only lightly. Not only do women bear much better than men continence enforced by circumstances, they attach much less significance to the sexual act. This applies to the physical as well as the moral aspect. A good deal of sexual unhappiness could be avoided if men only knew that women value the overture far more than the performance, they want to be gradually moved and not rudely attacked, and even the measure of aggressiveness which almost every woman enjoys must be carefully measured out and must never lose the character of a prelude. All the subtle technique of love-making is valued as grades of a mounting intimacy and contact, and the actual intercourse must be only the last step to the summit.

The same principle applies in the moral sphere. A few fleeting moments in which two souls miraculously meet may amount to a real adultery. On the other hand, contrary to the opinion commonly held by men, it is psychologically quite true to say that to be sexually unfaithful means much less to a woman than it does to a man. The impotent rage of a jealous man seems to the 'guilty' woman much ado about very little, and her calmness during the dramatic scene need not be due to spitefulness or affectation, but more often to helpless incomprehension. On the other hand, men, for whom sexuality centres around, and almost exhausts itself in, the sexual act itself, therefore commit an act of sexual unfaithfulness by any sexual association with 'another' woman. This is one of the occasions previously mentioned, when a woman feels she has kept her dignity intact in a situation when a man will feel his honour badly shattered.

I know that such general statements, made in so brief and peremptory a manner, will arouse immediate opposition, because everybody recalls unpleasant memories of situations in which he or she felt differently. In order to placate some of the critics I want to stress that this difference between the sexes applies only to the question of mutual unfaithfulness. The reaction of a man or a woman to his or her own behaviour is a quite different problem. After a coitus provoked by circumstances rather than inspired by love the woman often feels ashamed: not because she has been unfaithful, but because she has done badly something which she knows she could have done much better – as shown in an example quoted further on. Whereas men usually deal with their own action in a more matter-of-fact way, or shake off a slight feeling of remorse rather lightly; the conflict exists for them only when they are the victims and not the culprits.

Or, to put it in still another way: from a man's point of view his own action is something fleeting, passing away without leaving a mark on the actor, hence is of no great importance and easily forgotten; whereas the man feels that the woman, as the object of his action, the material affected by it, is afterwards changed somehow, worsened, 'dishonoured'. A woman, for her part, does not experience herself as object or matter, but, safely anchored in her essentiality, may feel disillusioned or deceived, but certainly not worse than before – if she is a real woman and, even more, if she happens to be drawn into such a situation.

But these psychological differences in the attitude towards the sexual act by no means imply that women have been given by Nature a passport to sexual libertinage; on the contrary, they feel the binding force of moral law and the rules of decency very deeply, just because sex means so much to them.

*

The fact that sexuality in women does not awaken spontaneously makes masturbation in young girls unnecessary, and although it is naturally difficult to assess exactly how many girls masturbate, it is certain that many do not. Those who do are, in contrast to what we know about boys, abnormal, that is to say, for various reasons their sexuality has been prematurely and artificially stirred up. It is equally certain that many adult women do not masturbate, not for want of sexual desire, but because feminine sexuality is, so much more than the masculine, dependent on mutuality. For this reason such a unilateral action as masturbation becomes, for a normal woman, senseless and often enough repulsive. Some women refuse even mutual masturbation with their male partner. To a few of them one may give the benefit of the doubt and assume that by virtue of their normality they want the real thing or nothing, but more often than not one may suspect a neurotic attitude, a kind of insistence on the pound of flesh, in order to humiliate their often impotent partners by refusing substitutes.

The clue to the understanding of female sexuality is the fact that women have an *a priori* awareness, an instinctive knowledge, of sex, long before they can have had any practical experience of the essential nature, the meaning, significance, and importance of sex. Hence they must insist on perfection, cannot be content with the second-best. Exemplariness, as I have defined it in the first chapter, is the innate feature of feminine sexuality. But this dormant awareness must be awakened into manifestation. This awakening cannot be done by instruction or lascivious stimuli or just by any man. There are quite a few woman who have been married for a long time, and have had children, and have grown old, but have never been awakened: they have been misused by their husbands, their children are, from any but the legal viewpoint, 'illegitimate', and they themselves have in the truest sense of the word been living 'in sin'. It must be one particular man who possesses the key to this particular lock, who is united with the woman in love, with whom she feels secure. Then the coitus is, as a very young woman put it, 'a shattering experience. Every cell in me was buzzing with life, an experience with the halo of glory. I could not bear an imperfect cohabitation, and when it once happened because I consented without a special desire, I felt a deep sense of guilt because I was not able to respond. The idea of an "obedient wife" in sexual matters is abhorrent to me to the degree of absurdity. Intellect and sex are the two things in life which must be perfect or not at all.' Women insist on having a proper sexual life for reasons beyond the sexual field itself. The wife of an impotent man told me once that she had never masturbated because she had not felt a physical urge to do so, and she still does not do it, because no sexual needs have yet been awakened by her husband. When I asked her why she is so insistent on his being cured, she said: 'Sexuality, I feel somehow, is the only way of self-expression for a woman, and you cannot express yourself in an idiom which your partner does not understand.'

Such experiences may help us to understand that women – and among them the most feminine – feel the man to be just an instrument not for stilling their physical-sexual needs, but for accomplishing the full realization of their femininity. That some women have had an orgasm only on the few occasions when they conceived, which means when the coitus was really complete, has been mentioned before. A less degree of completeness is the coincidence of mental and physical orgasm, so much so that the mental participation is the condition of the physical gratification. But there are cases which one has no reason to classify as abnormal in which this psycho-physical unity appears to split. A woman described it as 'relief although no orgasm'. And she meant that she was mentally relieved without the specific physical sensation. Another said: 'In spite of great physical rapture no real orgasm', in which case 'orgasm' meant the complex sensation of thorough gratification. Another woman complained of having had an orgasm 'in spite of myself'. This latter experience is not infrequent among raped women: the purely physical excitement is so great that it overrides all the mental resistance to it. A very strange experience is the following: a young woman complained of frigidity, but a few questions revealed that she actually had a full physical orgasm with complete physical and mental relaxation. Despite this she insisted that it was not the real thing – which she knew from one single experience in a dream. The explanation of her attitude was this. Almost her sole purpose in life was to 'defeat men'. In her marriage she had ample opportunities to demonstrate her superiority over her husband, and the emotional upheaval which led to her physical orgasm was joy in her triumph because her husband was so tremendously excited by her and afterwards satisfied and exhausted. As she was a very sensitive woman with proper feminine instincts she felt dimly that this was all wrong. And after the dream experience she knew why. But this is a case already bordering on pathology.

If we now return to the description of the sexual development of women we remember that masturbation is not a necessary stage of their development. But what meaning, if any, has the affair for women? Is it as important for a girl to have premarital experience as for a young man? The answer is decidedly in the negative. Not for any moral reasons, which as we know are outside the scope of a psychological study, but for reasons entirely immanent in woman's nature. The essential characteristic of an affair is its transitoriness, and the essence of feminine sexuality is permanency. A girl puts her whole self into every relationship. Partial participation – be it only of the body, or associations based only on love, or only 'part time' relationships – is contrary to her nature. Nor are affairs essential for the development of a woman, because her development is very different from that of a man. A man develops, and not only in sex matters, from the stages of imperfection towards a state of perfection. The woman is, right from the beginning, 'perfect' – in the sense in which we use this word here; she only unfolds as the bud becomes the full flower. The man adds part to part, the woman expands her original wholeness. In every affair, at every stage of her development, a girl gives her whole self to the man, that is to say, as much as she can at this stage. Her 'development' consists in an increasing faculty of giving herself more richly the more she grows in her personality; whereas the man learns to give more and more parts of himself. In other words, the man grows into maturity, the woman grows within her maturity.

For the man an affair is a preliminary form of the mature sex relationship, for the woman a diminutive form. Hence there is only one way in which the woman, too, benefits from an affair; she gains experience, gets to know men and herself. But essentially to have an affair is for a woman only a compromise, a form of resignation. She may instinctively adapt herself to the demand of her lover for a temporary relationship, or she may voluntarily bow to the necessities of practical life, consciously renouncing what is essential for herself. If she really wants her beloved friend she does not mind the price. Never, perhaps, has this supreme resolution found a more uncompromising expression than in the famous passage in one of the letters of Héloise to Abelard: 'However sacred and honest the word "wife" may be for you, for me it always sounds delightful to be called your sweetheart or even your whore.' These words came from the heart of a mature woman after she had gone through all the blissful happiness and all the depths of despair of one of the greatest love stories in history. And a great modern poet, who knew things through his profound insight into human existence, wrote: 'Her [i.e. woman's] self-abandonment wants to be immeasurable: this is her happiness. The nameless suffering of her love has always been that she was expected to limit her devotion.' (Rilke.) Or, as I once heard a woman say: 'My love must be enormous.'

What every woman always wants is finality, which in the sexual sphere is marriage. She wants it not for the sake of material security, but for existential security, which is her condition and reward for being herself, because constancy is her way of being. As a young woman with no special claim to sophistication but all the greater profundity of instinct put it: 'The more often I have been with my husband the more I like it. Each time one enjoys all over again the previous pleasures. Familiarity is more stimulating than novelty.' Thus, if an affair has come to an end, as come it must, the woman finds herself deserted, disillusioned, betrayed, a great expectation has come to nothing, a generous investment has been wasted.

A rather surprising conclusion drawn from all these facts is that the much maligned 'dual morality' has not been invented by men for their own pleasure and comfort, but has a solid psychological basis. The 'essential' morality of sex applies naturally to both sexes alike, but the ways leading to a state of maturity – which alone permits of realizing this morality and putting it into practice – are very different for young men and girls. In the phase of pre-maturity a misunderstanding between the sexes is inevitable owing to this incongruity. At this point an objection to the entire conception of the relationship of the sexes presented in this study is too obvious to be overlooked: it may be necessary for men to have premarital affairs – the argument may run – but since affairs are contrary to woman's nature, how can men be justified in thrusting themselves on women? The answer is that there is no answer to this problem, as to many others which result from a conflict between the laws of Nature on one side and on the other side inevitable socio-economic developments (e.g. the retarded maturation of youth, economic difficulties of early marriage), avoidable sexual conventions or, last but not least, factual difficulties – e.g. that a woman does not find the man she would like to marry, or that the man who would be the right one cannot marry her. Should a girl, under these adverse circumstances, renounce love in the form of a, however temporary and therefore imperfect, union with a man and the, however modest, measure of happiness which fate has meted out to her? I think she need not, provided her degree of exemplariness permits of such a compromise. Because we must never forget: *His degree of exemplariness determines a man's destiny.* It is a hopeless, and even more useless, endeavour to nail these subtle distinctions down to hard and fast rules, or to simplify complex problems unduly in order to be able to give simple answers. Thus, to suggest premarital chastity for both sexes is a facile solution, because it simply shifts the burden on to the male sex, and a dangerous one, as will be learned from the following chapters. The only possible answer, not nearly as smug as it may seem, but squarely facing the issue, is that sex warfare claims its victims as does any other war. Not through the merciless greed of men, but because, as we see it happen incessantly, Nature achieves her aims through sacrifices. The French realized this when they created the wise saying: *L'amour c'est à mourir un peu.* That is, each time we love, a bit of us must die – but, as a woman friend explained, in order to make the rest develop and grow. This, too, is a law of Nature.

And yet there were women, many of them, who thought the sacrifice worth making. In the halcyon days of Imperial Vienna there was a type of girl, working in offices and shops, selling flowers in the streets, simple, unpretentious creatures, who in their touching naïvety considered the affair as their natural form of sex relationship. They refused material gain in any form, knew nothing of self-fulfilment or self-development, they enjoyed the present while it lasted, oblivious of any future: they wanted nothing but to love and to be loved in the purity and chastity of youth. When such an affair had come to an end, which they well knew must happen sooner or later, many a little heart was broken and died *un peu.* But when it was all over they married contentedly a friend of their schooldays or their neighbour's son, and the young student or lieutenant whom they once so hotly loved 'for ever' was soon forgotten. These girls were very characteristic of Vienna, distinctly different from their near relations, the German 'Gretchen' or the Parisian *midinette*, and these lines are written as a memorial of a bygone tradition and art of loving.

*Excursus into Pathology*

Although it is not in the plan of this book to discuss pathology in detail, it will be necessary to include some pathological forms of sex life in our analysis, not only to bring normal psychology into full relief against this background, but because a good many character-traits of women, among them some of the most clamorous and least pleasant, are unrecognized neurotic symptoms. They are erroneously taken to be parts of women's normal nature, even by competent observers, because so many women suffer from neurosis. Besides, many symptoms of sex pathology are nothing but normal emotions, motives, and reactions carried to an impermissible extreme.

Although it has always been known that a part of our mental activity, particularly the emotional, takes place in the subconscious part of our mind, it was Freud who showed how important subconscious activities are. Under normal circumstances the conscious and the subconscious mind co-operate, but under abnormal conditions they militate against each other. The conscious mind disregards the subconscious warnings at its own peril, and the subconscious opposes and interferes with the intentions of the conscious. We feel these inhibitions and frustrations without being able to account for them. We say 'I cannot do this' when in fact the subconscious part of us does not want to do it. Therefore what appears to be an incapacity is actually an act of unwillingness, and the effect which we consciously deplore is in fact of our own making.

The functions of our inner organs, the heart, intestines, and pre-eminently the sexual organs, are under the exclusive control of the subconscious. If we are sexually excited and want to perform a sexual act, this intention reaches the sexual organs only via the subconscious, and if in a given case the subconscious disagrees with this intention, it does not transmit the message, and consequently the sexual organs do not react. If a man under such conditions anxiously wants to have an erection, he 'cannot' have one; this inability is due to the fact that actually in his subconscious he does not want to have an erection. This state of disagreement between the conscious and the subconscious mind is called 'neurosis' and the resulting inhibited function of an organ is a 'neurotic symptom'. All anomalies of the sexual function among men and women, of whatever kind they may be, however alarming, or however long they may last, are neurotic symptoms, that is to say they are of psychological origin.

All the actions of our mind, conscious and subconscious alike, have a motive and a purpose; and so have the neurotic symptoms. They do not happen, do not befall us as does pneumonia or a fracture of a bone; they are intended, part of a scheme, results of our own design for living. The purpose common to all neurotic symptoms is self-protection, they assist a desire to withdraw from a situation, to avoid responsibility, to escape.[1] The motive for this defeatism is a fear of being incompetent, the notorious Inferiority Complex. This attitude of defeatism, of despair, is obviously a reaction to one's environment, and a certain group of medical psychologists has gone so far as to subsume the psychology of the neurosis under social psychology in general. This is not permissible if one uses the term 'social environment' in its strict meaning, because social circumstances never produce a neurosis, and reactions to social influences are distinctly different from neurotic symptoms. A grain of truth can be detected in the above contention only if one limits the concept of environment to a very special one, the family. The neurosis is a kind of teething trouble: under the influence of the home environment, reacting to all the emotional cross-currents pervading this small but infinitely important social group, the small child develops the patterns of emotional relationships and builds up his self-esteem and self-confidence. Under unfavourable circumstances it develops abnormal emotional fixations to the members of the family and produces all those fear-inspired, defensive, morbid traits which we call neurotic symptoms.

1. Some time ago I read a report on the present condition of the literary world in Germany. Quite a few writers had stayed in Germany during Hitler's régime. When they were afterwards asked what they were doing during these years, most of them said they felt it was their duty to stay on, but they did not take part in the holocaust. One of them, Frank Thiess, called their mental attitude an 'inner emigration' in contrast to the, obviously despicable, outer emigration of others. (Reported in *Horizon*, xv, 1947.) However this may be, and whatever Mr Thiess's contribution to German literature, he has enriched the medical vocabulary with a most useful term: all neurotic symptoms are truly an attempt at 'inner emigration'.

Previously we have learned that some of the behaviour patterns of women are reactions to their social status. But they were all quite normal reactions. It is normal, indeed very normal, to try to win a place in the sun, to hit back if one has been hit, to compete fiercely if one finds oneself thrown into the midst of a competitive society, etc. On the other hand, in some women there is to be found a large group of traits which are definitely of a neurotic nature. To put it in another way: what a woman experiences in her social *milieu* affects her as a member of the social group 'women', but what she has experienced in her parental home affects her as an individual woman. Up to a point these two sets of influences overlap. Thus, for instance, it depends on the views common in a given society whether parents are disappointed if a newcomer is 'only' a girl, but it is almost a law of Nature that a mother prefers her first-born son to his younger sister, and it is an individual misfortune if a father dislikes or, perhaps still worse, adores his daughter.

It is of the greatest importance, not only for the general psychology of women but also for the proper understanding of the psychology of any particular woman, to keep these kinds of reactions strictly apart. The effect of a neurotic disfigurement of a woman's character cannot be overrated, and many statements about the character of women in general, as well as of a particular woman, are almost valueless because the neurotic element has been neglected. I, personally, am certain that all the talk of 'masculine features' in a woman can be discounted as based on insufficient knowledge of psychopathology. If, for instance, a woman with a strong personality suffers from a neurosis, the combination of these two elements may produce a striking result: her genuine efficiency may be enhanced, or a strongly complex character may emerge, and both the efficiency and the complexity are usually, but quite erroneously, attributed to her partial 'masculinity'. Similarly a small personality may, under the influence of a neurosis, appear almost interesting through the iridescence and half-tones which the neurosis often lends to a personality, or she may become still more tiresome. As a matter of fact, I know no case in which an expert analysis has not unmasked an alleged masculinity as a neurotic symptom – or as bad manners and lack of self-control.

Or take, for instance, the case of jealousy. Is there any sense in assuming an 'innate feminine jealousy'? In a society where marriage was the be-all and end-all of a woman's life, jealousy of a successful competitor in the race for men was a natural social reaction. It may have disfigured the mind of many a woman, but it was never a part of the feminine character. But jealousy as such is, in men and women, one of the most typical manifestations of an Inferiority Complex. Jealousy, far from being an essential concomitant of love, springs from confusion between 'belonging to' and 'possessing' someone, and from distrusting one's capacity to hold what one may be in danger of losing. In other words, jealousy is a neurotic symptom and, if felt by a particular woman, is only the result of her personal anomaly.

From all that has been said it must be obvious how deeply a neurosis must affect the sexual behaviour. Any defect of self-confidence must reduce sexual efficiency more than any other, because in the execution of any other task we may secure assistance from outside, whereas in sexual matters we are entirely left to our own resources.

Instead of continuing this abstract analysis of the sexual functions under abnormal conditions, it may be better to give some illustrations by relating the history of a few patients. The first is of a girl who went through a very difficult development:

B. C., a very attractive girl aged 18. She was sent to England from overseas to forget a love affair. In London she got into very undesirable company and spent her nights in night clubs and her days in bed. She was sent to me to get out of this rut. And this is her story:

Her parents lived the not very distinguished life of the wealthy upper class of their country and had made every possible mistake in the upbringing of their only daughter. The result was the usual one – the child lost all respect for her parents, and, consequently, for herself. She became lazy, shy, untidy. During her schooldays she made a vow: to shut herself up in order not to be hurt by people, and not to be disappointed by failures. Sticking rigidly to this principle, she developed the 'don't care' attitude to perfection. Why should one bother about people? Why should *noblesse oblige*? Why should one cultivate one's talents, which after all are one's own property? Why should one not waste time, money, oneself?

'I am no good, anyway; what is the good of living a mediocre life?' and so on and so on.

I discussed all these questions gently and patiently, and one day she reported the following delightful experience: the night before when she took her dog out she seemed to notice a small gate in the hedge which surrounded the garden. She knew it would not be difficult to pass through this gate and into a new, hitherto unknown, world. When she actually made a step towards it the gate was no longer there, and the hedge stretched, unbroken, in front of her. She at once understood the symbolism of this vision as the first glimpse of hope of her salvation.

She went to Paris for a holiday. In a night club she met a professional dancer – 'an awful man' – but his technique of dancing and the perfect rhythm of his movements fascinated her. To her horror he told her that her dancing, the only thing she thought she was really good at, was utterly amateurish – what she needed badly was 'style'. That word struck her like a revelation, she suddenly knew that dancing is more than fun. It is an accomplishment through perfect style – and so is Life!

Thus, assisted by an Austrian psychologist and a French gigolo she had acquired a better conception of herself and a sense of style. The third discovery she owed to a British officer. One day he took her to a small private party. Unfortunately the host got drunk and became rather objectionable. Next morning the young officer called on her and apologized for the embarrassing incident. She was deeply moved. At home one would have laughed the whole thing off, but here someone found it necessary to apologize for it and – even more surprising – found her worth apologizing to. She could be affronted, therefore others obviously had respect for her.

Against this rather sordid background her sexual development was most astounding. Ever since she was a child horses and riding had been her great passion. One day she 'noticed' the stable-boy who looked after her father's horses. His well-trained body, his joy in living, the recklessness of his youth fascinated her. She instinctively tried to emulate him, live up to him. He gave her a 'sort of standard'. She loved him with the tender unselfconsciousness of a first love – 'The world was wonderful, full of wonderful things; it was good to be alive'. This fragrant experience was the cause of her exile, and the brutal separation was a 'crushing pain and disaster'. She was still almost completely free of sex curiosity or sexual desire, but in spite of this unawareness she had a deep instinct of sexual self-preservation; kissing and all the small pleasures which go with it meant so much to her that she tolerated them, if need be, but never reciprocated them. She even deeply regretted this tolerance when Lord X kissed her when they first met, 'because I felt at once that I was going to love him'. And so she did. He was a man who 'always gave her something' just by his sheer presence. She adapted herself to him quite consciously, felt the desire to grow up to his standards, became patient on occasions when previously she would have lost her temper. She received from him 'richness' instead of the 'cheap profits' (fun and thrills) she had hitherto drawn from association with men.

Again her parents stepped in. She was recalled home. Shortly afterwards she met a young scientist. They fell violently in love with each other and got married, successfully in every respect.

The sexual development of this girl was remarkably normal, so much so that it can be taken as a paradigm of normality. It was remarkable in three respects: firstly, because of her intuitive certainty of the meaning of sex; secondly, because of the instinctive preservation of her emotional chastity in the midst of the rotten life she lived, and last but not least in that this bud burst into full flower when the right occasion came. And by that I do not only mean when she had met the right man, but also after she had gradually and with almost conscious effort built up her general personality.

Not all women, indeed only very few, are so lucky under similarly unfortunate circumstances, because unpropitious educational influences not only interfere with the development of the general character of girls but directly affect their attitude towards sex. The result is a condition which we call frigidity.

A frigid woman either has no sexual urge at all or she is unable to get her satisfaction from cohabitation; the latter condition can be all the more exasperating as it is often accompanied by a very strong sexual desire. Frigidity is always a neurotic symptom and as such it is subconsciously arranged by the woman. It has a meaning and purpose in the pattern of the woman's life. In brief, frigidity is an insidious 'secret' weapon in the sex warfare, i.e. in the woman's struggle against her Sense of Inferiority and against the assumed superiority of her partner. Once more it must be stressed, this Sense of Inferiority is not due to the status of women in the social sphere, is not felt because a woman cannot become Prime Minister or must give up certain kinds of employment when she gets married; such grievances can be remedied by methods of political warfare. The battle fought in bed is caused by the erroneous notion that women are essentially inferior to men, or worse still, that this individual woman must defend herself against the superiority arrogated to himself by her partner. It is an intimate warfare, a civil war on a small scale.

It is fear – fear of all sorts of imagined dangers that causes the trouble. There is a group of cases, comprising mostly very young women, uneasily balanced on the borderline of normality and pathology. They suffer from an exaggerated degree of the kind of fear which assails most girls in face of the most decisive experience in their lives. The following case demonstrates this experience with rare lucidity:

C. D., aged 23. Parents were divorced when she was still small, and she lived with her father. She was his 'pal' and joined him in all his sporting activities, which made her decide to 'become a boy'. She knew of her father's numerous amorous adventures and unfortunately could not help witnessing them occasionally. She was disgusted with him because he did not behave like the fathers of her friends. Up to 16 'sex was something that did not exist for me'. Occasionally she permitted boys to kiss her without reactions on her part. At 17 a 'real' kiss was a new and exciting experience. When she was still small she invented a peculiar practice; in bed she lay on her tummy, closed her eyes so tightly that 'stars' appeared, and then she had the most enjoyable sensation of falling through this sky deep, deep down; afterwards she was tired and relaxed. No doubt this was a most ingenious form of masturbation in which she had discovered the essential feature of female sexuality – the falling and sinking.

The father married a second time, and as things at home did not go too well she was sent to England to finish her education. Here she had her first 'affair' and was in this and two other liaisons completely frigid. And this is the reason why: she knew that the right thing to do was to understand her partner and to adapt herself, to surrender part of herself – and this was what she was afraid of. In the sexual act when the excitement mounted she felt as if she was sinking into a deep well, the world receded. 'Everything became so small, as if one were looking through the wrong end of a telescope.' Actually it was not so much the sensation of sinking, but of being ruthlessly pushed down and of falling, not with her partner, but quite alone.[1] She sometimes had the sensation of trembling just on the brink and then she pulled back. She knew somehow that this letting oneself loose and sinking was the true nature of the sexual experience which she would have to go through sooner or later – but not yet. 'I have no confidence, I cannot trust him, or myself' – this was the clue. And then she added: 'I may be overtaken, it may happen without me, I am afraid of the Unknown, of what may come, what I may be afterwards; it must not be too easy, too quick. I must watch and never lose control.'

The neurotic element in this girl is quite obvious, but it has only intensified the normal feature of the virginal anxiety which we can observe in this case as under a magnifying lens. This feature is fear of letting those still unknown forces take charge of her. The male – her friend, men in general, her father originally – is only the embodiment of those forces, and the girl said once quite definitely that she knew of no reason why she should distrust her friend personally; actually she distrusts 'it', which means the whole process in which she and he are immersed. And then there appeared a motive which we already know (from the case of A. B.). She must be so infinitely patient for fear, which was justified by previous experiences, of being considered too 'weighty'; she must keep herself back in every respect instead of being permitted to show what she is. 'This is the lot of us women!' Lastly there is a hint at a moral element: to let herself sink and fall she associated with the phrase 'fallen woman' and the original Fall of Man.

Another element, most important for an understanding of the female character and sexuality, can be learned from the following case:

D. E., aged 27, newly married. She started masturbating at the early age of 6, and continued it into adolescence at times when she felt lonely, bored, or unable to go to sleep; it was a 'dull and mechanical practice, egocentric and meaningless'. A few flirtations left her cold. Then she met her future husband. 'He tapped my personality'; from the moment she met him she knew she would marry him, felt intimate and akin to him. After two months she

1. She used as illustration of this sensation the famous painting of Rubens, 'The Fall of the Damned'. Curiously enough, two other women patients, one frigid, the other a case of anxiety neurosis, mentioned the same picture to explain what they felt.

became tired of just playing at love; she wanted the real thing, and almost forced her friend to start a proper affair. She felt at home with him at once, a new and blissful sensation which she had never known in her parental home. Everything came so naturally to her: cohabitation was only the fullest manifestation of her sense of being at home, 'of the partner, by the partner, for the partner'. Great disappointment followed because sexually she felt nothing. She explained this to herself by saying that what she really wanted was marriage, and she wanted to preserve herself, i.e. the full sexual surrender, until then. Eventually they were married, but the sexual situation was not materially changed. 'A lovely feeling' was all she could achieve, but no orgasm.

Here again we have the perfectly normal beginning of a true woman's sexuality. Noteworthy is the suddenness – not infrequent with women – of the awakening: from meaningless masturbation right up to cohabitation almost without intermediate stages. She wanted 'to rush from the bottom to the top'. It is true woman's sexuality is like a bud opening up overnight. Remarkable, then, is the unfailing certainty of her instinct in the choice of the man. 'Single-mindedness is the root of love and sex,' she said. But why did she not respond sexually? Because gradually the sad truth dawned on the young wife that there was not enough to respond to: her husband, himself a pretty serious case of neurosis, did not give himself, not only not entirely or not sufficiently, but hardly at all. He never felt himself truly married, and thus she could not either. So she felt once more the sense of home and security slipping away from her, and worst of all, respect for her husband was gone.

The new aspect of the multifarious female sexuality which this case opens up is the fact that frigidity can, on rare occasions, be an adequate – in a sense virtuous – reaction to a sexual situation which falls short of what it should be. And one of the most important things which should be, in fact the indispensable condition for a proper sexual response from a healthy normal woman, is the virility of the masculine partner. A woman willingly accepts her part in her marriage, even up to the point of subordination under an authority which she can accept, but she withdraws from a man whose virility she cannot respect. Real human tragedies may ensue from such conflicts. His love, devotion, sincerity, may be appreciated by his wife, both partners may desperately cling to their love whose genuineness they deeply feel, and yet women insists inexorably on this one condition. What a woman wants from her partner is 'solidity' as a woman patient once summed up the whole problem with incomparable precision. Solidity implies the consistency of a man's personality and the natural strength which is derived from it – not forcefulness or, least of all, the gesture of power. Only neurotic women enjoy coercion and ask to be overpowered. A normal woman shrinks from such theatrical performances, and that a certain degree of 'sadism' is part of a man's sexuality is believed only by romantic schoolgirls and incompetent psychologists. How sensitive women can be in this respect I learned from a young woman. She was obviously mishandled by her first lover, with complete frigidity as the result. A second experience was no better. Thus she withdrew from men altogether. Eventually she met the right man, who succeeded in awakening her to the full enjoyment of sex. But whenever her lover showed the slightest tendency towards brutality during the act she became chilled by fear – because she and he lost 'their identity', their humanness, and the whole process appeared to be reduced to a merely biological function. In another case the wife of such an incompetent man described how her frigidity developed step by step: for a few weeks after the wedding she had a full orgasm because she entered her married life with confidence and trust; but soon she grew suspicious of her husband's virility and 'held herself back'; but during the last year she did not need to hold herself back because she was frigid. Obviously she had given up hope and had resigned herself to her fate.

Now, who is this 'right man' of whom we have talked so much and of whom every woman dreams? This is another question to which there is no answer in the abstract but which is answered by the inscrutable logic of life. The right man is the one man who happens to fit, in the mysterious, almost whimsical way in which Eros brings men and women together against reason and expectation. Frigidity, if the man whom a woman has married does not fit, can be, and usually is, general, i.e. no man can give these disappointed women satisfaction. Sometimes it happens only with one particular man or type of man –

as all frigid women persistently hope it may be in their particular case. Many do not give up hope, but try out unrelentingly one man after another, and if 'nice' women only knew the despair and misery of these 'loose' women, their contempt and envy would give way to pity. To what kind of man eventually falls the part of the saviour occasionally baffles the wildest imagination, as the following case proves. I had the chance of watching the sexual career of a woman through many years. She was in many ways a most attractive girl and married, comparatively young, a man who was the sort of he-man parlourmaids dream of, although the range of his successes went far beyond the confines of the servants' quarters. She was completely frigid with him, and the marriage was dissolved after a few years. She too was one of those who kept on experimenting with no success. At long last she found the man who succeeded where so many others had failed. Alas, the unfathomable irony of life! He had some time before the two met consulted me because of his impotence, and I had given him up as hopeless: his physical and psychological unmanliness made him – as I sometimes feel in such cases – almost unworthy of having a sex life. And her explanation of their success? Pity, motherly feelings towards him, this Samaritan spirit which animates many women did the trick. This woman was the counterpart of the one, previously mentioned, who got her orgasm through her sense of triumph over her husband. Thus we see that both triumph and pity can be canalized into the sexual channel and can be transformed into sexual enjoyment.

It may be worth pointing out that only neurotic women can have an orgasm out of pity, and this thoroughly abnormal reaction does not invalidate our previous statement about the importance respect for her partner has for a woman's love and sexual satisfaction.

But by far the largest proportion of all frigid women are the fighting ones: those who revolt against the part Nature has assigned to women – or, more precisely, who mistake competition for co-operation; women who erroneously believe that to need a partner for a job means being 'dependent' on him in the derogatory sense this word acquires in the sphere of competition; who, misled by their Sense of Inferiority, believe that to accept pleasure through someone means admitting his superiority, who try to make their partners look foolish and incompetent because they cannot do what every 'real' man is supposed to achieve. These women deny themselves the greatest enjoyment rather than give credit to their partner for being the source of their pleasure – rather a high price for an illusion, one may say. So it is, but no price seems too high for maintaining prestige. All neurotic symptoms are a bad bargain: they offer short-term solutions of sham problems, interim answers to bogus questions.

Occasionally, more often perhaps than one would think, frigidity is caused by the fact that a woman's partner is the 'wrong' man for her because she does not love him or does not love him any longer. That this could be the sole cause of the trouble is easy to believe, but it is not always easy to decide in a given case that there is nothing else the matter; in other words, that we are dealing with an honest but unfortunate woman and not with a neurotic patient. For how is one to know, particularly if a woman has had no previous experience, that her lack of satisfaction is due only to her unresponsiveness to this particular man, and not the manifestation of a neurotic repression and consequent aversion to all men? Every psychologist remembers one or another occasion when, to his slight embarrassment but greater relief, a woman patient whom he has been treating for frigidity in her marriage suddenly announces happily that she needs no more treatment because she has found out at last that nothing had been wrong – with her.

Sometimes a frigid woman discovers new characteristics of the female sexuality through the defectiveness of her sexual experience, or confirms those already known. A woman who was frigid in her first marriage found herself in her second marriage married to an impotent man. When I asked her why she was so anxious to have her husband cured, although owing to her own abnormality she was not likely to benefit greatly from the change, she said that she did not care for sexual satisfaction, nor were children very important for her, but she must have proper intercourse because this alone would make her feel really desired, fully united – in one word married at last. Her pathological condition had deprived this woman of the two benefits which are commonly held to be the only purpose of sexual activity – pleasure and children – but had brought into full view the essential meaning of sex. This woman, from a medical point of view defective, but from an essential point of view perfect, had grasped, better than many of her more fortunate sisters, the fact that marriage consummated and symbolized by the sexual act, and nothing but such a marriage, delivers man from his existential loneliness.[1]

★

From all that has been said a fairly accurate picture can be drawn of the structure of the female character.

In the centre stands the 'eternal feminine' composed of character traits which are derived from the woman's existence. This kernel is surrounded by a layer of traits resulting from the physical and mental infantility of women. Next come qualities springing from the individuality of a particular woman, such as ambition, charm, intelligence, stupidity, fussiness, cantankerousness, gaiety, etc. A further stratum shows the reactions to a given social environment. And this whole complex may be pervaded and modified by neurotic trends.

No wonder that the complexity of this structure has dazzled also many observers who according to their vantage point have seen in women beings ranging from utter dullness to iridescent fascination. Still less surprising are the attempts to dissolve on scientific grounds the warm, live personality into an unknowable 'x' reacting to a bundle of little-understood environmental influences. There are too many observers who ridicule the concept of a genuine feminine character for no better reason than that they have never been able to observe anything like it. It may be readily admitted that often, too often perhaps, this essential femininity is hidden by the outer layers I have described; nevertheless it can be clearly discerned even in every female character I have sketched in these pages, of women who have grown up and lived under the most unhappy circum-

1. This experience and the interpretation given it is not inconsistent with my previous contention that the sexual act is of less importance for a woman than for a man. On the previous occasion the act was considered only in its purely sexual aspect, but here it is considered as part of a life communion.

stances. Such summary jurisdictions are difficult to challenge unless one can persuade the critic to take to heart Pascal's dictum which I have previously quoted: 'One often writes things which can only be proved by asking the reader to ponder over himself.'

### (c) Psychology of Men

In the previous chapters a good deal has already been said about the psychology of men, so that in this chapter we have only to put these fragments together and to add some more details in order to compose a coherent picture of man's existence. But before we proceed it may be advisable to differentiate the terms which are commonly used almost as synonyms for a description of men. 'Maleness' denotes the biological function, and is the correlate of femaleness. 'Virility' means the character of men in a stricter sense as having vigour, strength, initiative; it has a definitely appreciative flavour and corresponds roughly to womanliness. 'Masculinity' is used by me as an existential term to denote the man's mode of existence from which the biological and psychological characteristics derive; it corresponds to femininity.

Starting again from biology we remember the fact that man derives from woman in that the function of the testicles changes the more neutral form of the female body into the masculine shape. The structure of man is therefore more differentiated than the woman's. This is supported by the fact that castration, that is the removal of the ovaries, has scarcely any noticeable effect on the woman's psycho-physical appearance, whereas the removal of the testicles affects the development of the masculine feature to such a degree that only a caricature of a man emerges, called a eunuch. From the biological point of view the dependence of a specialized organ, in this case the testicles, represents a higher stage of evolution. Furthermore, in recent years a great amount of knowledge has been collected about the effect of transplantation of testicles on females, and vice versa. White rats, guinea-pigs, and fowls are most suitable for these experiments. Their results show that females can be much more easily transformed into 'males' than males into 'females'. This can be taken as another proof that the female is more pliable, whereas the male is a completed and therefore much less changeable structure.

A second important fact is the greater sensitiveness of the male. Ovaries stand transplantation from one individual to another very well, even if the donor and the receiver are not of the same species – e.g. monkey to human. Transplanted testicles degenerate very quickly. Injections of the solution of female hormone are far more effective than those of the male. One reason for this is that the more sensitive male hormone is easily destroyed by the chemical process for the preparation of these solutions. Again, it is a well-known fact that the mortality of new-born boys is higher than that of girls. Many facts prove that, even when fully grown, the woman possesses a greater resistance to physical afflictions and a greater capacity for enduring hardship than man.

All these facts lend themselves readily to the interpretation that the male represents a 'higher' stage of evolution and can claim a genuine superiority over the female. But even from the – necessarily limited – biological point of view, this conclusion is far from decisive, because it can be argued with as much plausibility that a higher degree of differentiation and a greater sensitiveness are signs – or causes – of degeneration, as every animal breeder knows. The matter becomes still more confused if we consider the facts which caused Havelock Ellis to believe that the female is the type towards which the human race is developing, because in many anatomical details the modern civilized man approximates to the female type by growing away from the robust type of the more primitive male. There is no point in entering into a criticism of either theory, because both are rather matters of opinion, if not prejudice, than of fact. I mention them only in order to show that even recourse to biology cannot support the claim that the human race is the masterpiece of creation, and the human male the high spot of evolution. This in itself should suffice to expose the futility of any attempt to establish the superiority of one sex over the other.

The *masculine existence* can best be described by contrasting it with the feminine. I likened the woman's existence to matter and called it static, solid, fecund. The man's existence can be likened to the spirit and may be described as dynamic, volatile, productive. In contrast to the oneness of the feminine, the masculine existence is individualized, and intentional communication with the world must replace the genuine, spontaneous communion in which the woman lives. The woman 'is' with things, animate or inanimate; the man must contact them. Woman creates; man produces; man fertilizes, woman bears fruit. Or, if we expand this structure of the biosexual relationship to a general principle, we could say: *The Spirit gives shape to Matter*. This is, perhaps, the most comprehensive definition of the relationship of the sexes, and it opens to view a still wider and more fundamental and fascinating aspect of this problem. Before it can be understood we must make an excursion into dark regions of the human mind and distant periods of human history.

Scientists of all kinds, ethnologists, philosophers, theologians, and linguists, are agreed that the original form of human mentality was mythical thinking as part of a 'magic' existence. Its main characteristics was a sense of universal oneness. All the distinctions which our way of thinking has developed did not then exist; reality appeared to this mode of thought to be still homogeneous and undifferentiated. Time, for instance, was not yet split into past, present, and future, but men lived in a perpetual present. Reality and dream were one. Life and death were parts, successive stages in one and the same process: birth was return to life and death continuation of life. All later concepts of reincarnation or of a future life and immortality were derivatives or applications of this mentality. Symbol and reality were the same; hence the belief in the efficacy of magic formulas, incantations, and rites. Cause and effect were not yet separated, everything could cause everything, wherefore the concept of hazard was unthinkable. Animals and humans were thought to be the same, a conception which underlay the almost universally accepted Totemism. The part was thought identical with the whole, wherefore this way of thinking is termed 'holistic'.

Measured by evolutionary standards, self-consciousness, the concept of a self as a self-contained unit, is a late, almost a recent, acquisition. Through a gradual process of differentiation of the original oneness, the concepts of mankind, races, tribes, families, and, at last, of the individual, have developed.

This process is still continuing, but many remnants of the holistic concept still live on in our thinking. First and foremost among them are religious concepts such as the brotherhood of man, the *anima Christiana universalis*, transubstantiation, and the like. The superstitions came next. And last but not least are all phenomena commonly, but quite incorrectly, described as para-psychological. As an example it is only necessary to mention telepathy as the best-known and most safely established phenomenon of the kind. Telepathy is the capacity for being in communion with others separated by space and time, without visible means of communication. This capacity, clearly a derivative of an all-embracing oneness, is still widespread and most efficient among primitive people, e.g. Negroes in Central Africa, and forms the basis of the mysterious transcontinental spreading of news. It is also, to a much lesser degree, the gift of some – comparatively few – individuals among the 'higher' civilized people in Europe.

It is known that a beehive or an anthill is not a community comparable with the human one composed of a number of separate individuals, but a living whole in the truest sense of the word. It is as if a certain 'quantity of life' was distributed among many bodies and centralized in the queen; therefore the life and health of these insects depend on the life and health of the queen so completely that insects working in the fields at some distance from the hive stop short when the queen dies. Such closely knit communities still exist also among humans. It is reported that among some tribes in the South Sea Islands a chieftain may sentence one of his subjects to death just by ordering him to die, and wherever this unfortunate man is, having received this sentence without any visible or audible communication, he sits down and dies obediently. Religious people in the Western world, by the way, mean much the same when they say of a dead man: 'The Lord has called him to Himself.' Later on kings sent knights who had fallen into disgrace on suicidal errands. In our day courts-martial sentence officers to suicide by tacitly suggesting it, and most of the victims take the hint. These three examples represent three stages in the process of loosening of the original communion, in that the involuntary, almost automatic, 'happening' of death is being replaced by increasingly voluntary action on the part of the victim, and finally the effect of a once magic influence becomes the result of a business-like calculation. Ordinary people commit suicide if the balance of their successes and failures in life shows them bankrupt and they despair of their ability to put things right again. What a sorry decline! Incidentally, viewed in this context suicide appears to be just another form of 'natural' death; in a case of what is commonly called 'natural death' the body has ceased to function, and in a case of suicide the mind has given way; the means which bring about the actual death are rather immaterial.

The same process in another field of reference manifests itself in this way. The original oneness of everything alive, being gradually restricted to the idea of mankind and later to groups based on consanguinity, has, through the recession of the mythical consciousness and the progress of conceptual thinking, been devitalized into artificial, man-made groupings like states and the many diverse institutions of which states are composed. The 'natural law', so dear to the hearts of the Schoolmen and Romantics, has been scientifically 'disproved' and replaced by scientific laws, and natural growth and intrinsic development have to give way to planning. And man, at one time thought of as created in the image of God and as a brother among brothers, finds himself depleted to hardly more than the bearer of a national registration number. Under the heartless rule of reason human existence cools off like the planet on which we live.

Love is the last surviving relic of the lost paradise of the magic existence; in the unconsciousness of the sexual orgasm man once more sinks back into mystic union, and the embrace of the lovers transfixes them into the all-embracing oneness of the magic existence. This is the secret of the essential mystery of sex.

Moreover, it must be now abundantly clear that the woman is the custodian of this arch-type of human existence, the keeper of the sacred flame, and that every single trait of the 'eternal feminine' is truly eternal, in every detail part of the magic existence which in the heart of the woman lives on for ever. For this reason men feel something mysterious about women and, rather bewildered, say they are incomprehensible and unpredictable. It is for this reason that love and sex mean so much to women, and not because they are oversexed or overemotional. Or take women's attitude towards Time. The much cursed unpunctuality of women is often enough due to neurotic reasons or lack of training, but there is more in it: the main characteristic of the magic existence is, as we remember, wholeness, which in terms of Time means continuity. Hence women experience Time not as a sequence of distinct bits of Time, so to speak, but as a continuous flow in which they cannot exactly single out one particular moment wherein they will do something or be somewhere. But far more important, for this same reason, women want marriage, because marriage alone represents and guarantees continuity and finality.

Masculine existence is the opposite of the feminine-magic existence. It is based on reason, built up by experience, and consists in 'doing'. In order to 'do', to handle things, one must split the whole into parts which can be measured and counted, combined and regrouped for varying purposes. There must be rules for conduct, for relations to others, for any kind of activity – and it is obvious from what I have said earlier that man's existence is the kind of existence towards which the development of mankind is moving – that is, away from the magic existence towards a form of existence which is based on reason, conceptual thinking, laws derived from experience and rules designed for specific purposes. This fact is the existential reason for the predominance of men over women. If women try to compete with men they try the impossible, impossible because it is against their intrinsic nature and against the trend of history. The best they can achieve is equality in action in such superficial strata as, for instance, the economic sphere or military service.

But does not this trend of thought justify the concept of an essential superiority of men? By no means. It is the old story all over again: only the propensity of mankind to attach values to facts is responsible for the misconception that a later stage of development must, of necessity, also be a 'higher' one, and that up-to-dateness and therefore factual domination is due to or synonymous with essential superiority. Similarly only from the point of a special philosophy can the spirituality of man be pronounced a higher stage of development than the materiality of woman. In fact, the respective merits of man's and woman's mode of existence could be just as well assessed the other way round: that man's existence represents a step on the downward grade, an alienation from reality, genuineness, and immediacy – and therefore man would appear as what we doctors technically call a *dégeneré supérieur.*

It is a strange historical fact, to my mind not sufficiently appreciated, that throughout history the publicly recognized position of women varies inversely with the esteem in which they have been held in private. The reason for the variation in public recognition of women can be found in the greater or lesser emphasis that a nation or a period lays on the spiritual element in our existence, and the degree of emphasis decides the character of the people or of the historical period. The most striking example is offered by the Orthodox Jews. The Jewish religion is the most patriarchal even among the Oriental religions, and not for nothing are the Jewish archfathers referred to as 'Patriarchs'. Women are relegated to a much lower religious status than men. They, for instance, need not hold all the numerous religious rites – not, as modern rationalists put it, because they are too busy to do so, but because their status does not require such a measure of religious observance. Or an oath made by a woman can be simply annulled by her husband, etc. But as a housewife she enjoys the greatest respect. It is she who actually rules the house, and on the eve of the Sabbath she lights the sacred candles and says Grace. And as a mother she is supreme: the child is her child, physically and spiritually. Although under Jewish law the father is responsible for the religious and spiritual education of the children, in case a Jewish woman marries a non-Jewish man the children of this marriage are considered Jewish – not out of tribal possessiveness but because we are our mother's children in the flesh and the spirit.

And here is an example from more recent history. The seventeenth and eighteenth centuries prided themselves on being the centuries of Reason. The seventeenth-century French philosopher Descartes, to-day acclaimed as the originator of the French spirit, took as the starting-point of his philosophy the famous sentence *Cogito ergo sum*, which means 'Only from the fact that I think do I know I am alive'. Kant wrote at the end of the eighteenth century his *Critique of Pure Reason*, the gospel of modern philosophy, and the French Revolution erected altars to the Goddess of Reason. This is 'masculinity' *par excellence*! But – if we think of these centuries we look upon them as times of grace, subtlety, refinement, wit, and charm. With nostalgia we conjure up the images of those lovely women who ruled in Versailles and entertained in their *salons*. Superficially these centuries may seem extremely feminine, but from an existential point of view they are the most masculine in modern history.

Only modern psychology rediscovered the wisdom that life is so much bigger than the narrow scope of Reason, and that the real problems of Life cannot be thought out by pure reason but must be solved by the immanent logic of Life and by its intrinsic laws of growth. For women all this is self-evident, and it is an alluring speculation that to women has been assigned the task of taking Life's revenge on Reason: women tell the 'Truth', they know what really 'is'. Men tell the 'correct' thing, that can be proved, and when practically applied furnishes useful results. Men approach reality only through the medium of reason, and only that section of reality is accessible to them that can be grasped by reasoning.[1] Kant's great concept that man cannot know the 'Thing as such' but can only know reality through the screen of the categories of Reason is totally incomprehensible to women – not because they are too stupid to understand his theory, which may or may not be so, but because this way of approach is alien to their nature. One day I showed to a woman who is unquestionably one of the select the portrait of F. W. Hegel. Not knowing that she was looking at one of the greatest thinkers of all time, she was struck by the majestic beauty of the head, the dome-like forehead, the unfathomable eyes full of the sadness of a man who carries the burden of his high office. But with equal strength she felt anxiety and hostility to the arch-enemy, the antipode, the force

1. Schiller, the most 'masculine', that is spiritual and therefore erroneously called 'idealistic', of all German writers, wanted to write a poem, called 'The Bell', in which he described how the ringing of bells accompanies our life from the cradle to the grave. For weeks he went to a foundry in order to study the making of bells. But he could not get what he needed. At last he studied a text-book of metallurgy, and then he knew; only by means of this 'predigested' reality was he able to create his masterpiece.

essentially alien and opposed to herself: the rich wisdom of a woman recoiling, almost visibly, from the piercing impact of the supreme Intellect.

With women knowing and being coincide, both are the same function, whereas it is given to men only to 'know', for which reason they can never, unaided, get down to reality, to the being, to the 'thing as such'. This aid they get from women. A woman is intuitive always, from the beginning, where men try to get by means of a laborious analysis, surprised at the result of their efforts, which was self-evident all the time for the woman. Men rejoice in reducing any single experience to a principle, but it is difficult for a woman to think in generalities. Her design for living, her plan of campaign as it were, is always ready, intuitively and hardly conscious, but her difficulty is to translate it into the concreteness of thoughts and words; she can do it only by concrete action, because she 'knows' only through living. A woman, supremely great in her femininity, cut short all my attempts at luring her into making general statements by saying: 'I cannot tell. I have not yet been in such a situation.' Another woman, ready to forgo the security of her sheltered life and to embark on the dangerous adventure of testing her own strength, said: 'In theory I know that I can do all I like but I must have it in my body in order to "know" it really.'[1]

And pursuing this trend of thought one cannot help feeling that women in their frantic efforts at 'emancipation' are betraying their mission in the scheme of things.

The benefit which we derive from this rather long-winded détour into the history of mankind and the philosophy of existence is that we are now in a position to formulate conclusively the essence of the relationship of the sexes, their 'compensatory unlikeness': Matter without Spirit is shapeless and barren, Spirit without matter is volatile and sterile. The woman is the

1. This difference in approach on the part of men and women to the ultimate reality seems a perfect analogy to the difference between revealed and discovered truth. Many years ago I discussed this problem with a Jesuit, and in the course of the argument he said: 'There is only one Truth. To us it has been revealed and we possess it in its fullness. You scientists must gradually grope towards it, and in the end you will arrive at the same result, sooner or later. Probably later, but the Church can wait.'

solid ground of reality from which the man can start his flight into the realm of the Spirit, and to which he returns as the giant Antaeus in the Greek myth had to lie down from time to time and kiss Mother Earth in order to suck new strength from her inexhaustible store.

This interrelatedness and interdependence of the masculine and the feminine existence by which one sex opens up to the other hitherto unknown, in fact unknowable, depths of human existence constitutes what I called being in love with the sublime way a woman interprets reality through the medium of her womanhood. This femininity may manifest itself either just by her perfect way of being a woman or by some activity such as her skill in needlework, or her perfection in artistic or scientific achievements. To love a woman in that way or to love this kind of woman may not be given to every man, and men capable of this kind of love lay themselves open to the suspicion that a 'feminine' streak in them is attracted by the 'virile' element in such a woman. Still worse, there are psychologists insensitive enough to denounce this noble sentiment as masochism. In fact the reverse is true. These men are particularly masculine, because the high degree of their own spirituality makes them particularly susceptible to the 'material' component in these women, and through this fusion these men find the way to the realm of matter. If, for instance, a man lacks the sense and therefore the proper approach to art as such or to a particular kind of art, such as painting or music, and he is fortunate enough to be in love with a woman who practises this kind of art, she may become the mediator, provide the missing link between him and art: his existential union with her may open up and make accessible to him this hitherto concealed, almost forbidden, part of reality, and faith in her essentiality may reveal to him Truth. No man artist could render the same service, because this vehicle of faith cannot be established between man and man; even the master-pupil relationship is of a totally different nature.

Love is not the right word for this kind of relationship, or it is a particular kind of love. Nor is it friendship, which is the contact of two similar people, whereas in this case two different people complement each other by their different ways of being. It is love, but, so it seems to me, an impersonal kind of love:

pure Masculinity delights in pure Femininity; the particular man and the particular woman embody only the two aspects of human Existence, and their union creates human Existence in its wholeness. Accordingly, the emotion that accompanies this kind of relationship is also a particular one. It is 'tenderness', that sweet, fragrant, indefinable sensation. Tenderness, like any emotion engendered by the contact of the sexes, tends to physical expression – urgent and imperative but 'tender' and shy. There is a strong element of protection in the feeling of tenderness, and the caressing embrace is very different from the possessive embrace in a sexual relationship. Fascinated, the two look at each other in deep mutual understanding, they touch each other like people who have met at last, they kiss. However similar in appearance, this glancing, touching, kissing is of a totally different nature from similar actions which are part of the sexual contact – so much so that the very thought of really sexual contact is abhorrent to lovers of this kind. And in fact it is something essentially different: two worlds meet, Spirit and Matter are reunited.

In the biological sphere the woman bears the man's children and thus delivers him from his isolation, weaves him into the pattern of the generations and gives immortality to his name. In the social-economic sphere 'the germ of social organization was, indeed, the woman and her children and her children's children'. (W. I. Thomas.) Or, as V. Klein puts it: 'Women formed the social nucleus of primitive organization, that fixed point to which men returned from their exploits.' Women first practised agriculture and the handicrafts, and set men free to go about their jobs – fighting and hunting. Fighting they still do, and as for the hunting, only the quarry has changed; instead of the beasts of the wild now they pursue power, wealth, and fame. But above and beyond these vital pursuits men have built up an entirely new world, the universe of spiritual values, our civilization. On several previous occasions I have described the essence of civilization as a process of splitting up of genuine units, and we see now that this trend fits perfectly into the analytical, atomizing mentality of men. But besides this purely destructive effect civilization has also a constructive effect, to produce order – man-made order serving man's purposes superimposed on the purpose of Nature, on the natural growth of things. If we find somewhere in a field three large stones put together so as to form a pyramid we know at once that this structure is no chance product of Nature, but has been purposely erected by human hands as a signpost. Even in his noblest achievement, building civilization, the woman is man's indispensable helper. An excellent example is provided by religion. However religion may have originated, men have created the religious organization, the Church, have erected the Gothic cathedral of theology, have in modern times invented a philosophy and psychology of religion. But all these achievements, true products of man's spiritual adventures, rest safely on the solid ground of the humble, naïve, unquestioning, and unshakable faith of woman – as every religious leader or propagandist knows.

And here in a nutshell is the solution of the problem. A native woman was carrying a heavy load patiently behind her husband along the road. When asked – obviously by a tactless European – why she and not her husband was carrying the load, she said: 'If a lion attacked us and my husband were hampered by a load, what would happen to me?' There are a surprising number of lions about in our world, but there are considerably fewer prudent women.

*

The question whether the '*eternal masculine*' exists has never been asked, presumably because no one has ever doubted that it does. We men are taken for granted, mostly by ourselves. Actually, to characterize man would be to do no less than analyse human existence as such. Attempts to do this have been made in the late Germany by Heidegger, Jaspers, Scheler in the philosophical field; from the religious point of view mainly by Haecker; in the medical sphere by myself, and in this country by Kenneth Walker in his book, *Diagnosis of Man*. The problem has recently been taken up in America, and dealt with *inter alia* by Alexis Carrel in his book, *Man the Unknown*; by Erich Kahler in *Man the Measure*; by Lewis Mumford in *The Condition of Man*.

For our present purpose a few remarks on this subject must suffice.

I have said earlier that the difference between the sexes is rooted in the difference in the sexual function of either sex. This is fully valid for the woman, much less, if at all, for the man, because the woman fulfils herself in her sexual function, the man does not. What sex is for the woman, work is for the man.

Man is a doer. As we already know, doing is not the same as being 'active'. In films, for instance, or at political conferences, a great deal goes on without anything being done, achieved. Conversely, great things are often done by patience and by waiting, attitudes that seem to be passive but in fact may require great efforts of self-constraint. The elements and characteristics of 'doing' are intention, planning, taking risks, and responsibility, and making things. Needless to say, women like all other human beings do things, for 'doing' is part of human nature, and because one cannot live in this world without doing. But doing is not the woman's way of being, as it is for the man, whose mode of existence it is and whose days it fills. Furthermore, the woman's creation, the child, is part of Nature, it augments the already existing products of Nature, and the products of woman's activities are things one imperatively needs for maintaining life. Man's creativeness enriches the world by producing things that are not part of Nature, nor are they necessary for maintaining life, but are produced for their own sake and exist in their own right, such as science, art, philosophy, etc. It is true that some of these products can be 'applied' to practical purposes, as e.g. technical inventions, and that a good deal of man's activity is also entirely devoted to the provision of the necessities of living – but these are not the specifically masculine tasks. The nature of laws provides a good example of the interrelation of the spiritual and the practical in man's creations. Laws are necessary for the 'life' of a community, but this is only their practical application: they were invented, and the theory and philosophy of Law was evolved in order to embody, bring down to earth, the Idea of Justice. The transcendence of the purely vital sphere is the task and privilege of men.

There are also women artists and scientists, but not many, and only a handful have achieved pre-eminence. On the other hand, men have surpassed women when they have taken up typically feminine occupations such as cooking or dressmaking, not because they are better, but because they are by their very nature doers and therefore make things better. But it is most significant that in the field of fashion we meet the same distribution of labour between the sexes as in love life: men invent fashions, but women reserve the right to accept or reject them. And they do the latter if the fashion does not serve their main purpose of attracting men; no foolish or purely stylish suggestions last for any length of time. Incidentally, our clothing provides another interesting example of the devitalizing and cooling off of our existence, and shows that men are leading in the process. When the French Revolution reduced '*monsieur*' to '*citoyen*', it changed the colourfulness of the *ancien régime* into the drabness of our time. The clothes of modern men are designed only for usefulness at work and sport, and are merely a protection against the vicissitudes of the climate, and at the end of this downward development stands the overall. In fifty or a hundred years hence no man will dream of attending a fancy-dress ball dressed *à la mode* nineteenth or twentieth century.

Here just one word may be said about the much glamorized concept of the 'Great Man'. This is an extremely tricky question, because it is at the focal point of any philosophy of Man. Keeping clear of any form of romanticism, we can define greatness only as a specific manifestation of man's existence: to realize the eternal moral values, to embody or, in the truest sense of the word, to 'incarnate' them. This is man's task in the scheme of things. Here I want to point out a fascinating – or perhaps depressing – fact of history, in part mentioned earlier. All the great problems of man's existence have already been formulated and all the possible answers have already been given in the Jewish–Christian religion in its narrative and dogmatic-theological parts: Jesus, the mediator between God and Man, made Man realize that God's will is the core of Man's being. And a leading modern philosopher could not better define Man than as 'mediator between values of reality'. (N. Hartmann.) From a psychological point of view the greatness of a personality is measured by the degree of its harmonious unification. Moral greatness consists in the degree to which a person not only knows but lives those moral values. But most controversial of all is the definition of historical greatness. Certain it is that, contrary to common opinion, this kind of greatness does not consist in the commotion a man has caused in the world, or in the fact that he has turned history into a grandiose film in which a great deal goes on and nothing is achieved. In my opinion, a great actor on the historical stage is one who is given the genius to sense the intrinsic trends of historical events and who helps to bring the meaning of history to fruition; whether this means bringing the Kingdom of God on Earth or – if it must be – drawing up a planned economy. What for instance earned Napoleon the attribute of greatness? It is a puzzling question. For all his military conquests his dream of a United Europe collapsed before he died, and all that has survived this meteoric phenomenon is the Code Napoléon, the constitution of the Comédie Française – and a legend.

Greatness as I understand it is not confined to the supermen; it is in fact synonymous with what I call 'exemplary existence', and therefore it is, although in varying degrees, within the grasp of every man. Nor is it a privilege of the masculine part of humanity, as everyday experience proves. On the other hand, it is a fact not without significance that the register of saints in the Catholic Church contains the names of many more men, at least of the first order, than women.

The man does not 'live' in his house, he only lodges there. He is 'at home' where he works, in his office or workshop or study. His congenial surroundings are always organizations – the local public-house, his club, meetings, and the like. It is, then, natural and necessary for him to be with other men, and men like, occasionally at least, to spend their evenings with friends, and not only because of the divers activities with which they fill the time. It is different with women. A woman needs one or two women friends, but women's clubs, for instance, always appear as slightly ridiculous imitations. A woman 'lives' at home, the home is she, she is the soul of the home, and her absence reduces the 'home' to the status of a 'house' far more than does the absence of her husband. And if someone contends that these are outmoded views, he may be reminded that our civilization moves away from rather than towards the realization of the essential.

Finally, men and women alike pass through a painful experience which in the case of woman is due to Nature and in the case of man is institutionalized. The life of a woman as a female comes to an end through the change of life. Similarly, a man's life – not of course as a male, but in all that makes a man's life worth living – comes to an end through the institution of a legally or conventionally fixed retiring age.

## *Masculine Sexuality*

Whereas the woman fulfils herself in her sexual life, the sexual act is for the man just one activity among others, and the sexual relationship is a relationship, like many others, into which he may enter.

But there are differences. The sexual relationship is the only relationship which is an end in itself; by its nature it is a co-operation for the end to which both partners contribute equal shares. It is important to keep this fact in mind, because it disposes of the still widely held opinion that the man has to bear the whole responsibility for the sexual act, whereas the woman is often depicted as the innocent victim of the man's greed. This is obviously wrong, as both are 'active' in bringing about the result, the man, at any rate under normal conditions, by demanding, the woman by consenting. And it might even be held that the woman's responsibility is the greater, because it is so easy to say 'yes' to temptation, but needs far more moral courage, or awareness of the consequences, to say 'no'. Surprisingly many men are ignorant of the fact that women want them just as much as they want women, and that there is no sacrifice on the woman's part. The reason, or at least the essential one, for this erroneous conception is that these men believe that to take the initiative is the same as being active. The second difference between the sexual and any other relationship is the stake that is required. In any other relationship one invests and risks 'possessions', such as money, honour, reputation, health, etc. In the sexual relationship we must invest ourselves; nothing less than the whole personality will do. For the woman this is natural, because to stake all or nothing is her nature, and being sexual means being herself. For the man this self-surrender requires a definite resolve, because the sexual relationship is only one of many relationships, and he has been taught, or has learned by experience, that to take all in a bargain is usually foolish if occasionally heroic; only the fully matured man realizes that in sexual matters this is the normal thing to do. In this attitude towards sex rests the true responsibility a man takes upon himself. Whatever a man does with a woman and to her, so long as he does it in this attitude, it is fair play, and if he loses the game it is just one of these tragedies of which our life knows so many. But if he approaches a woman for any other reason or is willing to invest anything less than himself he incurs guilt.

The attitude of men towards the sexual act itself is complex. Man's nature, being what it is, makes him see in the act the aim and climax of the relationship. More than one woman has complained that all men want only one thing, and always the same. And men who postpone the climax do it, almost against their nature, out of consideration for their partners or out of technical refinement. On the other hand, man's capacity for splitting wholes up into parts makes him experience the coitus as a 'mere' act divorced to a considerable degree from the rest of his personality and, therefore, more or less devoid of meaning and inferior in importance to any other expression of personal contact. This is aptly illustrated by the story of a distinguished elderly gentleman who honoured his parlourmaid by inviting her into his bed; when afterwards the girl tried to kiss him good-bye he indignantly forbade her this 'disgusting intimacy'. The perfect male! But there is a lesson that can be learned from this rather disgusting story. The sexual act can be degraded to a purely physical action devoid of any meaning – not so the kiss. What coitus is to sex, the kiss is to tenderness; it always contains or expresses a strong personal attachment. Women are very much alive to this fact, and even a street-girl occasionally tries to snatch a kiss from her reluctant lover, in order to create the illusion of having been loved for a few minutes.

Thus, initiative, responsibility, and determination in action are the three constituents of male sexuality upon which its success or failure depends.

*

The capacity to fulfil a proper sexual relationship is called 'potency'. Its component parts are: desire to associate with a woman and the physical urge; an erection which must come at the right moment, be firm enough to permit of an insertion and last long enough to allow the woman to reach her climax; emission, which must not come too early or too late; the sensation of orgasm and satisfaction afterwards. All these elements must be there and must be properly co-ordinated. It is a frequent error to think that potency means only the ability to have an erection, and many a man takes it almost as an insult if one calls him impotent, although he has erections but is for one reason or another incapable of performing a proper coitus. Here, if anywhere, applies the law of 'all or nothing': either a man can do the job or he cannot; there is no compromise or half-way solution.

Men often ask how long a 'normal' coitus should last. The answer is that it must last until its purpose, which is mutual satisfaction, is achieved. But to all practical intents and purposes it means until the woman partner is satisfied; because of his own satisfaction the man is in control anyway. It is really astounding how many men, otherwise very decent ones, forget that, at least for this co-operation, the principle of 'equal pay for equal work' must be respected; having obtained their own satisfaction, they consider their work done and do not bother what happens to their partners. It must be admitted that quite a few women make it not easy for their partners to know when they have had their orgasm or whether they have had it at all, concealing this event out of false modesty or for neurotic reasons. On the other hand, some women who for neurotic reasons cannot get an orgasm, but are anxious not to disappoint their partners, play their parts so cleverly that even the most experienced men could be deceived. This is the weakness in our definition of the normality of an intercourse, that the orgasm of the woman is sometimes not a reliable indication; some women cannot get an orgasm at all and some others are so extremely slow that even the most potent men cannot satisfy them. But if we add the qualification 'under normal circumstances' the definition is still not only the best, but the only possible one. But pressed, and not only by men patients, to give a more precise answer, the most I could say for certain is that the widely accepted view that 'a few minutes after the insertion' would be sufficient is definitely too lenient. Although it is, for obvious reasons, very difficult to get reliable data, as women tend to be slightly immoderate in their demands and men are rather optimistic as regards their achievements, I should say that fifteen minutes is a poor average and half an hour is not yet an athletic feat beyond the capacity of a man with sufficient technique and with still greater devotion to his task.

If we now proceed to analyse the component parts of the male sexual function it will be advisable to treat the normal and abnormal modes of this function together, partly because it is not always easy to draw the line dividing the normal from the abnormal, partly because the characteristics of the normal function will by way of contrast be the better discernible. We had better state once more precisely what we mean by the term 'normal' man. He is firstly a man who does not suffer from any of those physical diseases which affect the sexual function. To name only a few of the most important ones: diseases of the brain and spinal cord such as progressive paralysis, tabes, etc.; some abnormalities of the metabolism such as diabetes and excessive obesity; abnormal functioning of some incretory glands such as the gonads, pituitary gland, and suprarenals; and last but not least, congenital or traumatic deformations of the genital organs. But such patients do not concern us here, because in them sexual disorder is only a part symptom of the primary disease, and such men are not sexual patients in the strict sense of the word. Hence we can unreservedly uphold our statement made in the preceding chapter, that *all defects of the sexual function are of a psychological nature· they are symptoms of a neurosis* that is a mental condition in which the subconscious objects to the conscious intention to establish a perfect union between the sexes and express this personal union in a perfect union of the bodies. For the purpose of this sabotage the subconscious mind makes the physical basis of the union impossible, thus producing what we call abnormal sexuality. The symptoms are: no desire or urge, abnormalities of the erection (no erection at all, insufficiently firm erection, an erection which collapses before or during the act), abnormalities of the emission (the emission may come too quickly or too slowly or not at all), lack of the pleasant sensation during the act, or lack of orgasm. Finally, abnormal reaction after the otherwise normal act. Which one of these means of sabotage the subconscious chooses in a given case is immaterial, because, as we said earlier, a defect of any one component part of the function makes the performance of a proper act impossible.

But even freedom from a neurosis does not yet qualify a man as normal. We must never lose sight of the basic fact that sexuality is not an isolated function but an integral part of our personality, hence sexual pathology is only one manifestation among several others of a pathology of the whole personality. *A personality is normal if it is wholly integrated*, if body, soul, and mind are welded into a complete unity, if the body is only the executive organ of the soul and if the soul desires or intends nothing which is not in harmony with spiritual values. *I have called such a state an 'exemplary existence'*. A person in whom this wholeness is disrupted so that these component parts can act independently is, in the strict sense, subnormal – temporarily or permanently immature. It may be argued, and indeed more than one man with whom I have discussed these problems has so argued, that life would be much simpler and more comfortable if one were not always impeded by these spiritual fetters – if we were permitted, for instance, to seek purely physical pleasure when we feel like it and to adhere to the principle of a bird in the hand being worth two in the bush. This is undoubtedly true in a way, but it is a small way only. For the celebrated commonplace that 'crime never pays' holds good, in a milder form, in the sexual sphere as well. The man who seeks only the satisfaction of his purely physical urges knows only the cheap pleasure of a fleeting moment, but the blissful happiness of a perfect sexual union will be denied to him for ever. This is the price he has to pay for his short-term policy.

I said before that if a man postpones having intercourse, and during the intercourse postpones reaching his climax, he does it out of regard for his partner, or out of technical refinement. Actually there is a third possibility, and this leads to still another aspect of the concept of normality. A man can not only know by variegated experience but he can genuinely feel what the woman wants and needs, by insight, as it were. Does this capacity indicate a 'feminine streak' in him, or is it an indication of his completeness? In my opinion this alternative makes no sense, for the real understanding of the essential idea of sex is common to men and women, and from this common root of wanting the same thing the mutual understanding of all intimacies derives. Then and only then each of the two sexes specializes and develops its own special character to the full. And now we realize at once that our problem acquires general significance: which represents the ideal norm – the all-round human being or the highly specialized one? Who is the better doctor, the general practitioner or the perfect specialist? In the medical field the question has been answered in practice by the fact that a kind of 'compensatory unlikeness' forces the two types into co-operation. In social life our taste has pointed to an answer inasmuch as the man or woman who is specialized in one field but ignorant on general matters is often found a bore, and in the sexual field the 'he-man' is generally considered a perfectly insufferable character. As in many kinds of corporative activity, each partner must play his part to perfection, always mindful of the common ground from which they have sprung and the common cause which reunites them. Or, to use a simile closer to the facts, it illustrates: in a play the hero must be heroic, the heroine lovely, and the villain villainous. But the actors turn tragedy into travesty if by overacting their parts they burst the frame of the play and leave behind the common ground of humanness in which the characters of the play are rooted.

*

Before I turn to an analysis in some detail of male sexuality and try to sketch some types of sexual behaviour in man, I feel I must first correct an erroneous conception which might easily have arisen from what I have just said about the masculine character. Sexuality is by no means a negligible factor of the male existence. Men need sexuality just as women do, not only for pleasure or the relief of the physical tension, but essentially. Nevertheless sex plays a different part in the lives of men and women. The woman needs sexuality in order to 'fulfil' herself by bearing a child and becoming a mother, and her sexual activity is only a means to this end. The man needs sexuality in order to feel himself a real man, to know that he can 'do' it, and his sexual activity is an end in itself. Superficial as this need to 'do' may seem, it is a very urgent one, in its way just as essential for the man as her way of needing sex is for the woman. Many times I have asked male patients why they were so anxious to put their sex life right, as their particular circumstances hardly seemed to justify their insistence – as for instance when a man has reached middle age without ever having felt the need for sex; or when a man, after a few years of a fairly satisfactory sexual life in marriage, cools off as it were, and he and his wife would be quite content to carry on a sort of companion-marriage. Invariably the answer has been that they really could not say, but that they somehow felt it must be done. On two occasions the strength of men's feelings about this was brought home to me in a most drastic way. A man was a prisoner of war abroad. One day he was seized with panic lest he might be impotent although, as he was young, there was no reason for this fear. But the idea became so compelling that he tried to escape from captivity and succeeded after the third attempt. No sooner had he reached this country than he attempted sexual intercourse with the first woman he could get hold of, and failed, as every man would have done under the circumstances. A short treatment assured him of his normality. The second case concerned a fighter pilot in the Fleet Air Arm. He was shot down in the Pacific. While his plane was sinking and he frantically tried to extricate himself from his seat he had only one haunting thought: 'I have never known what sex means. I must have it somehow.' He had it shortly afterwards.

*A man's sexuality in all its aspects is a function of his virility*: he must feel himself a man and then he will behave and act as a man. Virility means nothing heroic or dramatic, it is nothing but a simple, natural, instinctive confidence in oneself. The sexual capacity of a man is independent of his physical build; in fact the discrepancy between the physical structure of a man and his sexual avidity is often striking. Strong men fail where poor specimens succeed easily. Consumptive patients, for instance, in the last stages of their illness show a very strong increase of their sexuality, often a bad omen of the approaching death. Nor is physical tiredness a real impediment to sexual desire. Among sportsmen it is well known that after great physical exertion sexual desire and capacity is particularly strong, and winter-sport hotels derive a good deal of their attraction from this coincidence. After an unusually strenuous day's work a man may be dog-tired and drop into bed with no other desire than to sleep; but continuous tiredness is no valid explanation for permanent sexual abstention, though it is often used as an excuse. If a man is occupied with an absorbing mental task, particularly of a productive nature, his sexual interest may cease, not because he is physically exhausted but because his mind is absorbed. Even great worries need not necessarily affect adversely the sexual desire; on the contrary, the close union with another human being may provide the greatest solace. Generally speaking, sexuality – not the sexual instinct but the whole complex phenomenon – asserts itself in a normal man's life against all adverse influences.

As we already know, sexuality is not an isolated function existing in its own right, but an action with a reason and purpose, determined by the pattern of life a person has designed for himself; it comes and goes and varies in all its details according to this scheme. There is perhaps one exception to this rule: the frequency of a man's sexual associations is, it seems, almost entirely dependent on his bodily constitution. Just as one man can lift a certain weight and another a many times heavier load, so one man is able to cohabit several times a night whereas another must content himself with one coitus in a week or even in a fortnight. Intensity of desire is a different matter. As a rule desire and the capacity to satisfy it go together; sometimes the desire outruns this capacity, just as sometimes appetite for food is greater than the capacity to eat and to digest it; occasionally the desire is, subconsciously, suppressed, and varying degrees of neurotic frigidity result in men for the same reason as it occurs in women.

That a man's sexuality is a function of his whole personality is, *inter alia*, proved by the fact that, generally speaking, a normal man behaves in bed just as he behaves in his office. In both places the pattern of his behaviour is governed by the same basic motivation. This basic fact is illustrated by the following example:

G. H., aged 35, married. For two years he had had an affair with the girl he later married, with perfectly satisfactory sexuality. But as early as one year after marriage his erections became less good and soon an almost complete impotence set in.

He had been a precocious child in many respects, and everything came easily to him, for which reason he did not need to work very much at school. At the age of 15 he was the best football player in his town, so much so that a visiting footballer promised him a great future. From this moment on his interest in football slackened and before long he gave up playing.

His wife was the most beautiful and the richest girl in town, and as he came from a very poor family it meant a great triumph to him to have conquered her. But from the moment this conquest was secured by the marriage, his sexual interest slackened, and before long it disappeared completely. His considerable success in business was never made through disciplined hard work, but through chance, intuition, and daring. No sooner did he get a new enterprise going than he lost interest and left it to his staff to work out the details of administration. Only recently on one of his frequent journeys he met a woman who attracted him physically more than any woman had for a long time. As soon as he realized that she was only waiting to be asked, she suddenly lost the best part of her attraction for him, and he gave her up.

This man represents a type to which, curiously enough, a great many very successful men belong, successful sexually and in other respects. But they are like racehorses which can only stand a short course. They do not want to possess the object of their effort but just enjoy effort and success as such. They are like the bad type of collectors who only love their collections but cannot appreciate the intrinsic value of the things which compose their collections. For some people life must consist entirely of 'First Nights'. By their failing these men demonstrate that the element of aggressiveness and daring in the male personality must be no more than a means to an end, and that this end is to final conquest and safe possession. The general rule that a man behaves in bed as he does in his everyday life needs some qualification when applied to any not quite normal, i.e. neurotic, man. Men who need triumphs for the maintenance of their mental balance seek them either in sexual life or in the field of general activities, according to their ideas of where these triumphs are easier to obtain. These ideas depend on the kind of inferiority such a man feels. One man may dread competition in all spheres of practical life but feel that women are waiting for him and are to be had just for the asking. Thus a kind of Don Juan may result – a pseudo Don Juan, of course, easily recognizable by the kind of women he chooses and the kind of laurels he reaps – whereas the real Don Juan is, in his way, as genuine, although much inferior, a type as the great lover: the accomplished virtuoso of love. Another man may most successfully brave all sorts of dangers and difficulties in life but fail lamentably in bed. Serious as this situation is for those who are in it, sometimes one cannot help wondering at the whimsical complexities of human nature: I numbered among my patients a fighter pilot of 'Battle of Britain' fame, an officer of the Chindits who distinguished himself in the Burma campaign, and a parachutist – all three completely impotent with their girls. Alas, the superiority of men!

*

It is probably an over-simplification of a highly complex matter, but one may say, in general, that fear of the practical side of life is due to the father, who frightened the boy, and fear of sex is due to the mother, who gave the child a somehow distorted idea of women. If modern medical psychology can claim one credit, it is the fact that it has clarified and duly emphasized the importance of the parental influence on the development of the child's character. This was not, perhaps, a very new or revolutionary discovery, but all the progress of science lies in the difference between just knowing or suspecting a fact and dissecting and describing it so exactly that the knowledge can be practically applied. We cannot enter into a thorough analysis of the all-important problem of parental influence, but must content ourselves with a few observations. The mother's task is a dual one: to care for and protect the child, and to assist it in breaking away from her later on. The more deeply a child has been rooted in the love of its mother, the better prepared it will be for this break and future independence. The unique intimacy between mother and child, and its feeling of unqualified belonging to a human being, makes the child feel at home in the world. The mother's implicit and unqualified love gives her child the sense of his intrinsic value.[1] As a reminiscence of the magic existence the mother is the mediator between the world and ourselves. And everlastingly lonely will be the adult who has not as a child consciously and emotionally experienced the existential communion with his mother. This problem of the mother-child relationship is still further complicated if the child is a son, for from the first moment the mother sees in her son a 'man' and often enough wants to bring him up as her sole comfort and solace for all disappointments which she has experienced in her marriage. And it is the hardest task of a mother – so hard indeed that many a mother fails in it – to bring up her son for another woman. Everybody knows these days that the conflict produced in a child by too great attachment to one's mother constitutes Freud's notorious Oedipus complex, but too few know that this concept is not the product of the unsavoury imagination of a sex-ridden psychologist but stark reality.

The father's contribution to a child's development is of a different kind. He sets up objective standards, creates the sense of duty, and stands for the idea of authority. By recognizing and appreciating the capacities and achievements of his child he builds up the child's self-confidence. A child who did not get, or thinks he did not get, adequate acknowledgement from his father grows up with a sense of failure, and therefore actually often becomes a failure. Then, what a child needs more than anything else is security. This sense of security he gets from a peaceful atmosphere and routine life at home. A child is like a sensitive instrument which reacts to all the emotional cross-currents in a home. Nothing is more harmful for the child's development than to have to face unexpected and unpredictable events. In this respect fathers are the main culprits. A man most successful professionally but rather a failure sexually in his marriage recollects how when he came home from school he always hesitated a few minutes before he

1. The great French *diseuse* Yvette Gilbert used to recite a poem: A son has torn the heart out of his mother's breast because his girl wanted it. Turning away he stumbles and drops the heart – and the mother's heart anxiously asks: 'Did you hurt yourself, my child?'

rang the doorbell of his home, wondering what might this time be waiting for him behind the still-closed door. Will father be friendly or will he be in one of his moods when no one is safe from his frightening criticism? This fundamental uncertainty of what the next moment may bring became the great handicap in this man's life; he has overcome it in the practical field, but not in human contacts, hence his sexual failure.

In order to build up the child's character it is not enough to teach him moral values, or to make him do certain things. What matters is to be a living example: not what we say or what we do, but only what we 'are' matters in human relationships. Often, indeed too often, parents thought they did their best for their children, and produced only failures – because not what they did but what they 'were' was not good enough. Herein real tragedies may originate, when the real and sincere personality of a father or a mother clashes too strongly with their parental duties. Only in passing we may mention the commonly known fact that sons of a famous father usually lag very much behind the achievements of their parent; and it is still open to argument whether the reason is of a biological or psychological nature. Also on lower levels children come up against a similar difficulty. I know a charming and intelligent 16-year-old boy who finds it rather difficult to get on in school. His mother was the only child of a most remarkable father, who brought her up as the sole companion of his far-flung travels; she crossed with him on skis the snowy plains of the Far North, and they climbed mountains together in Switzerland. In the strictest existential meaning she knew no limitations of Space or Time. Once she spent a long time meditating in complete solitude, and later developed a remarkable talent for sculpture. In spite of all these most unusual experiences, she is a very charming, modest, almost humble woman, who now lives a strenuous and narrow life in exemplary devotion to her family. And yet she 'is' existentially too big, too oppressive for her son, and the tragic thing is that she knows it and desperately tries to make herself small – the one thing no one can do.

This existential fate, as one may call it, is a factor in men's lives that cannot be overrated and is not yet sufficiently understood. Both these facts may justify giving another example which shows how this principle works and how distinctly even a boy could be aware of it. A 14-year-old boy could not at all adapt himself to the life in a school community and was in violent revolt against any form of authority. The cause of his psychological difficulty was his elder brother. The patient – if one could call him that – loved his brother dearly. And yet: 'I am jealous of his birthright,' he said, but immediately added that jealousy or envy are wholly inadequate terms because he feels no hatred for his brother. He finds it unbearable that 'seniority gives one some rights'. He does not want things his brother has been given but he is annoyed that he should not have them 'just because of these stupid two years' difference'. – I think that to make this distinction between jealousy and annoyance of the age difference is an outstanding psychological achievement. And the difference between psychology and existentialism can hardly be better illustrated than by the fact that the boy did not want the presents himself but just resented the – unalterable – reason for his handicap. The boy's revolt against authority was an attempt to alter it where he thought it could be done. The most successful psychological treatment (not carried out by myself) made the boy gradually realize that it is the nature of Fate to be accepted, and that there is ample space for developing one's personality within the boundaries of one's destiny. The obvious difficulty of putting up with one's essential Fate produced a truly ingenious idea in a 5-year-old boy. He too was the younger child, was devoted to his four-years-older brother, and showed no visible signs of jealousy. One day, for no particular reason, he said thoughtfully to his father: 'Daddy, if I stand on this chair I am taller than John, and if I could only manage to have my birthday twice a year I could be older than him, too.'

Sometimes it is pathetic to watch how a mother struggles against herself but fails. A young man described his mother as a 'complete angel'. He and his mother had always been together, shared the same interests and together braved the rather mild dictatorship of the father. When the son went to a university they wrote to each other every day for years. The result: 'The only woman I ever loved was my mother,' he said. 'Even when I was a small boy I always hoped to marry Mummy one day. Every woman I met later on I compared with my mother, but none could stand the comparison.' As soon as the mother noticed how things were, she encouraged the young man to meet girls, and invited all his girl friends to her house. At last he found a woman who was 'nearest to my mother in looks and personality' but he was sexually a complete failure with her – and has been ever since with any woman. The dream of his childhood had come true – he was 'married' to his mother, and in spite of her belated attempts, they were not able to break this fateful bond.[1]

This concept of maternal possessiveness must be taken in a wider sense than is commonly understood. It need not manifest itself in almost brutal action, such as that of a mother who melodramatically entreats her grown-up son to keep away from women, as all unhappiness in life comes from them; or as when a mother makes her young son promise never to leave her alone for the rest of her life; or when – in a more practical way – a mother finds fault with every girl her son brings to their house – for inspection, as it were. Force can be met by force, and a son with sufficient determination can liberate himself from this frustrating interference. Far more effective and dangerous, because more subtle and plausible, is the retarding and inhibiting influence, almost amounting to a spell, which mothers exercise on their sons through the kindness, sweetness, motherliness of their characters. There is a psychological law that every deviation from the average can become harmful, and hence too good a mother can be just as much a disadvantage as a bad one: sons of such ideal mothers must find it almost unreasonable to leave the paradise of their childhood – or, for that matter, the fleshpots of their parental home. There is still another pitfall not sufficiently recognized. Many a mother prides herself on the unlimited mutual confidence between her-

1. Two famous well-documented instances of the deleterious effect of a strong mother fixation on the sexual development of men are: Stendhal confesses in his autobiography, *The Life of Henri Brulard*, that he loved his mother 'with a mad passion', 'as criminal as possible'. This was undoubtedly the reason for his incapacity to love although he was much loved by women. And D. H. Lawrence's autobiography *Sons and Lovers* reveals his deep attachment to his mother, who evidently saw in him the substitute for her husband. And it is pathetic to watch how, hampered by this fixation, the young man had laboured to find his way to normal sexuality through a phase of homosexuality and impotence. (Cf. also his autobiographical novel *The Rainbow*.)

self and her son. 'There is nothing we hide from each other'; 'My son knows he could come to me with all his troubles', are typical phrases which indicate the insidious means by which the mother holds her unfortunate son in bondage. Needless to say, the main subject of these confessions is sex, and I know more than one case in which the mother had confided to the son all the, usually sordid, details of her own sexual life in marriage. That this psychological nudism is still more harmful than the physical is obvious. Such a son, tied and tethered to his mother by the last remaining fibres of the umbilical cord, as it were, must find it almost impossible to break away, and to transfer his loyalty to another woman, his wife, must appear as desertion, if not adultery. Some of these unfortunate sons express their plight rather naïvely in their dreams. A young husband dreamt that he was in a restaurant, sitting at a table with his mother and sister, and in a distant corner sat, quite by herself, his wife. He felt sorry that he could not assist her in this crowded and noisy place. Another man dreamt he was in bed with his young bride; just when they wanted to turn towards each other someone knocked on the door and his mother, of all people, brought in the morning tea, of all things! A patient, hampered by an over-zealous mother and gifted with a remarkable psychological insight, still vividly remembers the effort it cost him to kiss a girl, because he felt 'enclosed in a magic circle from which he could not step out'. These men are 'Sons and Lovers' of their mothers and incapable of fulfilling the commandment: 'Therefore shall a man leave his father and his mother, and shall cleave unto his wife, and they shall be one flesh.'[1]

This determining influence of the parents on the character of a child can occasionally be followed up through several generations, as the following family history illustrates:

The patient, a man of 36, is impotent through fear of women, who appear to him as the dominant sex. His mother is a domineering woman who holds husbands and children under her sway. Her father was a brutal tyrant who held his wife under tight control, whereas this father's mother – that is, the patient's great-grand-

1. A moving illustration of this sorry tale can be found in John Ruskin's biography, recently published under the title *The Order of Release*, by Admiral Sir William James (John Murray, 1947).

mother – was the ruler of her family, reducing her husband to a shadowy figure in the background. It is easy to see how this family curse worked through these four generations, and it did so in the two ways possible: The grandfather took up the challenge of his powerful mother and made himself powerful, whereas the patient succumbed to the strength of his mother and became impotent: it is to be hoped that his psychological treatment – the modern way of exorcising evil spirits – has laid the ghost for good. It may be worth mentioning that these people were Indians, and their story may be taken as an illustration of my contention that all men are alike – at least in their misery.

It is widely believed that a man's relationship to his mother has a decisive influence on his choice of a sexual partner; he chooses a woman either like or very unlike his mother. There is a great deal of experience to corroborate this opinion, but I think it is true only of men who had an abnormal relationship to their mothers in that they were too much attached to or too much frightened of them. The other extreme represents Alfred Adler's opinion that every average man must be able to have an average sexual relationship with every average woman. This is true in principle – that is, if one reduces the man and the woman to sheer maleness and femaleness – but it is certainly not true of complete human beings. We must admit that we know very little about the motives which make a man choose his sexual partner. It cannot be denied that a purely sexual attraction exists, that some women and men possess a definite 'sex appeal'. But in a real human relationship this element is far from decisive; in fact one may doubt whether it is of any importance if during a walk in the street one watches the men and women who have found each other in love or marriage. Hence, if a man complains that his sexuality does not work properly because he has discovered that his partner is less attractive than he thought, one must usually suspect that this is only a specious rationalization of a more important underlying disagreement.

Divers likes and dislikes, whims and fancies, in the choice of a sexual partner may betray often enough only thinly disguised peculiarities in a man's character, mostly of a more or less abnormal nature. If, for instance, a man has an affair with the nurse who looked after him during a long illness, and is perfectly successful with her but fails almost completely with the young wife whom he married after he had finished with the nurse, it is not difficult to know the cause of his different reactions to these two women: it was the element of a motherliness in the nurse's profession, not the woman herself, which stimulated his sexuality. We have seen in a previous chapter that men of a certain type visit prostitutes because the anonymity and meaninglessness of this kind of relationship best fits their personality. This mentality explains many peculiar habits and reactions of men. If, for instance, a man who had spent many years in Africa was normally potent with native women but invariably failed with women in this country, it was not just a matter of taste. He treated the native women not as 'women', hardly as human beings at all, and what appeared to be a normal sexual intercourse was in reality only a rather complicated method of masturbation. On the other hand, intercourse with a white woman 'meant' something to him; in fact it meant so much that he was afraid of doing it. The following case illustrates well several aspects of this problem:

H. T., aged 35, a vigorous sporting type of man. Ever since he started his sexual career he had had a slightly premature emission, which did not prevent him from leading a very extensive and variegated sexual life. The only occasions when he was as good as normal were when he associated with prostitutes, whom he visited on and off practically all his life. The last of his friends, a few years ago, was a Belgian woman, a 'great expert'; he could cohabit with her three times a night fairly satisfactorily. For the last two years he has been having an affair with a married woman of very high social and personal status, with whom he fails almost completely. He has very good erections but as soon as he intends to make use of them the emission occurs. This is all the more depressing as this is the 'great experience' of his life, and he thinks he is very much in love with this woman.

The psychological analysis of this case is very simple; right from the beginning this man refused personal contact with women. Hence his habitual premature emission. The Belgian woman he considered as his mistress, whom he kept, and did not mind whether he satisfied her – hence his comparative success. In his present affair he minds very much – hence his complete failure. By 'minding' he understands his strong desire and ambition to give this woman what she wants – but he is not aware of what it is that she wants, and of the price he would have to pay to give it to her. He means sexual gratification, but what the inexorable law of life demands is – giving himself. After I had explained all this to him he said: 'You frighten me – perhaps I never loved anyone. I never considered giving pleasure to a woman, never felt any responsibility, it defeats me.' He may have felt the need for responsibility but he was still far from taking it on, because he knew quite well that he was still keeping himself aloof. And here is an amusing tailpiece: At this time he went abroad on business; in Paris he ran into his one-time mistress – and all went as well as ever before.

This story, most typical of the sexual behaviour of many men, has a moral: that immorality in sex never pays – I mean, of course, not the conventional immorality of this man in keeping a mistress and having an affair with a married lady, but the essentially immoral notion that pleasure is the purpose of sex.

A similarly deleterious effect on a man's sexuality can result from an attitude seemingly the opposite of the one we have just discussed, but its meaning and purpose are much the same. Whereas men of the group we have mentioned deprive women of their natural value and dignity, the men we are now to consider give them too much of it by putting them on a pedestal and looking up to them, as if women were beings of a superior kind whom one must worship but not desire. To judge such a situation properly requires a good deal of tact and experience. This sexual attitude, like any other, is the result of the atmosphere in the home in which a man has grown up. If the atmosphere was a sincerely and genuinely moral one, and if this morality was imparted to the child not forcefully but by living example, then he will become a man who approaches women with respect. This is not an ideal but the norm according to my definition of norm given in the first chapter of this book. The acid test of the genuineness of this attitude is that such a man produces an effective sexuality at the appropriate time and when the right conditions are fulfilled, as they are in a true marriage. But there are men who do not pass this test, and they are the ones I am here discussing. They do not approach women with respect but, as I said, put them on a pedestal that is too high. This is just as bad as putting them too low. Whether one makes women into devils or angels makes little difference – as a proper sexual relationship can only be established with mortals. The method of hanging grapes high up and pronouncing them too beautiful to be eaten is just another way of dodging reality. It is, as always, fear that hides behind this pseudo-morality and the pedestal's only purpose is to keep the woman safely out of reach. This attitude is always the result of harmful domestic influences, as the following case shows:

T. K., a 36-year-old man, very virile in looks and personality, married for eight months, has so far completely failed in his sexual approach to his wife. He comes from a family of Quakers. His father was 'a most saintly man' to whom the son was deeply devoted. Three friends of his father were also very pious men who made a great impression on the boy. One of his masters at school, a 'most powerful personality', impressed him as a kind of Gandhi; he was 'the antithesis of sex'. Thus, the boy developed an 'undue sense of delicacy', was 'much too respectable', a 'perfect gentleman' – apparently much in keeping with the spirit of his father, friends, and master. His mother he described as a strict Scotswoman, a dominating person who ruled at home and was much admired by her husband. It is no easy matter for a child to grow up under such a régime, and it is quite safe to assume that the personality of his mother had made the boy shy away from women. Again, it is fear rather than awe that lies at the bottom of this patient's attitude. At the age of 20 it dawned on the young man that his great purity was not quite genuine, but he did not yet know what had gone wrong. And when, some years later, he married a very young, beautiful girl, he started the old game of adoration all over again, and was 'deeply impressed by the excellence of his wife'. The gulf between his inveterate idea that women are beings of a superior order and that sex is an activity of an inferior nature was too wide to be bridged, and impotence was the almost inevitable consequence of the emotional conflict that ensued.

This leads to the all-important question of the influence a religious upbringing may have on sexual development. One would hardly believe that a problem of this kind could arise but for the frequent assertions of patients that their 'puritanical upbringing' or 'religious consciousness' is to blame for their failings. If there were any truth in this argument, how can it be that the Jews, for instance, whose moral strictness on religious grounds is unsurpassed, have survived many thousand years? Moreover, the disastrous drop in their birthrate set in only when they allowed economic considerations to outweigh their religious allegiance. And the Puritans, in spite of their proverbial severity, succeeded in populating a new continent even before less morally minded aliens came to their assistance. But a still wider experience of a very different nature has led modern psychology to the unassailable conclusion that no genuine belief of whatever kind can have a harmful effect on the proper development of a man, as long as the belief is genuine. If a really religious man encounters difficulties in his sexual life, then they are invariably the result of the well-known trick of neurosis to make use of anything that may suit its purpose – in this instance sabotage of the sexual activity under the guise of religious scruples. I once treated a devout Roman Catholic, one of the purest and loveliest characters I ever met. The first woman with whom he came in close contact was his wife, but he was completely impotent with her. He was always so deeply impressed with the mystery of sex that he could never treat it as something trivial. He experienced communion with a woman in very much the same way as communion with God, and comparable perhaps only to the 'inside knowledge of things' which he sometimes experienced in his scientific studies. Admirable as this sentiment is, it could not be accepted as a valid explanation of his failings, because – even if we argue on purely religious grounds – communion with God must be actualized in good works and communion with one's wife in sexual intercourse. If this cannot be done, reasons other than purely spiritual ones must be operative – and there were plenty in this case, as in every other of this kind I have ever come across.

But why cannot faith help these men over their difficulties? This seemingly so naïve question raises big issues. I have discussed this question with priests of various religions and different religious persuasions, and from the not very illuminating answers two views crystallized. One was that in such cases the pathological elements in a man prevent him from contacting God properly or fully enough. This view would assign to psychology the task of removing these obstacles and thus raising the psycho-biological capacities of a patient to the normal level, from where he could then lift himself up to the spiritual plane. The other view is that such a man's faith is not strong enough, and the way to help him would be to purify and strengthen a man's faith, so that the faith would then eliminate all the impurities of his soul, which in medical terms we call 'pathological' symptoms of the body or the mind or both. But this is beyond the domain of medicine. On the highest level and in its perfect form this kind of healing constitutes what is called a 'miracle'. This is another of the problems that were familiar to the great men of the past. The following quotation reveals how much they knew about it. The great medical philosopher, Paracelsus, writes: 'Oh, you doubtful men, you Peters of little faith, who are moved by each wind and sink easily. You are the cause of all such diseases, because your faith is so little and feeble, and your own evil thoughts are your own enemies.' (*Philosophica occulta.*) That Paracelsus is referring to what we to-day call neurosis is quite obvious from the context, as he goes on to say that we have a powerful magnet in ourselves which attracts from all sides those thoughts which fit into our secret will.

But if we now return to the safer ground of psycho-pathology proper we find ourselves occasionally confronted with cases which reveal still another of the complex relationships of morals and neurosis.

K. L., aged 28. He has been married for two years, but is not yet able to have sexual relations with his wife.

At the age of 5 he was stricken by infantile paralysis, which left his left leg paralysed. The boy bore his misfortune with great fortitude and became an example to the other children in the hospital ward, exhorting them by words and deeds to face life with hope and courage. At school he ignored his handicap, worked hard, and his considerable success gave him confidence in himself. The strong religious faith of his mother, a devout Catholic, assisted the boy in his determination. From early on he 'designed' his life, planning his method of living. He wanted to get out – out of the squalid atmosphere of his home, out of the always being 'the youngest' (as he was in his family), out of the atmosphere of pity and sympathy with his deformity. Also he wanted to get on in life, and devoted all the strength of his youth to work. He succeeded in both his purposes – at a price.

The price was his solitude. He was a lonely child; at home and at school he made hardly any friends, and the concentration of all his efforts on work alienated him from people all his life. He was never deeply attracted to anyone. Even his social activities in hospital and later on did not come from love of people but from a sense of duty: he was convinced that he could do certain things better than others, and thus he felt he had to do them. Nor did he get on with people in business: he was too dogmatic, he hated to compromise and to adapt himself when he thought he was in the right. But he is quite sure that this rigid attitude has nothing to do with self-assurance out of a Sense of Inferiority. He puts it down to 'pure moral uprightness'. This, by the way, impressed me as being perfectly genuine and by no means smug. The field in which he had to pay the price was his sexual life. In the beginning all went well. At the age of 13 he had his first erections when in hospital he saw the legs of a nurse, and at 15 he began to masturbate. But this was about all. First he kept himself away from women because love might have distracted him from work, later he dismissed the idea of marriage because he thought it unfair to a woman to tie her to a cripple. 'It's not for me, anyway. Let's get down to business.' At last he met a girl who by her lovely womanliness convinced him that all his theories were wrong, and shortly after they first met they got married.

The case demonstrates with rare lucidity the complexity of the concept of morality. With fortitude and moral uprightness this man defied a handicap which would have broken the spirit of many a man. He achieved this triumph over disability by throwing himself with great determination into a life of action to the exclusion of everything else. Thus – and this is not the least interesting part of this life story – he made himself a victim of the common confusion between 'acting' and 'doing'. The concept of acting was for him restricted to the material world of 'doing' and 'planning'. 'Everything was so well calculated,' he said, and he subordinated himself and, as far as possible, others too to his schemes. This method of living did not issue from a particularly strong 'masculine' mentality, but was a defence mechanism, his way of silencing his fear of another kind of 'activity': contact with human beings. The loneliness of the child was due to his instinctive withdrawal from other children, caused by his great handicap; the loneliness of the man was the result of his deliberately blinding himself to a part of life which might imperil his designs. He said with conviction and plausibility that he was never really unhappy, but at that time he was wholly unaware that it was just his successful refusal of unhappiness which prevented him from ever being really happy either. And the service his sexual failure rendered him was to open his eyes to this fundamental truth, and his first real unhappiness gave him the chance of becoming really human. For when, at long last, Nature claimed her right and sexuality could no longer be completely repressed, when he dragged a human being into his neatly arranged, well-calculated but emotionally empty life, then he saw himself confronted with a task where 'drastic action was no longer possible'. When I asked him why he tried to force this disturbing element into his life he gave a most revealing answer: 'I must get my sexuality right in order to have a full life, because otherwise all my effort to this end would be wasted.' Thus we see that even now he has not grasped the true extent of his misconception of life, for he still considered sexuality merely as a means to an end. And behind his idea of a 'full life' stood the pride of having mastered life to the full. Thus it was the purpose of the treatment and the condition of his cure to make this man realize the essential immorality of this attitude.

Actually, the criteria 'moral' and 'immoral' are in such cases out of place because the problem has descended from the moral into the psycho-pathological sphere. The reaction of the child to his misfortune was proof of great moral strength, but later on, under the influence of a growing neurosis, this constructive attitude deteriorated into a mere technique of living. It would be unfair and wrong to say that the whole thing was from beginning to end but a neurotic arrangement. The correct diagnosis is that the neurosis made use of a genuine moral sense, and the strength of the boy's moral capacity only lent momentum to the neurotic misuse of it.

I have discussed this case at some length because the story is typical of those chronic invalids who take up the challenge of illness and grow in personal strength during the struggle. The development of their sexuality depends on how much they are able to keep their efforts within reasonable bounds. If they cannot succeed in overcoming the sense of inferiority, inevitable at the beginning, sexuality must suffer; if they do succeed, they will keep their sexuality intact; but if they overstress the compensations, as the above-mentioned patient did, sexuality goes down together with all other human relationships.

And here is a story which shows the reverse effect of the same cause.

G. H., 34 years old, equally virile in body and in mind, had the misfortune to lose one leg in the last days of the war. He married some months ago, and is not yet able to consummate the marriage.

The outstanding feature of the early development of his personality was a training in stoicism, to acquire the 'mask-like face of a Red Indian which never betrays any feeling, particularly discomfort or pain', which the boy often deliberately inflicted on himself. Later on he raised this child's play to the status of a philosophy of life, the main principle of which was that there are no limits to a man's determination, and that nothing is unobtainable. And in many respects he has lived up to his high standard. Then came the accident, and although he at first tried to ignore it, as it were, he soon realized that there were now limitations which he simply had to accept. Shortly afterwards he met his future wife, and this released a new wave of relaxing, as here at least was someone who made all pretences of heroism unnecessary. The sexuality of this man was never normal, the main trouble being that he had never had an emission when associating with a woman. That this defect had no physical cause was amply proved by the fact that the patient had frequent wet dreams and had an emission when he masturbated. The symptom was purely psychological, as all sexual anomalies are. Having an emission is the symbolic expression or the factual demonstration of self-surrender, of the most complete union with another human being. But this is precisely what this man never wanted: he did not want to show emotion, kept himself to himself, did not want to give himself to anyone: and for all these reasons he could not have an emission; it was an integral part of his scheme of living. A very short psychological treatment of this highly intelligent man put things right.

This case is interesting for two reasons. First, it shows how intimately sexual troubles are linked up with the whole personality of a man, and that in the sexual sphere the same trend operates as governs a man's life as a whole. But perhaps still more important is the fact that this man reacted to his misfortune in a manner exactly opposite to that of the previous case. It did not harden, but mellowed him; it made him not rebel against Fate but accept it; cured him of a sham heroism and made him wise. The price was the discovery of his sexuality. One may wonder why these new realizations had not cured him at once. This is difficult to say; probably because they had not yet been sufficiently assimilated to effect not only a change of mind but also a change of heart, i.e. of his subconscious mind. For this last stage of his transformation from a fictitious Red Indian into a real man he obviously needed some assistance.

While I was writing this paragraph I happened to meet, socially and not professionally, another specimen of this unlucky group. He was 25 years old, an ex-airman who lost the best part of one leg and is now at Oxford finishing his studies which were interrupted by the war. He is engaged to be married to a girl with whom he has happy and for both fully satisfactory sexual relations. I mention this 'case' in order to put a brighter light in this gloomy picture and to set the two other cases into a proper perspective. Those two men 'reacted' to their misfortune in different ways, that is to say, they had in one way or the other to restore the balance of their minds which was upset by their misfortunes. But the healthy mind of this young man needs no elaborate readjustment – and this is the supreme test of mental health; he takes things as they come his way and strides on, even with an artificial leg.

But the lesson we can learn from these cases permits of a much wider application. It could be summed up in the following thesis. External facts affect us much less by what they actually are than by what we make of them, that is, by the meaning we give or importance we attribute to them. Some psychologists are of the opinion, to my mind correctly, that plain, meaningless facts do not exist in human life at all. The standard example is: Fire breaks out during a theatrical performance. For most people this 'fact' will have the meaning 'mortal danger'; for some young men 'opportunity to be heroic'; to the fireman on duty 'a long-waited chance of work'; to the actors 'a nuisance'; to the producer 'a calamity'; to the people in the street 'a sensation'. But there is no one to whom it is just the plain fact 'fire'. In few other fields does this principle operate more strictly than in the sexual one. We have already learnt that neither physical tiredness nor bodily disablement need necessarily affect a man's sexuality. How much less should smaller, sometimes even trifling, circumstances be allowed to upset a man – or a woman for that matter. If, for instance, a man blames his sexual failure on the girl's perfume, which irritated him; or on the inappropriateness of time and place of his rendezvous; if noises outside the bedroom disturb him; if some sexual mannerisms of his partner inordinately affect him; if certain risks he may run worry him – can these men be given the credit of being particularly sensitive, or is this fastidiousness only a pretence and excuse for their evading the issue? This is a very tricky question, and a very thorough knowledge of the whole personality of such a man is needed in order to give him, at best, the benefit of the doubt. Even at the risk of being unfair to one or another of these men, it is always safer to assume first, at least as a working hypothesis, that his incapacity in such situations is caused not by moral, aesthetic, or any other kind of susceptibility, but by neurotic inhibitions.

Such cases appear as rather petty manifestations of a biological principle of paramount importance: throughout the animal kingdom from the amoeba up to Man, and through the development of the individual from infancy up to maturity, a trend towards an ever-increasing independence from outer circumstances operates, in other words a trend towards freedom. The human mind is the supreme means for attaining this freedom either by way of adaptation to changing circumstances or by devaluing their importance. Does perfume really matter? Do mannerisms do more than mar the surface? What does time or place matter, and isn't it the very nature of risks to be faced rather than feared? Does anything really matter but the fact of being with her whom I love? It need not be stressed that no man can achieve a complete independence and freedom, and it is obvious that our joy in life, our self-esteem, our capacity to work and confidence in success are in varying degrees affected by circumstances – affected, but not seriously imperilled, still less destroyed. Consequently, if a man succumbs to circumstances, particularly in the sexual, his most vital, function, he proves that he is no 'man' – that is to say he is either retarded in his development or psychologically abnormal. Many men sin against this law and – subconsciously – renounce their freedom to defy circumstances – and have to pay for it. All these cases can be brought under the heading of '*submitting to the devoir d'une situation*', a phrase coined by Stendhal and made the theme of his famous novel, *Le Rouge et le Noir.* What this means can best be seen from a rather trivial illustration. By sheer chance a man finds himself with a woman in a situation which, he thinks, compels him to make some kind of sexual advance: he has met a woman at a party, and it so happens that he offers to take her home in a car; or a man goes for a walk with a woman and finds himself in a lonely spot; or he pays her a visit and finds her alone in her house. Many a man feels he owes it to his maleness to make use of such a real or imagined 'opportunity', or he mistakes an innocent remark of a woman for an invitation and encouragement. Confused by the unexpected turn the woman relents; against his wishes and intentions the man finds himself in a critical situation – and therefore fails lamentably.

Why? Because by the force of essential morality we are compelled to be honest in our sexual activity, often enough even against our conscious ego. Just wanting to make love to a woman is not enough to set the whole sexual apparatus in motion. More is needed. Again, I am quite prepared to be told, mockingly or indignantly, that this may be so in theory but it is obvious not true in practice. It is not true of the type of sexual adventurer who builds up his reputation by cheap triumphs. To such men applies what I said about the customers of prostitutes, as indeed they treat every woman as a prostitute. Honesty cannot hold them back because they do not know what honesty in sexual matters means. It is not true of the 'exemplary' man, because it would never occur to him to avail himself of the many 'opportunities' which offer themselves, and he would never mistake an occasion for an opportunity. Nor would he allow a situation to challenge him. But the temptation to pick the bitter-sweet fruits and to defy the law of sexual honesty claims its countless victims in the broad stratum between these extremes, among what one may call the 'sexual middle class'. A man of this group is not so certain of his 'face' as not to be afraid of losing it; he is concerned about his reputation, which he probably never possessed; torn between his desire and the fear of making a fool of himself, he acts foolishly, thus becoming, instead of the architect of a situation, its victim – and victims are never potent.

The most important 'circumstance' or element of a sexual

situation is the woman partner. What effect has she on the sexual life of a man? The first question which presents itself is whether there is such a thing as the 'right' or 'adequate' partner. The Greek myth of the hermaphrodites, split in halves and each half searching for its complementary half, presupposes the idea of 'adequate' partners. Since those blessed days we have become less fastidious, and modern psychology dismisses as a myth or as the wishful dream of lovers the idea that they have been predestined for each other. In some cases this belief may be no more than a neurotic pretext for sexual indifference. The exemplary man, specific to the highest degree in all manifestations of his personality, is entitled to claim that he needs an equally specific partner who would complement him as a key fits into a lock; for such a man the existence of only one specific partner must be admitted. But the lower we descend from the top of the ladder towards the bottom, the less specific are the men we meet, and ever larger groups of women become suitable for them. The other end of the scale is represented by the 'man in the street', the more or less fully unspecific man for whom more or less any woman can be an adequate partner. Leaving aside the two extremes the correct formula would be: Instead of demanding an ideal woman as the ideal complement, a man should choose the woman with whom he is confident and determined to build a proper life in true co-operation. The insistent demand for 'the one and only' is a romantic illusion.

That not every man can be sexually attracted by every woman is obvious and fortunate. That, on the other hand, purely physical incompatibility sometimes occurs is equally true. But one must be very careful, and must know a man very well, before one can admit that such psycho-biological incompatibilities are the real cause of his sexual inactivity or even impotence.

This may be the right occasion to say a few words about that curious type, the inveterate misogynists or confirmed bachelors. It may be shocking news to them, but there is no denying the fact that their attitude towards women is a form of impotence. Many of these men are perfectly potent in physiological respects, that is to say, they are able to perform the sexual act, and even to do so frequently. But they are willing to go only part of the way and refuse to reach the real goal. As we shall learn presently, our definition of potency – being able to satisfy one's partner – is not yet complete, because the time factor has been left out. And a man fulfils his sexual task only if he establishes a lasting union with a woman in marriage. It is not a dogmatic overstatement but a true fact that in the last resort *every impotence is due to fear of marriage.* Many men feel intuitively that a coitus is not only a symbol of marriage, but an actual marriage *en miniature*, and they are impotent because they dread even the symbol or idea of marriage. Many bachelors are aware of their fear, although they may often enough not admit it even to themselves, and it would be amusing, if it were not so pathetic, to observe how skilfully they sometimes disguise their knowledge of the truth. A friend of mine, for instance, deplored quite earnestly his bad luck which caused him to fall in love only with married women; there was no point in explaining to him that this peculiar preference was less due to bad luck than to his subconscious device to guarantee his safety by protecting himself from every possible risk of being trapped. But the most frequent explanation of voluntary celibacy by such a man is that he must wait for the 'right' woman who, of course, never turns up, as no woman can live up to his expectations, which he deliberately puts so high. Extremely rare is the insight which such a man once expressed in this way: 'You see, doctor, the trouble with me is that I want only a perfect woman, although I well know that I should never be in a position to offer her what such a woman would have the right to demand in return.'

In the following I am going to sketch the behaviour of men in a few characteristic sexual situations. There is first of all intercourse with prostitutes. We know from a previous chapter what type of man frequents prostitutes, or better, limits his sexual life to encounters of this kind. But even within this group two different kinds of reaction to prostitutes can be clearly distinguished. The essential attraction of an association with prostitutes is the fact that it demands only a bare minimum of human contact; therefore the prostitute is accounted the ideal partner by all men for whom any human bond becomes a bondage. Everything is so clear and simple; it is understood that the whole thing is business, and that nothing more is expected. There are men who show the same business-like attitude and manners only thinly veiled in sexual situations also with 'nice' women. Thus, if a man feels an irresistible urge after the coitus to jump out of bed or even to leave the room, he treats every woman as a prostitute. Another reason why timid men prefer prostitutes is that they need not bother about success or failure, because neither matters. Still another reason is that the self-confidence of such men is comfortably bolstered by the social, moral, and psychological inferiority of prostitutes. It provides them with a sense of superiority which is, at least for many, a condition for sexual success. The habit of some men of humiliating their partners by their general behaviour and sometimes by perverse sexual practices, however slight, has the same motive and serves the same purpose.

Every feature of the association with prostitutes which proves helpful for one type of man can be a deterrent for another type. If a man of the first type is relieved by the thought that the whole thing is reduced to purely physical contact, another man is frightened by this matter-of-factness, by knowing that he must do a particular job or else the meeting would be pointless, since there is neither time nor opportunity for amorous or intellectual preludes. Incidentally, this sexual practicality and unpremeditatedness, in taking a chance as it comes one's way, proves for many men a help, if not a condition, of their sexual efficiency. A man who had failed completely with his wife told me that he was quite confident of his success if he could take a girl 'on a haystack'.[1] For men of this kind it is an exacting demand to make a date and to know in advance that they must be in full fighting trim at a certain place, day, and hour. The opposite type needs long preparation, and for them the sexual act must be not the beginning, but only the conclusion or climax – sometimes to the exasperation of a less fastidious and more realistic partner. Again, if it is helpful for one man to know that the prostitute is a professional with great experience, another man fears just this virtuosity which may make his own achievements appear rather poor

1. Although it is a neurotic symptom to need the unexpected for success, a similar attitude to a lesser degree can be said to be part of the sexual make-up of men. Women feel very differently about it. As a woman once put it: 'The unexpected occasion can only be enjoyable if the man is the expected person.'

by comparison with those of other men – a comparison, by the way, which no prostitute ever dreams of drawing. These men prefer the ignorance of the 'innocent' girl, to whom they may appear as heroic benefactors. On the other hand, the sexual braggart may be stimulated by the knowledge of the previous experience of his partner, because he hopes he is 'scoring off' his predecessors.

Some men like a certain degree of resistance from their partners, and this is quite normal, because the spirit of conquest is part of masculine sexuality. Some men cannot be potent without being aggressive, or at least making a show of aggression, and this is abnormal. One may object that this is a very subtle difference; in fact it is not, because it is neither more nor less than the difference between freedom and compulsion. Freud has already pointed out that no sexual practice is in itself normal or abnormal, but any practice can become abnormal if it is compulsory and the condition of potency. Lovers may do with each other whatever they like, if they do it for fun or for a change or because they feel that a certain way of making love brings them still more closely together – as long as they are still masters and not slaves of what they do, if they can do it or leave it, they are all right. This rule applies even to such seemingly unimportant details as the position in which two people perform the sexual act. It is, for instance, from the medical point of view, permissible if lovers occasionally change the normal position, so that the woman lies on top of her partner; but one must suspect a man of abnormal, i.e. masochistic or even slightly homosexual, tendencies, if he is potent only in this position and in no other. Vice versa, a woman who likes to lie on top of her partner may be accused of being masculine, or at least dominant, which is often correct. But sometimes it is not. A woman explained her habit by saying: 'I like to feel thoroughly supported.' How very feminine!

To return to the question of aggression. I once treated a young man for impotence with his wife. What upset him most was her permanent readiness. When, on his way home, he visualized her waiting for him in a dressing-gown and with all the signs of expectancy, he was tempted to turn back. One day – it was a very hot summer afternoon – he found her in a state of complete unreadiness, and performed the first, and incidentally the last, perfect coitus with her. No doubt many a man may sympathize with this young man and take his sexual reluctance as a matter of good taste; that this, unfortunately, was not the right explanation in this case was amply proved by the fact that on other occasions the same thing happened to him with more attractive and less insistent women. It is sometimes held that sadism is only an extreme form of the normal masculine aggressiveness. This is quite incorrect, and the women partners of these men know exactly where to draw the dividing line between normal and pathological aggression. Women often enjoy being overpowered by a strong man, but a normal woman detests the brutality of a sadistic attack. The sadist's aim is not to possess the woman but to hurt her, he does not enjoy the fruit of his conquest but the discomfort and pain he inflicts; the coitus is to him not a union with another human being but mere self-gratification and self-aggrandizement – in other words, only a complicated form of masturbation.

No one will be surprised to learn that there are men who not only enjoy but definitely need the explicit assurance that they are sexually wanted, in general, or on a particular occasion. As a patient put it, he needs to know that he has 'constituted rights' on his side. This being welcome or the superiority conferred by constituted rights need not always be expressed in words, but may be, unmistakably inferred by the situation. Thus a patient was particularly stimulated when he could pity his normally rather independent wife, as he did when she slowly recuperated after an operation, or even when he could help her in one way or another. Another man felt his potency greatly supported by the 'childlikeness' and the 'pathetically maternal mood' which his wife showed whenever she was deeply moved by sympathy with people in distress.

The power of imagination of men and women, their capacity for giving meanings to facts and for rearranging situations until they suit their clandestine purposes, is really astounding. But behind all these frantic efforts there is really one single motive. Which one? Before we give the answer it is necessary, I feel, to answer first a question which many readers may have asked themselves with growing urgency: Why look for clandestine motives at all? Why not take things for what they appear to be? First of all, because we do not always do this in ordinary life either. One calls it diplomacy or policy, if we deliberately and consciously camouflage our real motives and seem to act according to pretended ones; and if one does the same thing subconsciously and involuntarily one calls it a neurotic symptom. Since Freud explored and charted the vast territory of the subconscious mind this re-interpreting of human motives and actions has become the basic principle of applied psychology under normal and abnormal conditions. The answer to the question is simple enough: it is fear. Fear of failing in one's task. Fear of women and of giving oneself into their power; all these men are petty Samsons afraid of being deprived of their strength by their pretty Delilahs and delivered to the Philistines. Fear, at still deeper levels of the subconscious according to Freud's teaching, of incurring the guilt of incest and the punishment of castration.

After this lengthy détour we can now proceed with the analysis of some more typical sexual situations.

The wedding night is an unadulterated pleasure for fewer men than one commonly assumes. In olden days it was customary among many peoples to hang the blood-stained bed-sheet out of the window of the bridal chamber the next morning, to prove to all and sundry that the bride was a virgin, and that the marriage had been properly consummated. If this custom were still in force in our times, many a hotel window would remain undecorated. In most cases, but by no means in all, the bridegroom is responsible for this calamity.

For a large number of men, it seems, this occasion is their first acquaintance with sex. No wonder that many of them fail in the arduous task of teaching a young, inexperienced, and frightened woman the delicate and difficult art of love-making when they are wholly ignorant themselves. One can hardly blame them, because it requires a considerable trust in the strength of our instincts – and the instincts themselves must be unimpaired – to overcome the handicap of knowing nothing about the anatomy and physiology of the female organs or the technique of intercourse. Great skill and finesse are needed to handle this delicate situation and overcome gently the sometimes considerable resistance of the woman. But not only the beginner finds this situation embarrassing. Often enough a man with a satisfactory record of sexual experience is dismayed by it. He is the victim of the psychological law that our behaviour is governed, not by the facts of a situation, but the meaning we give them: and the meaning he gives to his allegedly so 'natural' act is that it is a test of his manliness, an examination whose result may decide success or failure in his marriage, as it often enough actually does. The fear of intimacy with a 'decent' woman, which a young man imagines to be so different from what he has known before, his exaggerated ideas about the difficulty of defloration, the notion – incidentally quite correct – that the consummation of marriage puts the seal of finality on the marriage contract: all these anxieties may in this critical hour shake the self-confidence even of a man experienced in sexual technique. Fortunately these initial difficulties usually straighten themselves out spontaneously and through mutual adaptation. Sometimes they do not, more often than not through the fault of the disappointed young wife.

An analysis of sexual fortunes and misfortunes in married life will be given in the next chapter.

Lastly, a few remarks about the effect a woman can have on her partner's sexuality through her purely female qualities. These are mainly two. I have mentioned earlier that an incurable sterility in a husband can destroy his wife's sexuality to the point of complete frigidity. In view of the essential importance children have for a woman, this reaction is not surprising. On the other hand I know of no case where sterility in the woman has had the same effect on the potency of her husband. Many years ago I saw a patient in whose case such an effect seemed to have occurred, but a careful analysis and the later experiences of this man proved that he was no exception to the rule.[1]

L. M., a 35-year-old Orthodox Polish Jew, had been married for five years. The marriage was sterile through no fault of his. For the last two years his previously normal potency went from bad to worse and then completely disappeared. If one takes into account that for an Orthodox Jew it is of the greatest religious importance to have children, one is tempted to assume that for this reason his sterile marriage had lost all meaning for him and his impotence was 'on religious grounds'. The only suspicious circumstance was the

1. This case was previously published in my book *Sexualpathologie* (Verlag für Medizin, Vienna, 1935) but its great theoretical interest justifies an abridged reference.

fact that this man sabotaged the marriage by being impotent rather than by taking the proper step of divorcing his wife, which according to Jewish law would have been quite possible. Shortly after the consultation he did divorce his wife, not on the ground of her sterility but because she became so quarrelsome that he could not stand it any longer. He then went to Palestine and a year later he informed me in a letter that he had tried to have intercourse with two girls, but his potency was not too good, wherefore he could not yet make up his mind to get married again.

These last words gave the man away: it became evident that he was impotent with his wife not on religious grounds but for neurotic reasons, and his impotence was not a moral achievement, as it may have appeared, but a typical neurotic symptom. He was fed up with his marriage, wanted to get out of it, and staged an 'inner emigration' (see footnote page 145). And in Palestine he maintained a semi-impotence as a warning not to put his head into a noose again.

The moral of this interesting little story is that we must always keep in mind that every sexual trouble is a neurotic symptom. If a patient offers another explanation, however plausible, we may, at best, give him the benefit of the doubt, but no more. And in ninety-nine cases out of a hundred a closer inspection will prove that the doubt was justified. In the hundredth case we may discover a genuine human conflict. This, for instance, was so with the woman whose story I have previously related. Her marriage was a true one; she had no intention of leaving her husband, and had she done so she would have killed something very much alive. On the other hand, sexuality, although an integral part of her marriage but not the whole of it, had become meaningless for her and therefore she gave sex up, but not the marriage. Her frigidity was nevertheless a neurotic symptom, which helped her to solve her conflict. But her case was one of the extremely rare exceptions in which a neurosis lends its assistance to morality.

Besides conception, a woman's function in a sexual situation is emotional participation. Thus, the question arises how a woman's frigidity affects the sexuality of her partner. There are men for whom the partner's satisfaction is the condition of their own: they require more than the purely physical relief. But these men are few and far between. A second group of men, by far the largest, comprises all those who out of *naïveté*, ignorance, or complacency, take the woman's satisfaction for granted; many of them never know whether their partner has had an orgasm, and as many women put on a clever show, it would not matter anyway if they knew. And the third group simply cannot be bothered with such sentimental niceties. Thus, if there is a problem at all, it is confined to the first group. To any such men the impassivity of the partner deals a mortal blow, and sooner or later they will give up their fruitless attempts and resign. Frigidity is, as we know, a neurotic device adopted by some women to induce their partners to take this step. But if we recall that over two-thirds of all married women are supposed to be frigid, we must say that most of these neurotic efforts are wasted, considering the comparatively small number of men who take the hint.

But there is a one-in-a-million chance that a man understands and refuses to obey the hint conveyed by his wife's frigidity. I knew such a case. Once upon a time – this seems an appropriate opening for a story which could have been a fairy tale or the product of Edgar Allan Poe's gruesome imagination – once upon a time there was a man who was deeply in love with his wife. But she was completely frigid. In vain he tried to bring the lovely marble statue to life. In vain he raged against her motionless resistance. In despair he felt the scornful smile behind those firmly closed lids. One night he strangled her. And when the limp body rested peacefully in his arms, he took her and released in a tremendous orgasm all his desire frustrated for so long: he had conquered her, and he too was at peace at last. This man was no murderer for sadistic or otherwise perverted reasons. It would be futile and stupid to affix such outworn labels to such a case. He was a man who simply fought for his love to the last. And the judge understood it.

But this story has a symbolic meaning far beyond the narrow scope of sex pathology. It reveals the extreme incomprehensibility and unconquerableness of Woman, which, in varying degrees, many a man must experience in utter helplessness. He experiences it in her blank refusal to understand his tormented fury when he knows she has betrayed him; he must experience it in her cool indifference to his despair when he realizes that he is losing her. It is the majestic impassivity of Nature towards the suffering creature – the resistance of Matter to the Spirit, the perennial hostility of the sexes – the mystery of the Eternal Feminine. In every woman there is part of the Sibyls, those gigantic statues into which Michelangelo carved his awe, despair, and hatred of the Feminine – those eerie figures with unseeing eyes staring into infinity with pitiless unconcern.

CHAPTER 9

# DISCOURSE ON MORALITY IN SEX

WE have now followed the whole course of sexual development from the earliest consciousness of the primitive sexual urge to its metamorphosis and unfolding in the mature human personality. Frequently our analysis has been brought to a temporary halt by the collision of bio-psychological factors with moral principles. Before entering into a discussion of marriage, the form of sexual life in which – as thinkers of the most divergent opinions agree – the moral problem finds its final solution, we may now pause for a moment in order to sum up my view on the kind of sexual morality which, to my mind, is the driving power of sexual development.

Roughly speaking, and adjusting a very complex problem to the limited purpose of our argument, one could say that there are three kinds of morality: the religious, the conventional, and the essential morality. Religious morality claims absolute validity by introducing a supreme lawgiver. Conventional morality, relative to a historical period, a social set, or professional corporation, raises the same claims on a considerably lower plane, weakening them by the arbitrariness of its precepts. Essential or immanent morality is the sum total of the claims that spring from the nature of things or situations. It is not backed by any authority, hence it cannot be defended, but it is irrefutable to anyone who is capable of understanding these claims. It is irrefutable because it is synonymous with Truth.[1] As the essential morality is the only one which fits into the

1. This concept is so vitally important for an understanding of sex morality that it may be illustrated by a quotation from St Augustine: 'Ask not what *is truth*, for immediately the darkness of corporeal images and the clouds of phantasms will put themselves in the way and will disturb that calm which at first twinkling shone forth to thee, when I said "truth". See that thou remainest, if thou canst, in that first twinkling with which thou art dazzled, as it were, by a flash, when it is said to thee: Truth.' (*De Trinitate*, Bk VIII.)

This is the way one conceives also of essential morality.

pattern of a scientific analysis of sexual life, we must try to make still clearer what is meant by this term.

It will be best to start with biology. Every organ of our body wants to function, and if it is prevented from doing so, the whole equilibrium of the organism is disturbed. Thus, a woman needs a child, not because of her maternal instinct or any moral sense of duty imposed on her from without, but because her whole organism is built for the purpose of bearing a child, and if her organism is denied this fulfilment the frustration affects her whole personality. Similarly, against all difficulties which may be put in his way an artist strives to practise his art, not for material gain or in order to 'express himself' but simply because he has been given the physical and mental organism for it and this wants to function. The next step of our moral development is marked by the recognition that not only our organism but also elements of the world around us put such imperative demands on us. We remember the scene in the nursery when a small child who is playing with his bricks is told by his mother to go to bed, and says to her: 'Wait a minute. I must finish this house first.' Child psychology has taught us that the child means: '"It" (i.e. the house) wants to be finished, and I feel I must comply with this demand'. This is the red-letter day of moral conscience. And when many years later the mother says to her child: 'You must do your homework first', she meets with a willing understanding only if the child has already realized that the homework must be done, not because the teacher or any other authority has ordered it, but because it is in the intrinsic nature of homework to be finished. A letter we have received 'wants' to be answered, apart from any practical or conventional reasons, because it is in the nature of a letter to be answered. A scientist having conceived a scientific law or a philosopher a philosophical problem is under the spell of this law or problem which wants to be 'discovered' or 'elaborated'; he has no choice to accept or reject this call. Nor has an artist the choice of the material in which to materialize an artistic conception: one landscape can only be painted in watercolours, another only in oils, one model's head must be carved in wood, another's hewn in stone. A work of art is true and 'convincing', and an artist is a real – and in the truest sense a 'moral' – artist only if this essential condition is fulfilled – a virtue which distinguishes an artist from a clamorous virtuoso. If a man knows that he must not do a certain thing because it endangers his health, and if he shuts his ears to this demand and goes on doing this thing, then he is not only stupid and 'weak' but definitely immoral, because he squanders his health, jeopardizes his work, and imperils his life – things which are not his own but with which he has been entrusted. And in the same way a beautiful woman should cultivate her beauty, because it is not her private property but a gift of grace. A lot of misery which people feel, and cannot explain, is due to their obstinate silencing of these voices, although they know they will ultimately have to obey them.

*This obedience is what we call essential morality.* It means being sensitive to the demands which a situation in human life makes on us.[1] And to possess this essential morality is the characteristic of an authentic or exemplary personality.

One may fail to see the important difference between essential and conventional morality, which is understandable in many instances, because a great many of the precepts of conventional morality actually derive from essential morality. Conventional and essential morality often overlap. But conventional morality includes a great many obligations which are entirely non-essential and only dictated by the views held at a certain period or by a certain social set – such as wearing a particular kind of dress on a particular occasion, special table manners, the institution of the chaperone, and the many things which were or are 'not done'. But the cleavage between the two forms of morality is still very apparent in sexual matters, although it seems to be a trend of social development, at any rate in our days, that the essential morality of sex life is being increasingly realized and freed from outmoded conventional frustrations. A young girl in our days knows how to look after herself, and no longer needs a guardian angel.

1. It may be felt that there is a contradiction here of what I said on a previous occasion about the mistakes some men make by blindly submitting to the *devoir d'une situation.* This contradiction easily resolves itself if we only bear in mind that those submissions occur because the real meaning of a situation and its demands have been misinterpreted: for instance, if a man invited to tea assumes that this involves an invitation to bed as well.

This idea of essential morality in sex (being sensitive to and obeying the intrinsic laws of love and sex) has been the guiding principle of our analysis up to this point, and will now be further illustrated in the following pages.

It need not be stressed that the principles of sex morality are the same for both sexes. I am going to expound these principles mainly from the point of view of the woman, because sexuality is a more intrinsic part of a woman's nature and life than it is of a man's and therefore, I think, more simple, less complicated by auxiliary elements and more essential. A woman, at least on the level of exemplariness, lives her sexuality far more genuinely, essentially, more according to the intrinsic laws of sex – that is more morally.

The concept around which the problem of morality centres is 'purity'. A person in the state of purity is untouched by evil or any temptation, in fact invulnerable, simply because the pure person is incapable of grasping the idea of evil. Purity, like all moral concepts, is as difficult to define as colours or any qualities: an analysis can only assist us to remember and to understand better our own experience of this quality, and elucidate it by remembering our reactions to people who possess it.

If we now try to point out a few characteristics of the art of pure living, the first one will be the tendency of a person to be concerned only with the essence of a thing or situation or task, not distracted by non-essential reasons or ulterior motives or possible consequences. The next one is not to be torn by conscious conflicts or subconscious undercurrents in ourselves, to live in harmony with ourselves and with our environment: in one word, to be essential. Purity and being essential are synonyms, and a pure life is essentially moral. All the reflective attitudes are impure and immoral. For instance, consider sentimentality: a sentimental person does not enjoy the real thing, but only his feeling about or reactions to a thing. He does not, for instance, feel how wonderful an evening is, but how wonderful he is that he can find this evening wonderful. Or he does not appreciate a situation nearly as much when it is actually happening as when he is looking back on it and wallowing in memories. Sentimentality is clearly akin to self-pity. An obviously reflective mood is sensationalism. Another example is obscenity. To be obscene is not a quality inherent in a particular action, but is something added to an action, giving it the peculiar, unpleasant taint which we condemn as obscene. Nudity as such is not obscene, but it becomes so if the emphasis is laid on the 'not dressed'. A half-dressed state immediately acquires the character of obscenity if its intention is to emphasize the 'only half-dressed'. To be obscene is to insult decency and shame. Nothing lovers do as expression of their love and the desire for ever closer intimacy can be obscene. But even a comparatively harmless look or touch becomes obscene if it is intended only to excite lust. A pure woman delights in love-play – however extended, variegated and refined – if it is meant as the preliminary to coitus and tends to this essential climax: but she may abhor as obscene the same actions if they are meant as ends in themselves.

From this inner and outer harmony in which the pure live they derive an unfailing sense of security and certainty. They know instinctively what to do, they are not kept on this path by obeying rules that tell what to do and what not to do, they are not in danger of being diverted and distracted by temptations, because they bear in their hearts the notion of their goal which is the real thing, the Truth.

These abstract principles come to life and are almost self-evident if we apply them to the field of sexual purity. Sexual purity does not mean being free of sexual impulses or desires, nor their radical repression, but it means satisfying them as they ought to be satisfied: not in order to still physical needs, not for the sake of pleasure or fun or the enjoyment of obscene or perverted thrills, not for any material gains or advantages – but as expressions of real love and as means of union with a really loved partner. But it is not essential, and therefore completely outside the scope of purity and essential morality, whether this is done inside or outside marriage. Marriage provides only a greater measure of fulfilment but does not affect the essence and hence the moral quality of the union.[1]

1. Perhaps the most unusual instance of essential sex morality I met in my non-professional life. It concerns a woman well in her seventies, still very attractive in looks and mind, enjoying her life in the face of many adversities which beset it. Shortly before she died she told me her story, which in its tragic simplicity is remarkable enough to be remembered. As a young, beautiful and much wooed girl she married a man much older than herself. The marriage was unsatisfactory from any point of

As the prototype of purity one usually depicts the state of childhood. But this is only one form of it: it is the purity of inexperience, of someone who still stands before or outside life. Real or mature purity knows life, in its essence and free from conflicts. Akin to the purity of the child is the innocence of a virgin, the purity of ignorance, and here again it is incorrect to identify a woman's purity with her virginity. The mature, that is the awakened, woman knows the power of sexual impulse and desire, and through sexual experience she loses her anatomical but by no means necessarily her moral intactness. But whatever she does exists for her only in the 'pure' form, i.e. as essential union with her lover. Purity is a basic characteristic of a woman, wherefore it cannot be lost; besides, a woman who has once possessed it can never get into a situation in which she could lose it. A woman who can allow herself to succumb to temptation and violate the essential law of sex love can only forfeit her respectability but never her purity – because she has never possessed it. There are women whose character and allegiance to essential and conventional normality are above doubt, but who lead a very complex love life before, during, and after marriage. For love overtakes a woman as her destiny, and she does not demonstrate her purity by avoiding its challenge but by the way she accepts and copes with it. Such women do not 'preserve' their purity in the midst of adversity, on the contrary their purity of heart purifies all they do: there is nothing sentimental or sensational in the way they

---

view. Some years later she met a man, and both fell in love with each other at first sight. But his social position made it in those days impossible for him to marry a divorced woman, and thus all they allowed themselves was to meet once a week for lunch – for twenty long years. And when I asked her: 'But why, why?' she said: 'Because, my dear friend, I knew as certainly as one only knows the truth that had I only once given away all would have been spoilt; I did not want a clandestine furtive pleasure, but I wanted the real thing.' At last her husband died and she married her friend. But as the power which rules our lives apparently does not greatly appreciate virtue, or acts on mysterious motives, or perhaps does not exist at all, her second husband died a few years after they got married. Yet every day of these few years, she assured me, proved that it was worth waiting for them. I should never have called this woman exceptionally 'pure', and I know that no moral compunctions in the conventional sense prompted her almost heroic control. Only her unerring feminine instinct made her in her sex life choose the perfect – as incidentally in many other respects as well.

live and love, but fullest devotion and self-surrender, undeviating and fearless directness, unerring certainty, magnificent unconcern – and humility.

In an exemplary existence purity is not just one part of the personality but its substance and fibre. Every action of such persons is permeated by a radiant lucidity, and there is an aura of saintliness about them. In persons of lesser exemplariness the unity of the personality appears to be split, and one finds in them elements of sexual purity combined with various manifestations of impurities in other, non-sexual respects. Not infrequent is also the reverse combination: women of unquestionably great personalities who are rather indiscriminate in their sexual conduct. This contrast between the two aspects is often striking and slightly embarrassing, because one's attitude towards such women is inevitably as complex and ambiguous as are their personalities. And it needs a good deal of confidence in one's instinct to be fair to them.

I think it is true to say that every woman possesses an element of sexual purity, because purity is an intrinsic part of femininity. But too often it is only a faint glimmer, hardly discernible under the coarseness of the non-sexual part of the personality. The diagnosis, as it were, of purity is occasionally difficult to make because purity cannot be proved by tests or measured by moral yardsticks; it can only be felt – and occasionally it can be mistaken for two conditions very similar in appearance but quite different in their nature. Some women give the impression of purity simply because they are more or less unawakened, either because no man has tried to awaken them, or because those who did try did not succeed. Other women are neurotic, frigid, full of inhibitions, and frustrations, wasting their lives in vain attempts to break their shackles; their 'purity' is also involuntary, forced upon them by the abnormal condition of their minds.

*

However much one may agree that purity is an essential element of every woman's character, however high one may assess the number of truly pure women, it must be admitted that there is a large group of women in whose personality structure purity is no criterion. This means that the question whether they are pure or not pure does not arise; they must be judged by totally different standards. Their moral value rests in the opposite of purity: in richness of experience. They have gone through good and evil, the heights and depths of life, through battles won and lost, covered with laurels and scars. Instead of *sancta simplicitas* an unholy complexity is the hall-mark of their characters. They have set out to embrace the in-exhaustible variety of life and love. They too embody a moral value which one may best describe as heroism. If for the pure type of women the psychological core is 'to be essential', for this other type it is 'to be brave'. To follow their arduous task unsupported by accepted beliefs and tabulated codes needs all forms and degrees of courage up to the thorny crown of tragic guilt. 'There is no other way to ethical maturity and spacious-ness', one of the greatest moral philosophers of our age ex-claims, 'but through the conflicts of life as it is, through moral experience – even through bad experience – perhaps the best of all.' The sexual life of such a woman is part of the pattern of her whole life. She follows the voice of her heart wherever it may lead her, and she accepts the challenge from without what-ever the risk may be. There is also a kind of purity in the way such women live and love, but it is not so much purity of soul as a purity of purpose. She belongs to the man she loves, en-tirely and exclusively as long as love lasts, and leaves him, if leave she must. This single-mindedness never allows the man liberties she takes to slip into libertinage.

A woman of this type must be carefully distinguished from the adventuress. The latter seeks danger for the sake of the thrill and sensation it entails; the former takes danger in her stride as an often inevitable obstacle in the way to her goal: and this goal is not to live dangerously, but spaciously. She does not measure her strength against the adverse forces of life in a futile contest, but uses her strength because, and in the way, strength must be used – just as an artist uses his artistic strength: as a faithful steward.

Each of the two basic types, the saint and the heroine, repre-sents a moral value of its own; they cannot be compared with one another, nor can one be preferred to the other. It is in no way permissible to proclaim purity as the only or the supreme value of sexual matters; it is no more than one of two alternatives.

It is interesting, although perhaps not surprising, that these two fundamentally different attitudes towards life have a different historical origin. Everybody knows that purity of soul is the supreme Christian virtue. It may be less known that the Greeks not only deny the moral value of purity but teach that only he who has gone through ethical conflicts has proved his virtue. The European mentality, being built on Christian and Greek thought, tends towards merging these two opposite principles. At first sight almost impossible, this formidable task can be – I very nearly said, easily – fulfilled if one frees the concept of purity from all conventional or dogmatic conditions and implications, simply defining it as: *to be essential in the midst of the turmoil of the fullest experience of life.*

In fact, this noble attitude is still very far from being generally or even widely accepted as the basis of our moral thought or action in the sexual field or in any other. Purity is strictly demanded but rarely and poorly rewarded. The pure young man, the Sir Galahad, is nowadays apt to be looked upon as slightly odd. And as for the women, one cannot but be sorry for those lovely and fragrant buds which, being denied the light of experience, cannot bloom and bear fruit; all too often they must wither in the shade of a conventional marriage, having preserved themselves for 'the one' man, who, through his lack of experience and understanding, trades this treasure for the small change of marital comfort. On the other hand, if a young woman has her own sexual life she has lost not only her anatomical integrity but she is dishonoured according to conventional morals, from the point of view of the Church she has sinned, and she may even suffer legal disadvantages. But in the light of essential morality she stands unblemished and pure, if she did what she did in a real loving union. Then also her sins against conventional morality, which are many, are forgiven, for she loved much.

## CHAPTER 10

# ON MARRIAGE

MARRIAGE is a permanent union between a man and a woman, legalized by the authority of the State and in many cases sanctioned by the Church.

The crucial word in this definition is 'permanent', and most criticism of and opposition to the institution of marriage, both by people directly involved and by those who are only indirectly concerned with it, such as legislators, psychologists, and all kinds of reformers, is concentrated on this postulate of permanence. But there is another, seemingly still more fundamental, objection raised against marriage as such. It is, so the argument goes, an unjustifiable intrusion into the privacy of the emotional life of two people to force it into the strait-jacket of legal control by State or Church. All these controversies start from the wrong end and miss the essential point, because they disregard the elementary facts of human psychology. There is ample evidence that permanent monogamous marriage is no invention arbitrarily imposed on mankind by ascetic priests or dehydrated moralists, but the expression of what one could almost call an instinct, deeply rooted in human nature. The human species is created that way, and if this were not so, it would be inconceivable that permanent monogamous marriage could have existed everywhere on this planet and ever since the dawn of history as an unchanged form of the relationship of men and women.

The proof that *monogamous permanent marriage is part of human nature* can be offered in several ways. There is first the psychological evidence. Charlotte Buehler's research into the psychological principles which control the development of man's life as a whole – and therefore every one of the activities which compose life – has shown that this development tends towards achieving something definite. This means not only that something definite exists or may exist in our life, but that it must exist: that a life in which nothing definite has been achieved is incomplete, almost wasted, truly abnormal. For instance, at a certain age we expect to live in our own house, from which we cannot be evicted; to run our own business, no longer dependent on the whims and fancies of an employer; to do work no longer forced on us for mere subsistence, but chosen for the satisfaction of our gifts and talents; to belong to a social set and a circle of friends – in a word, to be settled. True, there are people who never feel the desire and need to settle down in life and denounce any stability and permanency as dull, but these people are definitely subnormal, at least in this respect. This law of development towards definiteness applies also to the sexual part of life: we tend instinctively towards a definite or permanent form of sex relationship, and every normal and mature human being must want to achieve this aim. *The permanency of marriage is thus revealed as a biological fact, as a result of maturation and proof of achieved maturity*, and not, as commonly assumed, as a primarily moral postulate. This result can hardly be overrated.

Turning to sexual development in particular we need only carry to its biological conclusion what we have learnt about our sexual development in the preceding chapters. The sexual life of a boy starts with the appearance of the purely physical sexual urge, which eventually leads to masturbation. Although it is from a factual point of view justifiable to call masturbation the sexual activity of the solitary man, it must not be forgotten that, at least in its fully developed form, that is when mental images of erotic scenes provide the sexual stimulus, it is the establishment of a sort of contact, although only with an imaginary partner. A few years after the appearance of the physical urge, an emotional element develops, which in late adolescence joins up with the physical component. Before this happens the physical urge turns from the imaginary to a concrete object – the female body as such. Hereupon the growing boy enters the phase of association with prostitutes, which actually means sexual association with any kind of woman with whom a purely physical contact can be established. The main characteristics of this type of association are anonymity, transitoriness, and meaninglessness. The next stage is the phase of 'affairs'. By this time the young man has already developed the capacity for loving, and the sexual contact has become the expression of a personal contact with a personal woman. The girl has a name, although it may be only her Christian name that is used. The affair extends in Time, although its duration is limited. It has meaning in that it is the first experience of the co-ordination of mind and body in a personal union with another human being. After having acquired the technique of the purely sexual act in contact with females and the art of making love to a woman, through trial and error, the now sexually mature man is at last fit for marriage. The development of girls is much simpler and their maturation almost instantaneous, as has been previously explained on several occasions. Marriage carries the three characteristics of a sex relationship to perfection. The woman now has a name, adopting her husband's name as symbol of the complete union; the union is intended to last for ever; and its meaning is that marriage is, together with work, the essence of a complete life.

The second controversial concept in our definition of marriage is the word 'monogamous'. It could be pointed out that there have been periods in history when people lived in polygamous marriage, that this was the normal form of human marriage, and that monogamy is a sign of decay in men's virility and a way of giving in to the increasingly difficult conditions of life. This has in fact been said. Against this kind of reasoning, and in justification of the postulate of monogamy, one could put forward the biological argument that there are some species among animals which mate with only one female, a condition called monogyny, and that the human species is one of them. But the validity of the analogy might be questioned. One could then point out the idea of definiteness and finality includes the idea of exclusiveness: obviously it can be only one woman with whom a man enters into a lasting union. The high esteem in which loyalty and fidelity are held is only the moral version, or sanction, of this fact.

But there is still another aspect of this problem which, I think, is not yet sufficiently appreciated. It cannot be disputed that there is a tendency in the human mind to reduce multiplicity to simplicity, manifold variety to one single element or principle. Examples are: the age-old endeavour of philosophy to find the one principle from which everything else can be deduced; the tendency of natural science to reduce all sciences to one basic science, which for many centuries was held to be physics; the tendency of physics to reduce all phenomena of the inanimate universe to one single form of energy, which for two hundred years was thought to be mechanical energy and in recent years has been changed to radiation. But this trend worked far beyond the narrow confines of laboratories and libraries. Most significantly this principle has created the three great institutions which have profoundly influenced human existence: Monotheism, Monarchy, and Monogamy.[1] In modern times, particularly in scientific circles, the attempt has been made to explain this mysterious trend as the effect of the principle of economy. It is true that it is easier to understand and dominate a world which is only the unfolding of one single principle; it is also cheaper to have one king instead of two or one wife instead of several; but this way of looking at things fails us completely in the case of monotheism. This great idea sprang up suddenly in the soul of the ancient Hebrew people, and has gradually conquered the Western world. On the other hand, an attempt to achieve unification has been made from other motives: all the great empires were built on lust of power or greed. The recent endeavour to construct 'one world' is patently motivated by fear lest it be true after all that only the fittest survives, and it has given rise to efforts to construct political systems in which competition is made impossible. The monopolists strive for the same end for the same reason. From the fact, mentioned in the foreword to this book, that Man's life is the result of the interaction of a variety of forces, it is evident that economic factors must contribute to the genesis of sexual institutions, but they are only contributing factors, never the primary or the only cause. Indeed the development of no form of social institution can be explained on purely economic grounds. The materialistic theory of history is to-day but a philosophical museum piece. Thus neither economy nor the power principle can provide a satisfactory explanation.

If it is true that monogamous permanent marriage is

1. The syllable 'mon' or 'mono' is derived from the Greek word *monos* which means 'alone', 'sole', 'single', and the above three words mean: a single God, a single ruler, a single spouse.

one of the arch-types of human conduct, history and ethnology must prove its ubiquity in space and time. And so they do.

Animals are by instinct either monogamous or polygamous. Among men every possible form of marriage has been found: Monogamy (one man married to one woman), polygamy (one man with several women), polyandry (one woman with several men), matriarchy (social organization in which the mother is head of the family), incestuous marriage (marriage between near kindred), group marriage (whose existence is strongly disputed). But monogamy is the prevailing form of marriage. We have inherited it from our ancestors, the man-like apes, which lived monogamously almost exclusively. Mankind seems to have preserved this custom from the remotest past through hundreds of thousands of years to the relatively high stage of civilization which we now condescendingly call savage or primitive. Then came a period in which these other forms of marriage were practised. Polygamy, for instance, existed among the most ancient peoples everywhere in the world. But at a still higher stage of civilization, which roughly coincides with the rise of Christianity, monogamy became dominant again. This is the history of human marriage in a nutshell.[1]

If we inquire into the causes of polygamy we meet with the surprising fact that purely sexual motives, such as desire for variety, preference for younger women, etc., were no more than subsidiary factors. The decisive motives were social and economic. The number of his wives demonstrated the high social status or the wealth of a man. King Solomon, for example, is said to have had 700 wives and 300 concubines, and this in itself considerable achievement is dwarfed by the King of Loango, who is reputed to have had 7,000 wives.[2] The Koran permits a man to have four wives and as many concubines as he likes, whereas a slave could not have more than two wives. On the other hand, even in those early times a trace of moral conscience may already have been operative in the law that a priest in ancient Egypt was allowed only one wife. Even among peoples where polygamy was practised or not prohibited, it

1. Most of the facts about the ethnology of sex life are quoted from E. Westermarck, *The History of Human Marriage* (London, 1891).

2. Cit. from Westermarck, *op. cit.*

was by no means universal, but always restricted to the upper classes, a 'vicious luxury of the great'.[1]

Still rarer is polyandry, a form of marriage in which one woman is married to several men. It is most frequent among the Tibetan-speaking peoples. Here too economic causes seem to stand in the foreground, since polyandry occurs most often in poor countries and among peoples where women are in the minority. But neither of these factors is really decisive, because there are too many exceptions to either principle. That means that these forms of marriage existed under different economic conditions, and under similar conditions monogamy was prevalent.

Only a few words on matriarchy. The term denotes a society in which all the rights of a child, mainly its name and inheritance, follow in the line of the mother and not of the father, as with us. As the Swiss ethnologist Bachofen discovered, this institution was widespread among ancient peoples, but its importance and place in the development of marriage is still very much disputed. There are still two schools of thought. One maintains that matriarchy was a development stage through which all peoples passed before they entered the stage of patriarchy, whereas the other school thinks that patriarchy and matriarchy existed side by side and were bound up with the nomadic or agricultural economy of a tribe. However this dispute may be solved, matriarchy has no more than a historical interest.

Morgan has propounded the theory that the development of marriage took place in a straight line from chaos to monogamy, passing through the following stages: unrestricted promiscuity; consanguineous family; group marriage; matriarchy; patriarchy and polygamy; monogamy. This appealing theory is to-day discarded as an undue simplification; Nature does not work in such neat logical sequences.

If one scrutinizes more closely these various types of marriage, their structure, causes, distribution, etc., two basic facts emerge clearly. Firstly, that monogamy was always the basic and predominant type of human marriage, and secondly that even in polygamic or polyandric régimes a trend towards the monogamic principle can be discerned. This trend is revealed

1. Westermarck, *op. cit.*

in such features as the distinction between wife and concubine, the superior position of the first wife over all the others, the often limited number of wives permitted, the exceptional position of priests, etc. But most interesting is the psychology of women married to several men. Almost without exception these men are brothers, that is they spring from the same source, one mother, and consequently the woman marries one spirit embodied in several individuals: in fact, from a psychological point of view, she lives in monogamy.[1]

Looking back on the development of human marriage it would seem that Nature, having originally produced monogamy, started experimenting, and after some trials and errors decided that her first idea was the best one. Or, less metaphorically speaking, it is the rule that every civilization, having reached a certain still rather immature stage, tends to misuse means for inappropriate ends – in this case expressing wealth and power in sexual terms. And only later, in the course of development, is a new harmony achieved. For example, in past centuries feasts used to last several days, during which the participants consumed incredible quantities of food and drink. We no longer indulge in such excesses any more, and do not allow quantity to prevail over quality. The modern counterpart of medieval gluttony, equally distasteful and ridiculous, is the misuse of wealth by the *nouveaux riches*, whose behaviour is in such marked contrast to the style and culture of real aristocracy. On precisely the same principle men in a semi-advanced stage of civilization used their wealth to acquire many women, or several men shared one woman, owing to the scarcity of the

1. It was Freud who first pointed out that neurotic symptoms show a great resemblance to the rites and customs of primitive people, so that neurotics are not only infantile, which means retarded in their individual development, but might be looked upon as throw-backs to earlier stages of civilization.

I remember a few experiences which seem to suggest the relevance of this discovery with regard to our present problem. A young woman reported a dream in which she had married two brothers. Another woman told me that during masturbation she loved her husband and a friend of hers at the same time, with no sense of disloyalty to either. But it is not necessarily a neurosis which causes such an all-embracing affection. When I once sat during a long night at the death-bed of a young woman patient, she suddenly opened her eyes and said 'I have kissed now and said good-bye in this one kiss to all of them' (and she murmured the names of her divorced husband, her last lover and a friend who had just been killed in an air raid).

article. A change took place not when and because the economic conditions of life became easier or more difficult, but when and because women ceased to be considered only as a commodity. The moral development of man, which brought with it a respect for the individual value of women, established monogamy as the only form of marriage. Thus the history of marriage reflects the development of the individual, but on a grand scale: as soon as a young man has reached the stage in which he is capable of appreciating the irreplaceable value of a woman, he loses his need for prostitutes and his taste for affairs and marries this one and only woman.

Thus, having safely established on biological and ethnological grounds that marriage is a genuine and essential element of man's life, we may proceed to investigate the nature of the psychological experience which forms the substance of marriage. One thing must be stated at once and with great emphasis: contrary to the commonly held belief it is not love. What else? It is a feeling of belonging to another person more closely and more completely than in any other human relationship, it is the sense of being welded together with this other person into the unit of the 'couple', of the 'We'; the two mythical 'halves' have found each other for ever. These two peoples are transformed down to the core of their personalities, irretrievably. That applies to the man as well as to the woman. Once a husband he can never become his previous self, even if the marriage has been legally dissolved or broken up by the death of his wife. This is the psychological fact underlying the Catholic concept of the sacramental nature of marriage and the 'indelible character' of a married person. On the psychological as well as on the spiritual level marriage is indissoluble – so long as it is a real marriage and not just a legalized fleeting passion and perpetuated mistake. From a non-theological point of view, which is the only one from which we are qualified to speak, it appears unbearably harsh and inhumanly dogmatic to deny people the right to try to correct such a mistake in a second marriage. On the other hand, it is from a psychological point of view impossible to say whether such a unique experience as a real marriage can be repeated a second time. In theory certainly not, but the inexhaustible variety in kind and degree of human relationships defies any theoretical rigour.[1]

But we have still to justify the contention that love is not the essential substance of marriage. The reason can be found in the psychological and factual differences between the relationship between lovers and that between married people. Only a few of the many differences may be mentioned; the deep wisdom of language indicates the main one: one 'falls' in love, but 'contracts' or 'enters into' a marriage. This means that love is a destiny which overtakes us, but marriage is an achievement based on resolve and determination. It is a tragedy if love fails us, but it is mostly our fault if we fail our marriage.

Marriage too, like love, constitutes a 'world' of its own, but whereas the world of love is an exclusive one, the world of marriage is inclusive. What I mean by this admittedly somewhat arbitrary use of these terms is this: two people in love are absorbed in each other to the more or less complete exclusion of everything else. Through their love they grow and develop themselves, but only for themselves; the relationship fulfils itself in the act of loving, and if one of the lovers eventually remembers the existence of a world outside their love his partner feels this is a betrayal. The world of marriage by its very nature includes the outside world of action, moreover it weaves these two people still more closely into the world in which they live. The wife, far from limiting the freedom of her husband, is the mediator between him and the world. If a man can be sure of the appreciation of his wife, he needs no other recognition, but if she shuts her ear to his plea he feels himself a voice crying in the wilderness. In this respect, although in this alone, the husband–wife relationship repeats the child–mother relationship on a higher level. Therefore, when men refuse to marry for fear of losing their freedom, they do not know what they are talking about. They either mean by freedom lack of responsibility and consideration, or they have not yet understood the meaning and function of marriage. The truly married man's

1. It may be an experience similar to speaking a foreign language. If his mother-tongue is more to a man than just a means of communication with others, if he is 'wedded' to it, he may find it impossible to establish a similar union with the spirit of another language, however fluently he may speak it. I am always a little suspicious of polyglots.

freedom is the freedom of someone who feels secure, not satiated but content, who is at peace with himself and the world.

Although love is not the foundation of marriage, it plays its part in every stage of married life. Love with its sensitiveness for the intrinsic value of a person discovers the 'other half' among the many. Not that every man or woman who may be the right partner for an affair is necessarily the suitable partner for marriage, but one must love first the man or woman whom one wants to marry. Love is the match that lights the fire at the hearth which since time immemorial was held as the symbol of marriage. Later on, when the marital union has been established, love provides the sensational element which lends light and colour to married life. It is not childish curiosity or a superficial desire for thrills that makes many a young wife want to be treated by her husband like a sweetheart. Both the sexual urge and love are, as I said before, passing sensations if left to themselves; but just as sexual desirability is perpetuated by love, love is kept alive if embedded in marital communion.

Once more history and ethnology provide reliable assistance in our analysis of the intimate structure of marriage, by illuminating the relationship of love and marriage and by helping us to understand the nature of the psychological substance of marriage. Human beings never exist as isolated individuals, as bits of humanity, as it were, but always and only in groups, such as the family, tribe, nation, state, religious community, members of a club, a professional union, etc. These groups are not just biological or legal or conventional agglomerations of people, but living entities to which one not only belongs but of which one is part. This is particularly so with national and religious communities – and with marriage. In fact all three belong together: originally all religions were tribal religions and the religious blessing of marriage protected and guaranteed the existence of the tribe. Through having a child a man and a woman not only fulfilled God's demand but safeguarded the continued existence and increased strength of the tribe. Thus we see that religious and national allegiance are the real roots of the conjugal loyalty. There is no better and more comprehensive definition of marriage than the one given by the ancient

Roman law: 'Nuptiae sunt conjunctio maris et feminae et consortium omnis vitae, divini et humani iuris communicatio.' This means, in free translation: Marriage is the communion of husband and wife, which includes every aspect of life according to the divine and secular law. This trend of thought leads on to an important conclusion: the crisis of marriage which is supposed to exist in these days is not a crisis of marriage as such but is only the effect of a far more general crisis, which consists in a disintegration of the concept of humanity, in a deterioration of the genuine national spirit into a militant nationalism, and in a cooling-off of religious fervour.

That it is not passionate love that decides the success or failure of marriage is abundantly proved by those marriages which are contracted without love in a completely impersonal manner. I refer to those marriages in earlier centuries in the West and even nowadays almost over the whole of the East, when parents or councils of the Elders decided who should marry whom. These marriages were the best and happiest ever known. To marry was part of the religious or communal service, the law was experienced as a personal matter, and happiness was found in obedience. Life as a whole and marriage in particular were felt as moral and super-individual tasks. The sense of resting in the security of a higher will and of fulfilling the duties rooted in a tradition a thousand years old, humbly accepted, made these marriages joyous and safe.

'Consortium omnis vitae' – that is, being together and sharing the whole of life, the sunny days and the rainy ones just as they come along – that is the basic experience of being married. Nothing knits a husband and wife more closely together than facing the difficulties of life together, living together through the drudgery of workaday experience, and what lovers may feel as monotony, the quiet rhythm and continuity of life, consolidates the matrimonial bond. Familiarity breeds intimacy, the intimacy of thoroughly knowing each other, each other's mind and body alike: the line of a face that becomes more lovely the better it is known, the lock of hair that will never stay in its right place, the lifting of an eyebrow or jerking of a hand, which always occurs on the occasion it is awaited with tender amusement – always the same yet always somehow new. Similarly the amateur mountaineer admires the beauty of a mountain but seeks the sensation of ever-new experiences, and climbing a mountain means to him struggle and victory or defeat; but the real lover of mountains enjoys just the unchanging sameness of the scenery he knows so well, the familiar contour of a mountain range stencilled on the unchanging sky. Immersed in the stillness of these pointers to eternity, his own time stands still, and the experience of oneness with Nature brings him peace.

Just as in marriage the lives of the two have become one, so have their bodies. No shame can separate them, every function of the body changes its nature magically and acquires new weight and meaning.[1] The importance of living together is only surpassed by the importance of sleeping together. Sleeping together is the deepest symbol, the most intense manifestation of the marital union: in the stillness of the night and the unconsciousness of sleep the two sink back into and unite in the deepest stratum of pure vitality.[2] Married people who do not sleep together are not married, whatever else they may be. The essence of marriage is *being* together, without feeling the need to *do* something together. Many people say that they never get bored when they are by themselves, but that they always feel they must do or say something to entertain a companion. This is often so with a companion, occasionally so with a woman with whom one is in love, but ought never to be so with one's wife. Similarly, sleeping together creates the closest proximity even without any sexual 'doing'. Neither love nor sex is the substance of marital togetherness.

The realization that marriage is a seamless union between a man and a woman leads to a surprising conclusion regarding the nature of marital fidelity. If one conceives of fidelity as a

1. Intimacy must not be mistaken for carelessness and neglect; the dividing line is drawn by a sense of respect. The ruffled hair of a woman when she awakes in the morning may make her still more attractive; an unkempt woman is a horror. It is an unforgivable sin for a husband to take off his tie. A woman is in every stage of dressing or undressing perfectly dressed and attractive, a man is in every stage half-dressed and objectionable; to undress in style in the presence of a woman is a feat no man has ever accomplished – no love, however great, can pardon a man struggling with his collar stud.

2. It is significant that several languages use the word 'sleep' as a metaphor for intercourse: in English 'sleep with a woman', in French '*coucher avec une femme*', in German '*beischlafen*'.

moral deed, that is a resolve upheld against adverse circumstances, it appears that in a real marriage there is no such thing as marital fidelity – simply because there can be no such adverse circumstances as may put it to the test: for the complete devotion to each other makes the man and the woman insensitive to the sexual attractiveness of any other woman or man; one appreciates in a detached manner the qualities of the men and women one meets, but they are never felt as temptations. If they are, something has already gone wrong with the marriage, the union is no longer seamless, and through the rifts, unnoticed as they may have been, danger may slip in. A marriage has never been destroyed by the notorious 'third party', because he has no chance to intervene so long as the marriage is really intact. Marital fidelity as a moral deed, therefore, defends a fortress which is already almost ready to surrender. That this defence is so often necessary and can still avert disaster on one occasion and postpone it on another, sometimes even for good, is due to the instability of so many marriages and to the flexibility of human nature.

Similar deliberations help to clarify the concept of 'matrimonial duty' and to deprive it of its unfortunate moralistic implications. Matrimonial duties are not obligations arbitrarily imposed from without, but a mode of behaviour and action, the motives of which derive automatically from the nature of marriage. If a man has decided to spend the rest of his life with a woman, it is not felt as a duty in the accepted sense of the word to feed and clothe her; if he lives in close union with a woman he will not have sexual intercourse with her in order to satisfy dutifully her sexual needs; and he will be faithful to her for reasons which are remote from any command of abstract morality. He will do all this and much more for no other reason than because he cannot do otherwise. If a husband feels his obligations to his wife and children as a burden which he shoulders because his upbringing and his conscience compel him to do so, then this marriage is built on sand, and its days are numbered. A soldier cannot stand to attention for an indefinite time, nor can a marriage be lived for long if it is based only on the compulsion of moral precepts and taboos – or it is a marriage not worth the trouble of saving at this price.

But there is more in this concept of matrimonial duty. I said before that love overtakes us and deserts us, and we are not able to do anything either way. It is different with marriage; when a man decides to take this woman as wife, marriage becomes a task which must be carried out. And now something entirely new emerges: a husband and wife feel responsibility towards marriage as such, as if, in the process of marrying, marriage had come into being as a new super-individual entity which compels the man and the woman into its service, and this compulsion is only bearable, indeed loses all its compulsory character, if its aim is also voluntarily willed by the two. This experience of being united in the service of something bigger than they are themselves is the source and the measure of cohesion of husband and wife, and far more reliable than the mere satisfaction of personal needs or desires. It is the experience underlying or forming the indelible character of the married state. I had a friend, one of the great women of the day, who once confessed to me that she did not in the least mind the many amours her husband, a notable man in the artistic world, indulged in. She was confident that he would always return to her because, however much other women might stimulate him, she knows and he knows that she is the only one who waits for him as his wife. Or as another very real woman once said: 'So much in my relation to my husband consists in *that* and *how* we *are* to each other. I need not be jealous, because this – our being together – cannot be transferred to someone else.' The sure instinct of these women, and they might have spoken for many others, teaches us more about the problem of fidelity, temptation, freedom, and marital cohesion than many a learned treatise could. I suppose a woman who spoke of 'adult love' meant the same thing. It means a *state* of union once and for all established. Immature love would then be a series of *actions* intended to confirm one's loving. The former spells security, the latter restless doubts. Jealousy, which is just another name for the same thing, can never be stilled by facts and actions; on the contrary, they always only maintain and confirm it.

I wonder whether men could feel as these women do. I rather think not, after all I have said about the different meaning of the sexual act for men and women.

The outstanding importance of the problem of fidelity may justify a few more remarks and a few illustrations to show how it presents itself in different types of marriage. When fidelity emerges from real marital union it is a simple and self-evident experience. Husband and wife are faithful to each other because they cannot be otherwise; they need no one else, they are impervious and insensitive to any outside influence. In exemplary cases this union even outlasts the factual existence of a marriage, and the celebrated faithfulness beyond the grave is no uncommon experience. But this everlasting marital bond may also survive when the actual marriage has been legally dissolved. It then often assumes the character of a sense of guilt – guilt not so much, or not only, because one partner has inflicted pain and sorrow on the other, but guilt towards the marriage as such, towards that spiritual entity which one has once created, for which one is responsible and which one has now killed. It is a sense of guilt of which one need not be ashamed, and of which one can never hope to get rid, however justified one's actions may have been on factual grounds – but guilt of a kind of which it has been said that 'It is the privilege of man to feel guilty' (Hegel).

This fidelity is a manifestation of essential morality, i.e. part of the nature of man. But marital fidelity becomes a 'problem' only when the marital union in a given marriage has ceased to be or has never existed. The 'ought' or essential morality, replaced by the 'must' of traditional morality, becomes a 'duty' based on religious or civil authority expressed in the promise every wedding ceremony contains. And here are a few variations on this theme.

There are a great many husbands and wives who keep the letter of this promise faithfully; they live together in peace, abstain from any intimate contact with other men or women, and all seems to be well with their marriage. In some of these cases faithfulness, not so much to the partner as to the idea of marriage, is due to a strong moral conviction and determination. But these cases are in the minority, and the larger part of this group shows a very different character. If one has an opportunity of investigating these marriages more closely one cannot help feeling that many of them are hollow and lifeless, in spite of the dutiful observance of all moral obligations – or perhaps just because of it. Their fidelity, springing from propriety, is a state of neutrality between absence of essential cohesion and insensitiveness to temptations from without. These cases display a negative aspect of fidelity, as it were, due to a kind of emotional inertia.

Another variety of this kind of marriage is represented by those in which husband and wife have granted each other complete freedom, including that of sexual associations with outside partners. Curiously enough, such marriages often enough strike the naïve observer as particularly happy and successful. And in many respects they are: fondness, respect, consideration, helpfulness have taken the place of sexual association and often enough offer almost full compensation for its absence – at least, so long as both partners stick to the contract and both find their sexual satisfaction elsewhere. Companionate marriages they are in the truest sense of the word, but of course they can no longer be called marriages in the essential meaning of the word.

Between these two extreme types of defective marriages, the most conventional and the most unconventional, both psychologically rather uninteresting, stands a third type. People who live in such marriages have not the strength either to submit to tradition or to carry the burden of freedom. Their vacillation and inconsistency causes not only untold trouble, but reveals the problem of marriage only as a manifestation of the cardinal problem of our present-day existence: our state of suspense between a past that is not yet gone and a future not yet clearly shaped. What happens in such marriages takes almost invariably the following pattern: After some years of more or less normal married life, the sense of matrimonial union fades out for one of the two partners, and with it sexuality disappears too. If this happens in the husband, the wife may accept it as a normal development of marriage, particularly if she is not too interested in sex herself; and all may go well if, as often he does, the husband shows a satisfactory measure of kindness and consideration. But sooner or later, sometimes very late, she finds out that he is having an affair with another woman, and suddenly the whole unstable structure of this marriage breaks down. In vain he may point out to her that the situation has not materially changed, as this other woman has not robbed her of anything she, the wife, has possessed, and that in every other respect he is just as good a husband as he has been all the time. His pleading is of no avail, and nothing eases her despair. Often her reaction is caused by false vanity and injured pride, petty jealousy or insistence upon her pound of flesh – but sometimes it is much more: from a logical and practical point of view these husbands are right, psychologically they are utterly wrong. For marriage consists in a unique, irreplaceable and irreducible oneness, and as long as this exists even the absence of facts and actions, like kindness, attentiveness, even sex, does not greatly matter. Although sex is the outward indication of the existence of the marital union, many a wife blinds herself to the ominous meaning of the failure of the sexual life in her marriage. But when she becomes aware that her husband's sexuality has not simply disappeared but has been diverted to another woman, she cannot keep up her self-deception any longer. In her husband's flagrant infidelity she first realizes the breakdown of her marriage. That is why these women are inconsolable, mourning, at this late hour, a loss which they actually suffered long ago.

Nor is the concept of matrimonial duty related to 'possessing' or being possessed. No woman wants to be possessed, because this is against human dignity, but those who have grasped the essence of sex relationship love to be 'owned'. There is a slight but marked difference between possessing and owning. To possess means to dominate, but to be owned means to such a woman to submit to a person's influence or fascination voluntarily without protest, to become part of his existence, to feel and enjoy his strength, to be desired because of one's own value and not as proof of his might, to feel all the myriad shades of meaning and implications of being 'his' wife, to be touched and used for the common pleasure – as a delicate tool may enjoy being used by the hand of a master.

I know no better presentation of the essence of marriage in its simplicity, more adequate to its simple and tremendous subject, than the last few pages of Charles Morgan's novel *The Fountain.* A man and a woman had struggled against their love and against themselves, a battle they knew they were destined to win by losing it. A friend of the two, bidding them a final good-bye, felt 'that these two were doomed, that they were attempting the impossible and knew it ... to this adventure they had been compelled; this was the fate, the irony, the unrelenting natural stroke that had hung always over the love that they had believed to be encircled. Now they must carry that love with them through the world, vindicating and fulfilling it ... and he understood for the first time in what circumstance of love Lewis and Julie stood. They were not afraid of what might befall, but in awe of the prodigious and continuing power of what had befallen ... they were slow to advance into that external world towards which, out of their dream, fate and their own resolution were carrying them.'

Fate and our own resolution!

*

Marriage is the conjunction of the mind, soul, and body of a man and a woman. *Sexuality* is an essential part of a complete marriage: essential, in the sense of indispensable, but not in the sense of supremely important. Adolescents, of course, hope it will be so, neurotics fear it may be so, and Mr van de Velde even tried in his books to prove that it is so (with great success in some respects, but at the heavy price of much confusion and unhappiness for countless young men and women). The naturalistic idea that love and the marital relationship should be no more than a superstructure upon physical attraction, which is supposed to be the real substance of marriage, is untenable. It would be too much ado about too little to make such a primitive purpose, so easily obtainable and so quickly passing, the sole or even the main reason for a life-long association of a man and a woman.

Married couples share their whole lives – they eat together, enjoy life together, quarrel together, sleep together, and make love to each other. A marriage without sexuality is not a platonic or idealistic or white or clean marriage, but no marriage at all.[1] Although sex relations are the physical manifestation

1. This is also the view of the law, only recently stated in an interesting suit. A husband had stipulated in his will that the inheritance of his wife should be reduced by half if she remarried after his death. She did remarry, but the marriage was annulled after five years on the ground of the impotence of her husband. The judge decided that she should be reinstated in the full inheritance, as according to the letter of the law she was not married to her second husband.

of the personal union of a married couple, they sometimes help to strengthen or restore the union when it was slightly weakened. There is an old warning: 'No quarrel must last overnight', and two people can hardly go on sulking if they sleep together. Moreover if, in bed after a quarrelsome day, a wife turns lovingly to her husband, she is driven by the right instinct. For, conversely, the sexual act motivated by the right spirit of reconciliation re-creates the personal union. This is, I think, on the psycho-physical level an analogy to the function of prayer on the spiritual plane: some people scoff at set prayers as something unworthy. It is true that prayer is the manifestation of an existing union with God, but every truly religious believer knows that saying one of these set prayers in the right spirit helps to establish union with the Divine in a moment of spiritual slackness. A sacrament is the visible manifestation of something spiritual, and the sacramental nature of marriage applies to any part of marriage, for instance the sexual relationship as well, and the relationship between Matter and Spirit works both ways. Mystics, as I said before, often use sexual language to express their religious experiences, so why should not psychology occasionally borrow theological terms to express the spiritual core of psychological experiences?

The source of the sexual stimulation changes in the course of marriage: in the beginning the passionate element of love provides it, but in a second stage sex becomes the physical expression of the specific matrimonial bond, in other words, the wife becomes sexually attractive by virtue of her being one's wife. Familiarity breeds attraction. This dear face that I have seen so many times, gradually moulded by the imprints of good days and bad ones we have seen together, and I know so well – so well that I do not notice that the beloved features have gradually grown sharper and the lines deeper. Not so much the woman as the wife is now the source of attraction and the object of her husband's desire.

Even in an ideal marriage sexuality dies of old age, and if the marriage was a happy one in the past it will be happy in the short space of future still allotted to these lovers in retirement. In other marriages, often with a quite promising start, sexuality dies prematurely. That sexual attraction and desire gradually decrease is natural, partly for physical reasons, partly because some peripheral and merely supporting elements of the sexual stimulus change as times go by. Thus, the excitement of novelty disappears, curiosity is satisfied, and so on. Mortal danger threatens sexuality if a sense of safe possession encourages carelessness. As an experienced woman once said: 'You may forget anything in the presence of a man, including yourself, but you must never forget to powder your nose.' However, these are only accidental factors, and the widespread idea that it is the most natural thing in the world that after some time, often a short one, the mutual attraction should inevitably wither must be strongly contradicted. If this happens – and statistically it seems to be the norm, if statistics could establish the norm in human affairs – if this happens then something is wrong with the marriage. Either something was wrong from the start, or it has gone wrong since. I must say again what I have said so many times, that the fortunes of sex are inseparably linked up with the personal relationship of man and woman. The purely physical sexual urge passes through the same three stages as any other physical urge: stimulation, satiation, revulsion. But if the sexual urge is vitalized by love it acquires a certain measure of continuity, and if this complex sex love is embedded in the matrimonial union, sexual desirability and desire become perpetual.

Now we are in a position to add another contribution to the problem of fidelity. What has been said before about the different attitude of men and women towards sexual infidelity (page 231) and about the stabilizing effect of the marital cohesion is perfectly correct, but if a married man or woman has sexual relations with another woman or man, the marriage is definitely broken. The attitude of the lady I mentioned before, who gave such a long rope to the libertinage of her husband, is a curious mixture of profound femininity and over-sophistication. On the other hand, it may happen that, favoured by circumstances, a strong, irresistible sexual desire attacks and overwhelms a married man or woman, and they succumb to the assault: but this is no longer a human problem but simply a mishap. But if an extra-matrimonial relationship does not just happen, but is maintained for some time, however short, this marriage has virtually ceased to exist – not because someone or some law has decreed it but because finality cannot exist without exclusiveness. True, most people are too insensitive to feel what damage has been done, but some do – and we know that in human affairs the norm rests with the minority. Such 'broken' marriages can be, and often are, carried on very happily if their original liveness is now replaced or supported by good will and a kind of technique of living together; it cannot be learned, there is hardly a name for it other than 'courtesy of heart'.

★

Emotions and the moral conscience are powerful motives but not too reliable ones. Therefore we find everywhere in our lives '*institutions*' – sets of rules and regulations which support passing emotions and strengthen the wavering conscience, making them durable and reliable. Everywhere and at all times religious experiences have been congealed into doctrines, rites, and ceremonies, i.e. into churches or doctrinaire sects, however primitive or elaborate. A free or non-sectarian religion can no more exist than thinking without logic, or language without grammar. The set prayer does not diminish or debase religious fervour and communion with God. On the contrary, if the spontaneous religious aspiration slackens, if we have lost the way to God, the set prayer shows the way and restores faith. Codified law, curricula in schools, rules in sport, traffic regulations, ballroom dancing, set menus, office hours, food rations are other instances of institutions which exercise a vital formative influence in modern life.

So are wedding ceremonies and marriage laws. They are, of course, not the essence or substance of marriage, but the forms which give stability and permanence to the emotional experience of conjugal union. Form and content, living experience and objective institution, both together and only both together, constitute the concrete thing: marriage. Everybody has known periods of his life when God seems to have forsaken him, the spirit has left him, emotions dry up, life stands still. These are the occasions on which we gratefully submit to the strength and force of institutions, in order to be carried over the doldrums of life. No marriage could last without this institutional support. Moreover, now we fully understand the nature and scope of matrimonial duty. It is precisely our acceptance of this institutional support. Those who are willing to protect and continue their marriage are grateful for it; it is resented only by those who are not so willing. But – this institutional support must not be mistaken for a guarantee of safety. No institution can replace the live experience, but only support and thus strengthen it. In other words, if someone allows his experience of marital union to dry up, trusting that the institution of marriage will keep his partner in the marriage, he turns marriage into slavery, and slaves long for freedom. On the other hand, the strong desire of a woman to be properly married, however intimate and safe her relation with her beloved friend may be, has a very essential reason far beyond concern about her social status or economic security. The legal sanction is not accidental to but essential for marriage. It is this which makes marriage what it is. I have said before on several occasions, particularly in the foreword, that our life consists of many personal and functional relationships making conflicting demands on us. Now it can be added that marriage is, I think, the only human relationship in which the functional and the personal are so closely interwoven that the one loses its meaning without the other.

Another effect of the institutional character of marriage is the publicity which marriage thus acquires. It is no longer a private affair of two lovers, but a public business – in the truest sense of the word – of two members of a community which exercises its rights over them.

Here a few words must be said about the child and the part it plays in marriage. It is psychologically unjustifiable to assume that love and marriage culminate in the production of a child as their reason and purpose, and that marriage and family are almost synonymous concepts. Unjustified because marriage is an end in itself, entirely confined to the two people who contract it. True, it is lovely to have a house full of children and to find in them a legitimate object of one's surplus tenderness, but a barren marriage need not by any means be looked upon as a failure. Biologically it is necessary for a woman to have a child, as I have explained before, but not so for men. But as in an ever-increasing degree the biological elements of human existence have been overlaid by sociological factors, the sociological sphere becomes the proper domain for the problem of the child. In tribal communities where the child was not only the offspring of his parents but a contribution to the power of the tribe, it was of the umost importance for a young couple to have children, and sterility was the main reason for divorce. Our times have seen this natural right of the tribe develop into an absolute right of the State to consider the children as its property.

If a marriage is a real one and parents look upon their children as the embodiment and product of their union, children strengthen the marital bond; but this is the one kind of marriage that needs no strengthening. But if the bond has loosened, and needs strengthening, having children cannot serve this purpose. Children never keep a marriage alive, they only make divorce more difficult. It is true, people whose marriage has died long ago may keep on living together 'for the sake of the children'. But an empty shell is not a healthy place for children to live in, and every experienced educator knows that children suffer much more in such a strained atmosphere than from a clean divorce. A sociological problem of its own is the illegitimate child. If it 'just happens' it is no problem but just a misfortune, and the answer should be simple. But if a single woman needs and wants a child in order to bring all her womanhood to fruition, it is psychologically wrong, unfair, and immoral to permit her no other way of satisfying this natural and personal desire than through the indignity of an unwanted marriage. The answer is less simple if we consider the child's interest first. An illegitimate child suffers psychologically because it is brought up without a father, and socially it is stigmatized from its first day at school onwards. There is no simple answer to this problem, because the real problems of life do not permit of clear-cut solutions. If the rights and needs of one individual stand against the rights and needs of another human being, there is no arbitration possible, and the complexity of human life comes into its own.

As the views expressed above, that children are not an essential element of marriage, may appear to many people as wrong or even offensive to their feelings, it may be worth while to point out that the statement also represents the opinion adopted by the highest juridical authorities in this country. According to Lord Penzance marriage is 'the voluntary union for life of one man and one woman to the exclusion of all others.' Children are not mentioned in this definition, and quite recently the Lord Chancellor, Viscount Jowitt, said that 'Insistence on the procreation of children as one of the chief ends, if not the chief end, of marriage, requires examination'. On these grounds he refused to grant annulment of marriage to a husband whose wife insisted on the use of a contraceptive. Thus according to the law of this country the use of contraceptives is permissible and does not affect the validity of a marriage.[1]

The situation is still more complicated for Roman Catholics. The Canon Law states: 'The primary purpose of marriage is the procreation and education of children; the secondary end, mutual support, and the relief of concupiscence.' And Pope Pius IX says: 'The act of wedlock is of its very nature designed for the procreation of offspring ...' It is rather strange that the at one time supreme spiritual power should so uncompromisingly give precedence to the biological element in marriage, but it is only consistent with this view that the Roman Church condemns birth control as 'shameful and intrinsically immoral.'[2]

In marked contrast to the complexity and perplexity of the religious and common law, the problem presents itself much more simply from the psychological point of view. A woman needs to have a child as an essential part of her self-fulfilment, and a marriage in which she is, arbitrarily or by misfortune,

1. But the interpretation of the common law in this difficult matter is still far from being uniform. Shortly before the Lords decided the test case mentioned above, I was called as an expert witness in a case in which the wife sought annulment of her marriage on the grounds of non-consummation, because her husband suffered from lack of emission. This not infrequent trouble is due to a subconscious inhibition of the emission, thus being for all practical intents and purposes a kind of birth control. The judge granted annulment without hesitation. Before the case was heard, counsel was most doubtful whether we should succeed. When I remarked that the law must have defined in unmistakable terms when a marriage is consummated, the learned man replied with a weary smile: 'My dear friend, the English law never defines anything in unmistakable terms.'

2. Occasionally the flexibility of doctrine, properly exploited by the ingenuity of its interpreter, provides a loophole, as the following experience proves: A husband insisted on birth control, which his Catholic wife refused on religious grounds. She went for advice to her Confessor, who passed a Solomonic judgement: if her husband applied a contraceptive, he said, she did not 'use' but only 'tolerated' it, and thus would be blameless in the view of the Church.

denied this achievement, loses a good deal of meaning for her and is through the frustration of her maternal instinct for many a woman essentially null and void. Hence to force a woman to continue such a marriage means to force her to fret away her life as a woman. Although a child is of much less importance for a man, a husband must not be denied the benefit of a child if he wants one. In brief, although having a child is not a constitutive element of marriage, dissolution of a barren marriage must be granted if a husband or a wife seeks it because of its barrenness.

*

Most people are agreed that marriage, like many other social institutions, is passing through a crisis at this time. The truth is that the crisis of marriage is merely a reflexion of the crisis of far more fundamental issues, in fact of the whole existence of modern man. The formula on which practically all philosophers, historians, and psychologists who concern themselves with this problem are agreed is that modern man is uprooted and unprotected, his existence flattened out, he is a 'thinking reed'. Faith has been replaced by a shallow rationalism, spiritual values by utilitarian ones, pride in one's work by interest in the profit it brings, tradition has been divested of its glory by historical criticism, and social conventions are for many no more than an object of ridicule. As all these values, now discredited, are essential constituent parts of marriage, it is obvious that marriage is in mortal danger. But if this is so, it can be argued, why try to keep alive what is obviously no longer in tune with our way of life? The answer depends on the philosophy of history one favours: if one believes that the Decline of the West is in full swing, then there is really no sense in preserving relics. On the other hand, as it is a precarious business to predict the course of history, it may be worth trying to preserve what according to past history seems to be an essential part of human nature. Thus, one conclusion seems to be irrefutable: a reform of marriage in the sense of a new form of marriage cannot be expected before mankind has found and consolidated a new form of existence. And this may take a long time.

This is the negative or destructive aspect of the problem. But there is also a constructive one, as the worshippers of reason at least would call it. A great awakening is taking place all over the world, and one may say we are living in a second Age of Enlightenment. The awakening of national individualism in its ugly as well as in its beneficial aspect breaks up many social structures – and the women fling wide open the doors of their prisons without bars, thus breaking up time-honoured sets of values and social institutions. Marriage is in danger of becoming one of the victims. It need not be so. For what is needed is no more than a reorganization within the framework of marriage, giving the women scope for unfolding their newly acquired sense of social personality. None of these readjustments need affect the essence of marriage. This historico-sociological background produces a corresponding mentality in men. Thus from a purely psychological point of view the main reasons for the alleged crisis of marriage are: insufficient instinct for a proper choice of partner and insufficient moral strength to accept and carry out the responsibilities incurred by entering into marriage.

Fortunately the great problems of life solve themselves automatically, if the conditions which have thrown up these problems change in the course of history. What we can, and must contribute to the process is to make life bearable during the periods of transition, which means in our case to facilitate divorce.

*Divorce* is not an invention of modern times. Among many primitive peoples it was unknown, but among many others marriage was and still is not necessarily contracted for life. All degrees can be observed, between the great ease and informality with which marriages can be dissolved on the one hand and permanent fidelity on the other. The grounds on which divorce is sought and obtained are often ridiculously slight, in other instances very elaborate. Thus, according to Gallic law a wife could leave her husband if he suffered from fetid breath, whereas the Chinese law recognizes six reasons for divorce: barrenness, lasciviousness, inattention to parents-in-law, thievishness, ill-temper, inveterate infirmity. The two reasons for divorce almost universally accepted are barrenness and adultery. The civil authorities exercise their power to control divorce mainly for the protection of the children. The reason why peoples control divorce is in primitive states an economic one (it is expensive to buy another woman) and at higher stages of civilization a growing moral conscience. Generally speaking the two functions of civilization operate in successive stages: a phase of moral development which includes both the sense of essential morality and a set moral code is followed by a phase of progressive demoralization. Thus, in the history of peoples destined to reach the highest standards of civilization, such as the ancient Hebrews, Greeks, and Romans, we find that in the beginning divorce was extremely rare, but in the periods of decay in Greece and Rome divorce reached destructive dimensions as it has done among the Jews in modern times. From this point of view it is very interesting to note that the Catholic doctrine of the indissolubility of marriage was definitely established only as late as 1545 at the Council of Trent. During the last half-century the trend towards divorce has in increasing degree shown the virulence of an epidemic. In 1914 there were 856 divorces in this country; in 1921 there were 3,522; in 1928 there were 4,000. In 1946 the figure rose to 35,874, and in an announcement by the Lord Chancellor he expressed the hope that 'our normal number' will be 10,000 a year! In the United States according to the latest census the number of divorces was 3·6 to 10,000 people, in some states, as, for instance, in Ohio, even 6·2. Is this an alarming symptom that our civilization has already passed the culmination of moral development?

It is no secret that in all countries the laws concerning divorce are most unsatisfactory. The solutions offered by post-revolutionary Russia, that vast laboratory for experimental sociology, and in the small town of Reno, Nevada, U.S.A., or the Roman Church's alternative are not solutions – they simply shelve the problem either by condoning licence or by showing intransigence towards it. Nor are the half-way solutions practised by liberal régimes any more satisfactory, for they suffer from an inconsistency as fateful as it is inevitable. In no other part of our life, I think, is the relationship of the individual and the community as complicated and delicate as in sexual matters, nor is the infringement of personal liberty anywhere more resented, particularly if the interference is as patently unfair as the divorce laws make it. These laws are in the truest sense a trap. Neither Church nor State bothers in the least who marries whom; they bless the union, however unsuitable from every point of view the two candidates may be. Even immigration visas to a foreign country are granted only after a careful investigation into the physical, mental, and moral condition of the applicants, whereas the doors to Church and Registry Office are always kept wide open. But as soon as the two people are married and realize their mistake, they find the door has closed behind them, and they are trapped for good. In 1937 A. P. Herbert introduced a reform of the divorce laws, adding to the few existing ones some more grounds for divorce: desertion for three years, cruelty, habitual drunkenness, incurable insanity and life-long imprisonment. But the main ground on which people can obtain divorce is still adultery, and as in many cases where divorce is desired no adultery has been committed, and neither of the parties wants to commit it, it has become common practice to fake adultery and to submit false evidence to the court. Thus instead of protecting morality, the ideas of the sanctity of marriage and the solemnity of rites are turned into farce and blasphemy. Shortly after the First World War the American Judge Ben Lindsey propagated the idea of 'companionate marriage': the young man and the girl should live together in full marital union with the right to part after some time if they found the arrangement unsuitable. Even this absurdity has its history. In ancient Egypt and Japan this sort of marriage existed. Rabelais suggested a kind of monastery where monks and nuns should live together on probation for one year, and the context suggests that this time he was not speaking as a satirist. And during the period of Romanticism, German philosophers discussed the idea quite seriously. What such a companionate marriage amounts to is simply a legally sanctioned affair, and what is completely forgotten is the main difference between an affair and marriage: that the latter is from its inception intended to be permanent. It is easy to enjoy the amenities of a foreign country with a return ticket in one's pocket, but it is a very different thing to know that one has immigrated for good.

The unsatisfactory pseudo-solution of the problem of divorce is not due to the ineptitude of the law-makers and the incompetence of those people who make their work still more difficult. The problem of divorce is an outstanding instance of those situations in which the rival claims of liberty for the individual and stability for the community cannot be harmonized to the full satisfaction of all concerned. It is one of those real problems of life to which there is no answer. It is in the same category as two other problems that arise concerning the two other critical stages of man's life: the problems of abortion and euthanasia (sometimes called by the ugly name of 'mercy killing'). The legislation about these two interferences with human life is extremely strict and rigid. Every experienced doctor knows how much misery for the patients and heart-searching for doctors has resulted from the conflict between the human and the legal aspect of these problems; but as a doctor becomes older and wiser he begins to realize that this conflict is irresolvable. The line between the permissible and the impermissible has to be drawn somewhere, and there will always be people, perhaps many people, who will feel it has been drawn at the wrong place.

The matter-of-fact solution of the law is not only meant to produce the outward appearance of a moral society, but to protect the existence of society as such – at a high price. For these unwilling couples, forcibly kept in an unwanted marriage, and those undesired children, forced into a hostile *milieu*, seriously imperil the mental health of the community. Thus social gains are paid for with eugenic losses.

Fortunately these legal intricacies transcend the orbit of medical competence and influence. From a psychological point of view divorce as a last resort is essential, and it is equally important not to make it too easy. But there is still another aspect of divorce, not sufficiently known, which reveals the tragic element in the problem far beyond legalistic quibbles. I have said earlier that getting married welds man and woman into an inseparable unit, that their personalities are irretrievably transformed and that this cohesion results in a loyalty to marriage as such; the result of this complex process is epitomized in the term 'indelible character'. Although the transformation takes place in every case of real marriage, the fallibility of man makes it sometimes impossible for a husband and wife to live in a workaday world the new life which they have created between themselves, and to be these new persons into which they know they have been changed. And thus, a new conflict rises – the really tragic conflict of marriage and divorce. It is not caused by the struggle of husband against wife, but the rift splits each of the people inwardly, so that the married part struggles against the centrifugal forces inside each of them. This battle can neither be won nor lost, it must go on for a long time, if not for ever. I knew a woman who was married to the wrong man. When I asked her why she did not go her way and let him go his, she simply replied: 'I cannot, because I am married to him.' She knew that if a real woman gets married it is a real marriage, and it acquires for her the indelible character, whatever the partner may feel and however inadequate he may be. There can be little doubt that the greatest happiness in human life is a happy marriage, and that an unhappy marriage is a foretaste of hell. But still worse is the conflict we are discussing, because the victims from time to time think they should be able to solve it, but know so well that they have forfeited the right and chance to do so – long ago. And thus they go on serving their 'Life Sentence'.[1]

*

Why do marriages fail?

The central axiom of the psychology of marriage as developed in these pages is the assumption that marriage is essentially a permanent relation. Hence, every marriage that does not last is abnormal. This is not begging the question, because it can be demonstrated that the psychological conditions that lead to the breaking-up of a given marriage are always abnormal – abnormal not in the strictly medical sense of the term, but because they are of a kind that should not occur in a normal mature person. When a husband quarrels with his wife he maintains that his behaviour, to which she objects, is only the reaction to what she has done to him; to which she replies that this her action was nothing else than the reaction to what he has previously done to her – and they could go on

1. This term is borrowed from Rebecca West's short story of the same name, in which she incomparably describes this problem. It is part of her book *The Harsh Voice*.

arguing this way backwards until they would arrive at the original cause of their present quarrel: the fact that they have married each other. Every detail of married life and its future is fully determined by the characters of the two people who want to get married. It is not possible to discuss here the vast subject of choice of the marriage partner, but we must limit our analysis to a few typical instances in which the wrong one was chosen.

It actually means that two people are incompatible with each other; but this is a very vague and loosely used term, and we must try to isolate a few of its component parts. Medical psychology has discovered the fact that by far the larger number of our characteristics are not genuine, but reactions to environmental influences in our earliest years. But there are a few of these characteristics which must be considered as genuine and unalterable, as, for instance, the level of a man's intelligence. Another one is the 'speed' of life, which means that some people think and act fast and others slowly. This difference constitutes perhaps the most important impediment to marriage between such personalities, because it is not only unalterable but definitely irreconcilable. It is quite intolerable for the faster one to drag along his companion, or for the slower one to hurry breathlessly behind his speedier partner. The importance of this form of incompatibility can hardly be overrated.

Incompatibility of temperament is too well known to need to be more than just mentioned. In passing it may be pointed out that occasionally identity of temperament is just as hard to bear as difference. Although it is most annoying if one partner is left cold by an event which makes the other tremble with excitement, one can easily imagine the persistent uproar of a *ménage* if husband and wife are equally 'temperamental'. This instance alone proves, I feel, convincingly and disappointingly that it is not possible to work out compatibility with the certainty of a mathematical equation, because – must I repeat it again? – not the facts matter, but the meaning we give them, and meaning in this situation means willingness to live together.

It is, in order to give another instance, sometimes very pleasant for a husband of independent nature if his wife is independent too, but when in his weaker moments he longs for or even needs a submissive and obliging wife he may find her independence most irritating and unhelpful.

In real life there are only degrees of incompatibility, which make this mutual accommodation more or less difficult. Among the differences which, I think, are really difficult to bridge are differences of origin and background. However convinced one may be of the ultimate sameness of men of different races, the differences which overlie this sameness make themselves felt, often painfully, in the intimacy of married life. The differences between East and West, as well as between southern and northern Europe, need only be mentioned. The same applies to the difficulties which arise from different social and cultural upbringing

It has often been said that with some measure of goodwill these and similar difficulties could be overcome, that marriage is not a 'natural' thing which automatically functions but a task which must be achieved. All this is perfectly true, but only up to a point. In many of these cases the differences are too great and the task too heavy. That this is so, in spite of all the goodwill shown by one or both of the partners, is revealed by sexuality, which under these circumstances often fails. For moral obligations, however sincerely felt and discharged, are no sexual stimulus; nor is loyalty to marriage as such but only attachment to the concrete living person. The relationship between Morality and Sex is extremely complex: Sex does not militate against Morality, but Morality as such, on the other hand, is no motive for Sex. One may find that this statement patently contradicts what I have previously said about Oriental marriages. But this seeming discrepancy resolves itself easily if one realizes that in those marriages not 'morality' or 'obedience' in the sense of which we commonly use these concepts is the real motive power, but deepest harmony with God's will, a religious fervour which has become very rare among Western men.

Great as are the difficulties of such incongruous or disharmonious marriages for the people who live them, they involve a still greater danger if we consider the children that may issue from them. Every child has to weld into the unit of its own personality the character traits which it inherits from its parents, and it is obvious that this will be the more difficult the more disparate the personalities of the parents are. This applies not only to cases in which the parents are of different races, but also when the personalities of the parents and their families are too incongruous. One of the most unhappy men I knew provided a convincing example: his father's family were very successful business men through three generations, and his mother came from a family of artists. The result was not that their son became an artist who successfully commercialized his artistic work, but a man torn between two opposite attitudes to life. The split ran through his whole personality and the inner disharmony deprived him of all self-certainty, so that his great talents never came to fruition and he wasted his life in profitless dilettantism.

It is true that eugenists contend that the admixture of 'new blood' often improves stock, and that sometimes men of genius have such a mixed heritage; but the human race, and particularly the characterlogical elements in it, still defies all too often the rules of genetics. This fact makes very difficult, if not impossible, any advice about the suitability of a man and woman for marriage from the point of view of children. Every doctor experienced in these matters must know more than one case in which the record of both families as regards psychological and sometimes even mental illnesses was very unsatisfactory, and yet the children turned out to be ideally normal. That the reverse is equally true is, of course, common experience.

Again, I should not be surprised if I were reminded that many people know of cases in which marriages, incongruous from many points of view, have been successful. This should surprise no one, because the great malleability of human nature may achieve a relative success under the most adverse conditions. What I have said should only serve as a warning that such marriages are fraught with dangers. Besides, we always remember the exceptions better than the rule, because the exceptions do not fit into the pattern of our expectations, and the mere fact that we remember them shows that they are exceptions to the existing rule.

If we proceed now to less obvious and conspicuous reasons for failure in marriage, we must mention as the most important cause immaturity – which means that one or both of the partners are not yet fit for marriage. It is one of the leading aims of this book to show that marriage is an achievement, only possible when people have reached a stage of their development that enables them to grasp the idea of permanency and finality, and needs a long mental and physical preparation. These conditions cannot be fulfilled by men before reaching an age of approximately 28 or by women younger than 25. These figures, founded on purely psychological grounds, are confirmed by statistics; in this country, for example, the average age of marriage was 29 for men and 26½ for women until 1946. Then the figures were 23 and 20 respectively. This deplorable drop in sensibility was undoubtedly due to the war, which added a few more immaterial reasons for marrying to those operating in time of peace. Without exception every reason for marriage is immaterial other than the resolve to share life with a woman, not just because one feels lonely, but because one feels that marriage is a condition for a full life – and to share life with this particular woman not just because one is in love with her, but because one 'knows' that she will be the right one. How should young people desire to share life and how can they know what a 'full life' means when they have scarcely started their own? How can any man know that this woman is the right one, when he hardly knows what a woman looks like? Young marriages must be discouraged by all means because they carry in themselves the seeds of mistakes and failures. The basic error of judgement that leads to these premature marriages is due to the mistaken idea that to be in love with a girl is sufficient reason for marrying her, and that if one is physically attracted to her one must marry her first – in other words, these boys and girls do not know the difference between an affair and marriage. Many unhappy marriages are simply affairs dragged on long after they have ceased to be alive. And affairs are only the training-ground on which the battles for happy marriages are prepared, but not the battlefields on which they are won.

Even strongly morality-conscious educators admit that young people can hardly be expected to wait 10–15 years after they have reached sexual maturity before they are permitted to allow these faculties to function. Therefore it has been suggested that an improved social order should make early marriages possible. Apart from the fact that this may be a very long-term solution, this suggestion seems to me to tackle the problem from the wrong end. Early marriages should be discouraged, not because our economic living conditions have become so complicated but because we have become so complex. The civilization in which we live has affected our psychobiological status in that we reach mental maturity so much later than physical maturity. This is the crux of the matter. With some tribes in the South Seas it is a condition for the permit to get married that a young man should, as proof of his fitness to marry, present his girl with the head of an enemy he has slain. Although we need not insist on such a gruesome and exacting test, we may be justified in asking that the young candidate should have conquered, and should present, his own head.

But there is a still greater risk inherent in young marriages. Young people marry in a chrysalis stage, when even experienced entomologists do not always know what kind of butterfly will emerge. More than once I have heard a woman sigh: 'This is no longer the man I married.' This danger, to my mind the greatest in married life, also arises sometimes in later stages of marriages which have been contracted at a proper age, because some people – and occasionally the best ones are among them – develop slowly or resume a rapid development in mid-life. The other partner hardly notices the gradual change, he or she lives in a sense of security built up in the common past, and finds himself suddenly confronted with the catastrophe. These events are truly tragic in the strict sense of the word, because the two people become the victims of circumstances for which they are not responsible, against which they fight in the dark, and almost always a losing battle.

Here is such an example:

He is 50 years old, tall, physically and mentally very virile, highly cultured: he is a leading industrialist who has worked himself up from a very humble beginning and is an outstanding figure in the political life of his country.

She is 38, a sculptress, very sensitive, physically delicate, child of an old patrician family. They were brought together by common interest in art and politics, an active approach to life on a high idealistic level and still more by the fact that her feminine longing for support was happily met by his manliness. They had been married for seven years when things began to change. She noticed it first. She had had a rather difficult childhood, because her father, a very impressive man and therefore greatly adored by this daughter, preferred, or seemed to prefer, a younger sister. Reacting in a typical way to this typical family constellation, the girl tried to convince her father of her value by striving hard after any sort of success. Having now found in her husband an equally strong man devoted to her and giving her all the love and care which she, rightly or wrongly, had missed from her father, she relaxed and, almost for the first time in her life, allowed herself to be a woman and to be treated as such. But, and such is the irony of life, just at this time she became unusually successful in her own work. She quickly grew up, as it were, and became a fully mature, self-reliant woman. At this critical moment her husband's life took a turn in the opposite direction. Prematurely consumed by the hard struggle for his professional career, he was no longer fit enough to face increasing difficulties in business, some political disappointments – and least of all the problem of his marriage. Thus he did the two things so many men do in similar circumstances: he tried to escape from the tribulations of the world, at least for a few hours (he took to gambling, as other men take to the bottle or do still worse things) while becoming intolerably aggressive to everyone including his wife.

She understood the situation perfectly, realizing her problem and his. But understanding helps only in the 'handling' of a situation – and she handled it with courage and goodwill – it does not help in 'living' a situation, and consequently the liveness of her marriage died from the one poison no woman's love can survive: loss of respect for her husband because of his unmanliness and lack of self-discipline. She still fully appreciates his noble character and admires the greatness of his abilities; his quiet dependability in the past has given her enormous strength, but now she feels insecure, confused, left alone. She thinks she still loves him as much as ever, but her growing intolerance and unforgiveness make her slightly doubtful of her love. In the spiritual sphere they are still united but – and in a few words this woman revealed the deepest mystery of marriage and the unique essence of conjugal communion: 'We are deeply united but perhaps no longer married, because I stand with him, but no longer stand up for him.' That means united, but no longer one with him.

I do not know the end of the story, and probably never shall, because the couple have moved back to their home country. But the end is immaterial, for the purpose of telling this story is to show that the greatest danger for marriage is this drifting apart through the simple process of living, and the various reactions to problems which this process throws up. That this danger is immense if husband and wife are young is obvious, but the risk is ever present, particularly among highly differentiated people whose development never stands still but goes on throughout life.

I have previously said that young men need a period of trial and error in order to achieve the measure of maturity which would enable them to become successful husbands. Although this law does not apply with the same stringency to girls, one occasionally meets a young woman who feels the same urge to develop her potentialities before she enters into the bondage of marriage. I knew a young woman, in her late twenties, a most promising scientist, who suddenly left her husband after several years of an apparently happy marriage. An irresistible force drove her away; she had to find out whether she could forget the luxury of her parental home and forgo the comfortable security of her married life; she wanted to know what her own possibilities were, whether and how far she could be herself and stand on her own feet. 'Knowing' meant for her 'experiencing'. 'In theory', I remember her saying, 'I know that I can do all that I want to do, but I must have it in my body in order to know it really.' She could never learn anything by being told, but had to take the hard way, because she could become wiser only through 'feeling'. The obvious question how much lack of discipline had caused her to take this step she waved aside with the impressive assurance that nothing she did was ever done because she could not resist a temptation, but because she was always guided by the sensation of an unconditional necessity. But she was conscious of another motive in her bid for freedom: the need for romance. She believed she had had all too little of it, before her marriage. To have had romance was, she thought, a necessary condition of happiness though not its cause; and only after having had it did she think she could settle down to the serious business of life. All these motives fall into the proper pattern of this woman's personality and are seen in right perspective in the light of her concept of marriage: 'Marriage is the freedom from which life begins; until then it is just groping in the dark, coping with problems.'

This shows that she had remarkable insight into the nature of marriage, but it was only *a priori* knowledge, an image of things to come, and she was not yet capable of giving it reality. However, this attitude lent conviction to her argument that she was not running away from marriage but working towards it. And the cause of the whole trouble could not be better summed up than in her own words: 'I know that my husband is the only man I could ever live with as husband and wife, but it is a thousand pities that I did not meet him several years later than I did.'

This story is by no means typical, but very exceptional. Many women run away from their duties, whereas this woman – and a few others of her kind – feel it their duty to abandon an untenable position. Many take this step for lack of sense of responsibility; this one did it out of responsibility to herself. True, this young woman was no paragon of virtue; there were some other, less exalted, motives for her escapade: a neurotic reaction to her upbringing, a certain measure of self-centredness and insensitiveness to other people's feelings, fondness for admiration, and the like, but it was quite obvious – much more so than a brief account can convey – that these traits were only subsidiary to the genuine central impulse. In one respect, though, this story points a moral, and for this reason I have told it: it demonstrates the importance of the time factor in human affairs; great opportunities can be wasted and much harm can be done if we force situations, or allow ourselves to be forced into them, before the time is ripe.

I have previously mentioned some differences in the personalities of a husband and his wife which may lead to unsuitability and incompatibility. Here may be added one more typical cause of conflict which throws an interesting light on the problem of marriage and causes a typical conflict. It is often ascribed to the greater emotionality of women and the greater intellectuality of men. These terms are incorrect, because the root of all the trouble is not just emotionality against intellectuality, but the fundamental difference between the masculine and the feminine existence. The maturity, security, stability of his wife, her quiet 'being', become a challenge to the husband, and with strong personalities in whom the existential characteristics are clearly marked the clash is often thunderous, reverberating through all details of life. Against the specific weapon of men, critical analysis and discursive argument, women are defenceless. 'If he would only stop asking why I did something,' a wife moaned. 'I simply do not know, and it does not matter anyway, even if I knew.' And when a woman, yielding to pressure, gives a reason for her actions, usually the first she can think of, she becomes an easy prey to the man's superior logic. If a husband forces such an intellectual approach on his wife he destroys the best in her, because he makes her uncertain of herself. The sense of spontaneous happiness which many a woman feels, her madonnaesque beatitude, irritates some men and they dismiss it as unjustified and unmerited. Women's all-embracing oneness with the world puts them at ease with people; this makes men envious because they must 'establish' contacts by first discovering a number of qualities, adding them up and thus calculating, as it were, the character of the people they meet. A friend of mine, with whom I once discussed these problems, said with tragicomic resignation: 'If I talk to someone about the weather I know all about what he thinks about the weather, but if my wife does the same thing, she at once knows all about the man.' I owe to a very womanly woman this magnificent *aperçu*: 'To be content with a part only is a kind of dishonesty.' Highly intellectual men have the capacity of asking the one pertinent question which illuminates the crucial point of a problem, as a spotlight picks out the leading character in a play, leaving the rest of the stage in the dark – an artificial, eerie, almost tactless effect; whereas the holistic perception of women illumines the whole scene, bringing all the actors into plastic relief and proper proportions. Husbands often complain about their wives' lack of response or appreciation, because they want this response expressed in words and actions, and do not understand that women respond by being and living and are, suprisingly enough, inarticulate in those basic reactions. Many a husband feels oppressed and imprisoned by the exclusive devotion of his wife and blames her for not having friends with whom she could share interests and affections. There is truth in this observation. Women, those exemplary women, at least, about whom I am talking here, are lonely, they have no friends in the fullest sense of the word; their holistic way of being prevents them from entering into this kind of human relationship.

For friendship is the relationship between independent individuals, which corresponds to the masculine form of existence, wherefore real friendship is a prerogative of men. I cannot think of one instance celebrated in history or poetry of friendship between women as so many friendships between men are, and I do not believe that the slightly outworn explanation – that history and poetry are predominantly made by men – is good enough.

Every one of these conflicts I have discussed would be enough to make married life full of friction, but it is obvious that most, if not all, of them may occur together. But must they occur as a result of the basic misunderstanding of the sexes? By no means. In fact, most married couples will hardly know what I am talking about, and may take this whole analysis, at best, as undue sophistication. And up to a point they are right: we must not forget that most marriages are, to all intents and purposes, 'happy' and most people accept a certain amount of friction as inevitable; not many husbands blame their wives for not taking sufficient interest in their husbands' jobs, and not many wives are exasperated by their husbands' lack of interest in their artistic propensities. These existential conflicts assume greater proportion and importance only as we move higher up the scale of exemplariness. But even then they are not inevitable as results, as it is sometimes put, of the 'compensatory unlikeness' of the sexes. They are bound to arise if the 'unlikeness' is overemphasized, but they need not arise if the 'compensatory' nature of the differences is duly understood and appreciated. They do not arise, for instance, if a man does not misinterpret his wife's quiet way of 'being' as lazy-mindedness, or try to pierce her placidity by his power of intellectual analysis, but appreciates the products of her intuitive approach to things as valuable material for his intellectual constructions. That husband and wife should complement each other has become a commonplace, but the correct meaning of this complementing is often not understood. It does not mean the neutralization or levelling of difference. On the contrary, differences must be preserved and made use of for the creation of something new. What we said earlier about the dialectic relationship between a community and its members applies to the marriage relationship as well: the level of a community is the higher the higher the individuality of its members is developed. A man and a woman fulfil their respective tasks as marriage partners the more completely the more masculine the husband and the more feminine the wife are in all the depths of their existence. It is, to say it again and again, not the facts that matter but the meaning and interpretation we give to them. Marital conflicts arise, are bound to arise, only if this interpretation springs from a background of hostility.

But why should there be enmity between husband and wife – why should they choose war instead of peace? The answer introduces the fourth reason for marital difficulties: *besides factual unsuitability, developmental incongruity, and existential disharmony, emotional maladjustment or neurosis is the most frequent cause of unhappy marriages.*

Husband and wife cannot live in peace with each other but must fight a bitter war of attrition, often enough to the point of complete mutual destruction, when the neurotic disposition of the man or the woman, or of both, does not permit them to conceive of marriage as a harmonious and mutual co-operation but only as a struggle for supremacy.

And this leads to the crucial point for any understanding of conflicts in marriage: the revolt is in most cases not directed against the individual personality of the marriage partner, but against him, or her, only in their role or capacity as marriage partners – or, in a way, against marriage itself. A man may love a woman, he may highly appreciate her personal qualities of any kind, but he cannot live with her as husband because her neurotic character makes her more or less unsuitable for marriage; and vice versa. That marital proximity is the cause of mutual irritation and intolerance is proved by the experience – among many others – that surprisingly often divorcees rediscover their premarital mutual attractiveness, and restart a kind of intimate friendship, occasionally even an affair. This, I think, is possible only when the marriage has never been a real one, because the disappointment and resentment of such a fundamental failure as a broken marriage must of necessity exclude any other contact afterwards. Besides, both the capacity and the desire to enter into a lower form of relationship after the higher one has failed prove only how imperfect people and their relationships can be. If marriage has failed, one cannot keep up an affair with the one-time partner; if an affair has comes to its end one cannot replace it by 'friendship', and someone who once was a friend can never become a mere acquaintance. What was it this woman said? 'To content oneself with only a part is a kind of dishonesty' – the more so if one was once part of a whole.

What is it, then, that dooms the marriage of neurotic individuals to failure? We remember the main deficiencies of a neurotic individual: that he never reaches full maturity, that he avoids finality, that he never grasps the full meaning of sex, and that he is incapable of accepting responsibility – and if we realize that these four functions constitute precisely the essence of marriage, it must be obvious that, in principle and in fact, the neurotic is disqualified from marriage. The common denominator of these four deficiencies is lack of self-confidence. One must be very sure of oneself to risk the greatest adventure in human life with confidence, to be able and willing to surrender oneself to another person without mistaking this complete communion for captivity. Through this lack of a proper conception of himself the neurotic is too watchful of his prestige, and tries to raise his own by lowering the proper value of everybody else's. With this plan of campaign he enters marriage. The result is aptly illustrated by the following story:

G. H. She is 26, had a very unhappy childhood, mainly due to the influence of a domineering mother and unsuccessful competition with a slightly older brother. Ever since she can remember she has been possessed by a burning desire for independence; she could not bear to owe anything to anyone, least of all gratitude. She is an ardent feminist, cannot tolerate being contradicted by a man. She always envied men for being men. She thinks that women must always work hard and honestly, but men can live on their wits. She has wanted a lover and a child, but not marriage. It is patently clear that it was no easy matter to marry such an untamed shrew, nor can it have been easy for her to marry.

He is 28 years old, of slight build and gentle manners. He too had a most unhappy childhood caused by an insensitive and tyrannical father. A sense of inferiority, inevitable under these circumstances, held his development back and prevented him from cultivating his natural gifts. Coming from a distinguished country family he felt and behaved like an upstart in the world of high finance in London into which he was thrown by his marriage.

The combination of these two people, unsuited for each other, and both of them for marriage, held little promise of success, and this was in fact the only promise that was kept in this marriage. But why did these two choose each other of all people? Partly because they fell in love with each other, even passionately as they said. Partly for typical neurotic reasons; to her he appeared as an easy prey for her desire to dominate, and she was not slow in satisfying this desire after they were married. He, in a kind of self-defence, resorted to brutality in the form of 'mental cruelty', as all these men do if they feel that they do not possess sufficient personal 'weight', not enough genuine strength, to secure the measure of authority which they so passionately desire. The tragicomic part of this sorry affair was that each of them was firmly resolved under no circumstances to become like their parents – yet as soon as the opportunity arose, he was as tyrannical as his father, and she as domineering as her mother.

But he did something still worse to her: he grew up, at last. He became very successful in his business, grew in stature and respect among his colleagues, and before very long she found herself living in the shadow of a 'strong' man. 'This is no longer the boy I married,' she wailed. She did all in her power to obstruct his emancipation, and, at last, she insisted that all his success he owed to her.

Thus he had won the battle of life but lost the battle of love – and she too. The sexuality in this marriage was a complete failure, as it ought to be, in that he was almost impotent and she frigid. For sexuality means final Truth; in sexual matters one cannot deceive oneself or anyone else. His success in business was only an external success, as it were, a success of some of his practical faculties. But he himself, his personal substance, his real self, were still frail, and, as it is precisely this central part of ourselves that enters into the conjugal and, particularly, the sexual union, this man could not stand up to his wife, and failed sexually.

It is always very difficult to make men understand this seeming inconsistency, that they feel equal, if not superior, to their male competitors in business, but capitulate ignominiously to a woman. And she, like so many, but by no means all, neurotic women, regained in bed a part of her genuine feminine Self, and became submissive and receptive. 'It is nice,' she often said to him, 'when you are masterful.' 'Why don't you take what you want and be a man?' These poor women do not realize that they cannot have it both ways: no man can be their slave during the day and their master at night. And still more important, they cannot know that even their submissiveness has a false ring, is, however slightly, demanding. This is what their neurotic partners, oversensitive to any trace of coercion, sense, dread, and resent. This is the tragic comedy of errors in a neurotic marriage.

This case, as I said before, is typical of innumerable marriages. The structure of these neurotic marriages is formed by the interaction of six character traits, the varying proportion of which produces slightly different combinations, while the pattern remains the same. These traits are, first, the normal parts in the personality of the man and the woman, which have selected each other because they are in love with each other. Then the primary neurotic elements in both. His inferiority complex causes the man to choose a stronger wife on whom he can rely and who can take on the responsibilities and decisions of ordinary life. But every inferiority complex automatically produces its over-compensation; thus his sense of pseudo-strength causes the husband to misinterpret his wife's real strength as undue 'superiority' and her genuine support as intolerable domination. Thus, one part of his neurotic self resents precisely what the other part badly needs, so that practically everything his wife does appears offensive and reprehensible. Through the complex interaction of these three elements in her husband's nature, many a quite normal wife finds herself forced into an over-activity quite alien to her feminine nature, and resents bitterly the unfairness of the implication of being domineering. The inferiority complex of the wife, on the other hand, makes her choose, not as one would have expected a strong man, but on the contrary a weak one from whom she would not have to be afraid of being dominated. But her compensatory superiority complex, if I may say so, makes her choose a man seemingly stronger than she thinks she is to whom she may yield without losing face.[1]

1. This problem, in all its ramifications, is admirably presented by the German epos *The Nibelungen*, known all over the world in the version of Wagner's operas of the same name. Brunhilde, the virginal queen, had made a vow to accept as husband only a man who could defeat her in various athletic contests. King Gunther, who was in love with her but despaired of winning her under these conditions, persuaded his friend Siegfried to assist him in the combat by making himself invisible by means of his magic cap. The trick succeeded and Brunhilde became

But really masculine men do not, at least as a rule, marry neurotic women, nor can a real woman be deceived by the boisterous antics of a neurotic man. And this is fortunate, because the peculiar mutual attraction of neurotics lead to a kind of mutual neutralization of these socially and eugenically defective people, and protects normal people from much unhappiness. But we should not rely too much on the 'common sense' and salutary precaution of Nature, particularly as it is the idea and purpose of our technical civilization to assist Nature when her aims coincide with ours and correct her if they do not. Applying this warning to our problem would mean the prevention by legislation of marriage between people so unsuitable as those in the above-cited case. Psychological treatment would have prevented a good deal of damage, and every psychologist knows how much better the chances of treatment are when undertaken when the candidates are still free agents, and before incessant conflicts in their married life have too much embittered husband and wife against each other. And – still more important – before the psychological contagion, as it were, has been transmitted to the children. The couple whose story has given rise to this analysis had a child, a 4-year-old boy, who showed every prospect of becoming an expert neurotic himself. For some time he had done all sorts of things which were bound to annoy his mother. One day when his mother, tired of perpetually warning, scolding and punishing him, decided to ignore his doings, the child cried indignantly: 'But, Mummy, don't you notice how naughty I am?' Is more proof needed that a good deal of the mischief done by children, and adults as well, is deliberately 'designed', consciously as in this case, subconsciously in others, for a purpose? This behaviour of children is a forerunner of neurotic symptoms later in life, or more precisely it is already a symptom of a neurosis *in statu nascendi.* No doubt a compulsory premarital health control implies infringement of the freedom of the individual. But freedom is not a value in itself, and it

---

Gunther's wife. Shortly afterwards she discovered the fraud and her fury knew no bounds. This, by the way, is another illustration of the fact that all the basic psychological problems which modern science has proudly discovered were already well known to ancient peoples laid down in religious and profane literature.

is worth curtailing it if the sacrifice contributes so much to the well-being of the individual as well as of the community.

There is still another matrimonial problem which assumes ever-increasing importance in these days: the marriage of a professional woman. Actually this problem confronts any woman who has a full-time job, but it is more urgent among women in the professions – doctors, members of the legal profession, artists, journalists, and the like – because these women invest not only their time but also a good deal of their personalities in their work. The problem arises because the husband of such a woman feels that his wife's interest is divided between him and her profession. And yet, I wonder, whether we are here confronted with a genuine problem inherent in the nature of marriage? Even on a cursory examination it is obvious that in many such cases the husband's grievances are due to his unwillingness to revise his traditional ideas about his rights and the wife's duties in marriage: he takes it for granted that his wife should patiently wait until he comes home from his work, he expects her to be in full sympathy with his worries and to respect obediently his tiredness; but he is unwilling to concede the same privileges to her. Still worse, he is incapable of realizing that only the accidental or external elements of her personality belong to the world and her work; resentment of the fact that in this stratum of her life he does not 'possess' her blinds him to the far more important fact that the true core of her womanliness 'belongs' to him and to no one else; he resents her work, success, and fame, instead of being proud that this celebrated woman is his wife.

But in many cases neurosis, in the husband or the wife or both, creates or aggravates the problem. The husband asks: Is all this really necessary? Is she not overdoing her independence? Is it really a calling she is following, or is she only misusing her work as a compensation for her feminine inferiority? Is she not busying herself so much in order to escape her duties as a housewife? The answer to these questions is that it may be so and often enough is. But experience shows that many of the professionally most successful women are equally successful wives and mothers, while the neurotic busybodies fail both in their jobs as well as in their attempts at escaping their household duties. On the other hand, a husband's own sense of inferiority sharpens his instinct for his wife's neurotic antics and often causes him to mistake her genuine professional interest for a neurotic imitation. However, it is one of the most difficult tasks in life to be the husband of a successful woman.

And here is a bit of practical advice. More than once I have been asked by such a woman whether she should give in to the plea, or demand, of her husband to give up her work for the sake of the success of the marriage. Invariably I have warned her not to do it, mainly for two reasons. First, such a possessive husband is like a blackmailer, and a blackmailer can never be satisfied: first it is the job, then a pet animal, and so on, until in the end the woman has neither a job nor a marriage. Besides, a marriage which can be maintained only on such conditions is not worth maintaining. Secondly, it may be comparatively easy for a woman to give up a little shop round the corner, but if a woman is forced to give up her real work she loses an essential part of herself and is no longer the woman her husband knew and married. On the other hand, it is a very different situation if a happily married woman voluntarily gives up her job, because she feels that it has lost its place in her life which now belongs in its entirety to her marriage.

I have analysed this problem at some length because it seems to be a truly impressive illustration of the nature of marriage: the amount of time that husband and wife spend together is not material, their outside interests need not be identical, nor need there be maintained between them the traditional, and therefore so readily proclaimed to be the 'natural', distribution of superiority and inferiority, or rights and duties. The bond that keeps the two together is the sense of belonging and sharing – and nothing else. But if this bond does not exist a marriage is hollow and is held together only by accidental factors and external means which in themselves cannot carry the burden. Then it matters a great deal whether the woman has a quick drink with her colleagues after office hours instead of hurrying home, whether she wants to go to a straight play when he would prefer a musical show or to stay at home. Trifling disagreements may grow into catastrophes when the essential and genuine trust is absent. Neurotic jealousy then destroys the last bit of confidence and seizes upon the most harmless facts as proofs and justifications – a woman friend is suspected of being a Lesbian seducer, the housekeeper a tyrant, and even a child is a dangerous competitor for a wife's love. The changing social status of women does not of itself provoke a crisis in marriage, it only unmasks outmoded prejudices, and reveals the sham happiness of marriages which are built on superficial attraction but lack the essential marital union.

*

From all I have said about the nature and meaning of sex as well as about the idea of marriage it must be by now abundantly clear that matrimonial difficulties must necessarily affect the sexual relationship of husband and wife. Apart from relatively few exceptions, sexual differences are never the cause of matrimonial troubles, but their effect, and in many ways it is true to say that sexuality is the most sensitive and reliable seismograph indicating rumbles in the deeper strata of the marriage when the surface appears to be still quiet.

The cases of impotence of men in marriage can be divided roughly into three groups. The first one comprises men who had no sexual experience before marriage. If such a man seeks professional advice as to whether he is fit for marriage he confronts the doctor with a very delicate task. If a young man has abstained from sexual relations on moral grounds, essential for him and voluntarily accepted, he stands a good chance of properly succeeding in his sexual function in marriage. That even under these circumstances the novice may have to face considerable difficulties has been explained in detail in a previous chapter of this book. If his abstinence has been forced upon the young man by external authorities, to which he had only unwillingly submitted, the risks of failure when this pressure is suddenly lifted are considerably greater. But the situation is radically different when we have to deal with a case, not of continence, but of repression; that is to say, if the man did not, more or less voluntarily, abstain from sexual contacts, but, subconsciously, repressed his sexual desires and therefore could not have satisfaction however much he may have wished and tried. This man is a patient suffering from neurotic impotence, and it is a sign of unforgivable ignorance and almost criminal carelessness on the part of his advisers to comfort such a man by saying that all will be well after he has married. It never is. For marriage is a task and achievement, but no remedy for neurotic symptoms.

To the second group belong the men who had sufficient sexual experience before they got married, and much to their surprise fail completely with their wives. We have, in a previous chapter, analysed this type of impotence: these men are capable of having a mere affair, i.e. a temporary relation, but they are not yet capable of entering a permanent one. Also in these cases the diagnosis is: neurotic immaturity with ensuing impotence. It is to their credit how patiently most of these young wives bear their misfortune; some others seek and find satisfaction for their irrepressible desire elsewhere; a few bitterly resent the fraud, however unwittingly committed, and these cases are the relatively few exceptions in which sexual trouble leads to grave conflicts and eventually to divorce or annulment.

The third type of matrimonial impotence follows a period of satisfactory sexual relationship during marriage. These incidents indicate, as I said before, that something has gone wrong in the marital relationship. Every neurotic symptom is a clandestine means of withdrawing from an unwanted situation, which one is unwilling to continue and afraid of breaking up overtly. Hence, a man who produces impotence at some stage of his married life sends out a coded message, as it were, saying 'I have had enough; I want to get out'. These men, like those of the second group, were willing and, therefore, capable of staying on for a while, but are driven out of this relationship – which is erroneously termed marriage but is actually just an affair – as soon as they begin to feel the burden of finality which they are not yet capable of carrying. Curiously enough only very few of them intend a divorce; most of them would be quite happy to let things be as they are, if only they could be relieved of their sexual duties and keep their wives as companions and housekeepers. And many a wife accepts this revision of the marriage contract.

Far less conspicuous and far-reaching in its effects is frigidity, the feminine form of impotence. The fact that a large number of married women are frigid without making much fuss about it proves in itself that these women are quite prepared to carry on their marriages without sexual satisfaction. And as only very few men notice or care much for their partners' lack of satisfaction, frigidity is only seldom the cause of matrimonial friction.

Neurotic marriages are not irremediable, even when the conflicts are serious, if only there is a sincere desire on both sides to save the marriage. Any kind of advice, of course, however well meant and authoritatively given, is utterly useless; the only chance is a proper psychological treatment of the neurosis of one, sometimes of both partners. Even the treatment of one partner is often very successful, for marriage is such a subtle system of action and reaction that changes in the behaviour of one partner almost automatically change the reaction of the other one. This kind of medical work, sometimes strenuous and difficult, is often enough a most gratifying task for a psychologist if he commands expert knowledge, endless patience, and a great deal of experience in human affairs.

Very different, on the other hand, is the task of a psychologist and the chances of his success if the marriage as such is seriously ill or already dead. In such cases undue optimism, all too often based on moral rigorism, does more harm than good, and therapeutic efforts, however well meant, are usually wasted. The admission, 'I simply do not love him (or her) any more', must be understood in its hopeless finality in those mistaken marriages which are actually only protracted affairs. Again, 'This is no longer the man (or woman) I married' pronounces the same doom for a marriage in which the partners have grown away from each other. These cases are hopeless, not because the two people are unwilling to go on living together, but because they are incapable of doing so. And we doctors are powerless because no material is left with which the marriage could be rebuilt. To force the two to carry on with the sordid business because of the 'sanctity of marriage' or 'for the sake of the children' or for any other reason is not only inhuman but entirely beyond the domain of our professional duty and capacity. But so is also the advice to part. This, like any other factual decision, must always be left to the people themselves. Our power to help has come to an end when we have made them understand the situation, have sorted out the assets and debits of their marriage and assessed the measure of solvency remaining in it.

*

We have in this chapter on marriage said a good deal about the difficulties and failures of marriage. This is not due to the fact that a professional man gains his experience almost exclusively from his clientèle, that is, from people who have failed badly, and that he is liable to forget the vast number of people who do not need his help - or at least think they do not. The real reason lies in the complex structure of marriage and the great demands a happy marriage makes on the emotional and moral health of men and women. Even what constitutes happiness in marriage is controversial, and the question how many marriages are really happy may appear to many people almost a blasphemy, yet there is more in it than one might think. E. Kretschmer, for instance, professor of psychiatry and world-renowned for his book, *Physique and Character*, studied 100 marriages with all the paraphernalia of modern psychological analysis and came to the conclusion that only eleven of them could be pronounced perfectly harmonious. Seven of these successful couples belonged to the 'pyknic' type, that is to say, they were rotund, placid, easy-going people, who lived in a homely 'kettle on the hob' atmosphere. This, I am sorry to say, leaves to tall, slim, and mentally agile people a slender chance of being happily married: not more than 4 out of 100!

But, what, if anything, does this concept of happiness mean if applied to marriage? We were anxious to investigate objectively the nature of marriage and discovered a certain number of characteristics of what one may call a real and true marriage. The human mind, being what it is, tends to turn, automatically, objective data into postulates, thus changing characteristics into criteria, so that every marriage that does not show all the essential characteristics appears imperfect or subnormal. But these imperfect marriages need not by any means be unhappy, although a certain number of them are. Happiness on the other hand is a term of the subjective sphere and is so vague that it is almost impossible to define it. The only somewhat satisfactory meaning one could give to it is 'being content with things as they are'. When one applies this criterion to marriage, one will be astonished, to put it mildly, how little people need to feel content. The ancient Roman lawyers defined marriage as *connubium et commercium*, which means living together and sleeping together. By this standard most marriages are 'happy'. Most of all these 'jog-trot' marriages in which the husband returning home from business is content and happy if he finds a hot meal ready, not too much bother with the children waiting for his arbitration, and his wife willing if he wants to go to bed with her and not too tiresome if he does not feel like it. And if on higher levels some 'cultural' activities and interests are added to this bare minimum it does not amount to very much more. These marriages which mainly cater for the biological or vital needs of body and mind stand at the lower end of the scale; at the other end stands the exemplary marriage and therefore happy in the truest sense of the word. The broad stratum in between these two types is the domain of the difficult, problematic, unhappy marriages. It would be incorrect to assume that all marriages of this group are unhappy, but they carry in themselves the seed of potential unhappiness; these people have largely lost the instinctive security of the simple and straightforward life and have not yet acquired sense and strength to cope with the growing complexity of a higher stage of civilization. It would not be quite fair to identify these three groups with the tripartite stratification of society, although it may be true that complicated marriages are more frequent in higher social strata – partly because these people are more complex personalities, partly because the harder struggle for existence, caused by the anxiety and uncertainty of their livelihood compared with the security of the weekly pay-packet, makes them more vulnerable and less tolerant.[1]

It is really surprising how many of the elements essential for marriage may be missing without affecting the apparent, and perhaps even more than apparent, happiness of these marriages. And optimistic obscurantists who emphatically insist

1. But how careful one must be with such, however plausible, generalizations is shown by the following figures: American statistics prove that in country districts the divorce rate was almost 75 per cent above the national average (6·2 per 1,000 population *v.* 3·6 per 1,000 in the U S. as a whole).

that all is well with marriage conditions among a population to which they happen to belong must be warned that a great amount of professional knowledge is required to see behind the façade. Surprisingly many couples live quite happily together even after their sexual relations have long ceased to exist. Husband or wife or both may have affairs with the knowledge and acquiescence of their partner, and no shadow need be cast on the happiness of their marriages. In other cases sexual relations are the only bond when other interests have diverged widely. I know more than one such person who would hotly deny that anything is wrong with their marriage and honestly assert that the idea of divorce has never entered their minds. On the other hand, it is more than doubtful whether the opposite type of marriage represents an ideal, marriages in which husband and wife are immersed in each other, self-contained, standing, as it were, face to face with each other, turning their backs to the world. However happy these two may feel, great risks lie in store for them: monotony, unproductiveness and, most dangerous of all, awakening. In not too many of these marriages this attitude springs from genuine mutual devotion, in many more the motives are less sincere: he or she clings to the partner out of a sense of weakness, and what they want is not completion but support. Unless the extreme vanity of the stronger thrives on this dependence, the instability of these marriages is obvious. And it is obvious, too, that marriages much less closely knit correspond much more to the idea of marriage: marriages in which each partner enjoys a large measure of independence and goes, to a certain extent, his own way; coming home after the day's work has been done, each time freshly reunited, enriched, and enriching each other.

Curiously enough many marriages in which one of the partners is very much older than the other – differences of twenty to thirty years are not so infrequent as one would think – are most successful. Although they show many characteristics of marriage, sometimes even including sexual activities, one cannot help feeling that the younger partners are somewhat abnormal, a suspicion that can be substantiated whenever opportunity is given to probe into their psychology. The obvious infantilism of these young men and women makes them seek security more than anything else, which is gladly provided by the otherwise frustrated parental instinct of the older partners. This mutual assistance makes for stability and 'happiness'. Even incessant quarrels, as long as they are only quarrels about superficial divergencies and not conflicts due to essential problems, often do not affect the cohesion of a marriage. And this leads to a conclusion of really impressive absurdity: all the seemingly 'happy' marriages of the diverse type just mentioned are essentially unreal, in spite of their subjective happiness; whereas those marriages which are at breaking-point but cannot be broken, those 'life sentences', are through their existential cohesion essentially real! 'There are more things in Heaven and Earth ...'

If I had to present the problem of marriage in a nutshell, I would say that the final reason for the unsuccessful marriages of otherwise normal people is the fact that the wrong partners have been chosen. This, of course, is not a discovery of striking novelty. On the other hand, if one probes only slightly below the surface of the truism one finds oneself confronted with the difficulty of defining what a 'right' partner is. It is only fair to admit that we are not in a position to answer this question and in all probability never shall be. A right partner is not a man or woman who possesses certain qualities and faculties which correspond with similar or complementary opposite qualities and faculties in the other partner. This coincidence is helpful, but it is neither a guarantee of success nor does its absence necessarily produce failure. The previously mentioned conditions under which marriages often fail are not the causes of failure, but only increased risks, as there are, for instance, numerous happy marriages between people of different races, social status, etc. It is a mysterious selective power which brings the 'right' man together with the 'right' woman on the ground of an existential harmony and not as the result of a careful calculation. Or, to put the same idea in other words: There are people who are, as we say, 'integrated' or 'real personalities' or 'true characters'. We mean by these terms that everything these people feel, think, say, or do falls in an intelligible pattern. Consequently their lives have style, they are laws unto themselves, nothing just happens to them but all events are necessary and inevitable effects of this law. It seems as if a mysterious destiny governs their lives, but this is only a poetic metaphor for a very real sequence of psychological cause and effect. Among other decisions the choice of a marriage partner springs from this pattern, and is made with instinctive and unfailing certainty. The partner is the 'right' one because he fits into this personality pattern.

That so many people choose wrong partners and make similar grievous mistakes in other walks of life is due to the fact that they belong to the lower orders of humanity. That means that they are not closely knit personalities but rather bundles of qualities and faculties, and consequently they grope in a haze, make haphazard decisions less directed by an inner centre than caused by accidental circumstances. It is a privilege of the select to have a destiny, and of their marriages it can be said that they are made in heaven.

There is still another aspect of this problem which may be just mentioned in passing, without any pretence of doing justice to it. Every now and then a woman asks: 'Why is it that I always seem to choose the wrong partner?' In many cases we already know the answer: owing to his erroneous style of life a person is bound to repeat the same mistake. If, for instance, a woman, in order to assert herself, always chooses an inferior man, she must not be surprised if she always gets one; if a woman wants first of all a rich husband, she cannot complain if the personalities of these men are not always satisfactory; if a man out of vanity always chooses women far above his own standard it is almost inevitable that he is asking for trouble. But this is not as yet the whole answer. Sometimes it is obvious that the repetition of a wrong choice is no fault of the chooser. One cannot help feeling that it is just bad luck. Curiously enough, philosophers and psychologists are far from being agreed on whether there is such a thing as luck, good or bad. Fortunately we need not enter into the argument, and I mention it only as a warning that we must not always blame a patient for something which may have been beyond his responsibility, but that we must at least give him the benefit of the doubt.

Apart from these marriages which are doomed from their start because they were contracted in ignorance of the essential nature of marriage, the undoubtedly increasing number of unhappy marriages is due to the fact that we are rapidly losing the capacity of instinctively selecting the 'right' partner, and that we try to compensate for this defect by conscious planning. Thus, the much-heralded crisis of marriage appears only as a part of a much wider issue. Our whole mode of living has lost its roots in the reality of Life and is to an ever-increasing degree based on the uncertainties of Reason. Deafened by the blare of loudspeakers all around us, blinded by the glare of neon lights, numbed by the growing vulgarity of our everyday life, we can no longer listen to the 'tiny stuffless voices' of our intimate nature. True, reasoning is the specific power and adventure of man, but it becomes a constructive force only through working on, elaborating, recasting reality previously grasped by our instincts. Just as psychology can never replace common sense, but can only assist it, so reason can only reinforce instinct. Psychology is the science of human life, but Life is bigger than Science. The physical universe may soon yield its last secret to the unrelenting onslaught of science, but the human mind is, and in all probability always will be, inscrutable.

CHAPTER 11

# JOURNEY'S END

SEX is the only biological function that comes to an end long before the organism as a whole stops functioning, that is, before death. People who believe that everything in life has a purpose and enjoy speculating about the wisdom of Nature will easily find a good reason for the premature cessation of a function which dominates so much of our lives. And it may well be, as is assumed, that the means for propagation are withdrawn when the ageing organism is no longer fit for this purpose and the ageing person no longer suitable to be a parent.

As the female's part in propagation is so much more important than that of the male, it is understandable that the cessation of the sexual function in the female comes earlier in life and is more radical than in the male. The 'change of life', as it is commonly called – the professional term is 'climacteric' – takes place round about the fifties and lasts a year or eighteen months. The anatomical cause of this tremendous change in a woman's life is the degeneration of the ovaries. These organs, which through nearly four decades have produced the most vital cells and the most vitalizing hormones, are at the end of the process of involution nothing more than small hard lumps of connective tissue. The outward sign of this process is an ever-increasing irregularity of the menstruation, a symptom noticed by many women with sorrow and apprehension and greeted with relief only by a few. The final cessation of the menstruation marks the end of a woman's life as a sexual being and the beginning of old age.

Many women suffer a great deal from all kinds of pshyical symptoms during this period of transition. Some of these disturbances are directly due to the cessation of the ovarian function; they cannot be avoided, but can be greatly relieved by injections of hormones. The rest, surprising as it may sound, are of a purely psychological nature. Experience has shown that women who have led a harmonious life, in harmony with themselves as well as with outer circumstances, accepting all that life has brought to them, enjoying changing pleasures according to the passing years and accepting the gradual restrictions which these passing years impose on them – for these womanly, in the truest sense of the word normal, women the 'change of life' means not a sharp break but just one of many other changes, and they slide gradually, gracefully, down the unnoticeably declining curve of life. For them, the approach of old age holds no terror and, therefore, the climacteric produces no symptoms. Once more, for the last time, they adapt themselves to new circumstances and acquire a poise and dignity which culminate in a new kind of beauty.

The other type comprises women who have lived in disharmony within and without, who have spent and wasted their lives in a hopeless struggle against imaginary foes within themselves and in the outer world. They led a dissatisfied life full of disappointments, and as they always hoped the next day would at last bring the always hoped-for and always elusive happiness, they suffered incessant defeat from their arch-enemy Time. The stakes in this great gamble were their female attractions, and sexuality was the field on which they cashed in on their dubious gains. The threatening loss of these funds must leave them in fear of bankruptcy, and the lack of other resources robs them of their only reason for being. No wonder that so often this struggle against the inevitable is not fought in the best of taste, and too often the pathetic is turned into the ridiculous.

The worst of all is that all these worries are unnecessary, based on the erroneous conception that together with their menstruation women also lose their sexual desire and capacity for enjoying its satisfaction. This opinion was commonly held up till not long ago, apparently mostly by men who did not, or did not want to, know better, and those women who did were, for obvious reasons, probably not too anxious to reveal the truth. But experienced gynaecologists know that the majority of women keep their sexual life many years after the menopause. This fact, enjoyable in itself, presents an uncomfortable problem to those who believe that everything in life must have a purpose, and that the only purpose of sex is to produce children.

*

The situation is quite different with men. First of all there is no indication that the testicles ever cease to function. That the testicles still produce male hormones has been proved with men of the age of between 60 and 92. It is of course only natural that the testicles take part in the general involution of the male organism, but it is a harmonious ageing, and the testicles are never older, so to speak, than the whole man. Hence we are not justified in applying the term 'climacteric' to any phase in a man's life, that is to say, no symptoms, sexual or otherwise, with old men can be explained as due to an insufficient functioning of the testicles. It is true that some men between 50 and 55 pass through a peculiar period. They complain about trouble with their hearts and digestive organs, their energy decreases and they feel they are getting old; a strange irritability and depression complicate the condition. True enough that is a dangerous age for men, as nearly two-thirds of of all men die in the sixth decade of hardening of the arteries and consequent heart-failure, so that a certain nervousness and inclination to hypochondria is natural. But the symptoms of which we are speaking here are of a very different nature, and most if not all of them disappear within one or two years, and these men recapture their joy of life and efficiency.

For both sexes this age means the threshold of old age, the problem of death becomes a reality and they have to face it in a new way. And this way is quite different for men and women: for both sexes it is a kind of taking stock, but for women it is retrospective, for men prospective. Women must ask themselves what kind of life they have behind them; have they accumulated funds which will support them during the quiet years to come? Women are asked by Fate what use they have made of their chances, whereas men ask their Fate what chances they may still have. In order to make this clearer we must briefly consider the whole situation of a man of about 50. At this age a normal man ought to have reached the summit of his life. His economic and social position should be assured, the future of his family safe, the life of his children roughly designed – in one word, a considerable measure of stability should have been achieved. This ideal course is by no means the rule. The man whose subsistence depends on hard physical labour must face with apprehension the time when his physical strength will decline. Or at the other end of the scale, a highly differentiated man whose complex personality makes for a highly complicated life, or a man in big business whose great responsibilities may still increase rather than decrease, must watch with alarm the slightest decline of his physical and mental capacities. The growing tension between the still ascending curve of a man's tasks and the declining curve of his psycho-physical condition is cause and measure of his 'climacteric' trouble. And in a way one could assume that a pension would be a safe prevention of it all.

Does the sexuality of these ageing men fit into this general scheme of their lives? It cannot be denied that with a large number of men their sex life comes to an end round about the middle of the sixth decade: often enough without much ado, one may say, because many of them find this quite natural and accept it without complaint. But others refuse to bow to what they feel is neither natural nor inevitable, and call for help. Can it be given? No statistical figures are available which could help to say whether and to what extent, least of all how far in a given case, the resignation of the first or the insistence of the second group represents the norm. Nor is it helpful to know that some men keep their sexuality more or less intact for much longer, because they may be rare exceptions. I suggest as a working hypothesis to apply the principle that every sexual abnormality is a psychological phenomenon, even to men who lose their potency before the age of 60. Failures of psychological treatment will be more frequent with this age-group than with younger men, but, I think, one should give these men at least the benefit of the doubt – the more so as there is very little else to be done.

The only alternative is recourse to the so-called rejuvenation operations. The best-known and most spectacular is the method suggested by Voronoff (Paris) who transplanted testicles of monkeys into his patients. In successful cases – and in spite of the acerbity of the criticism, it cannot be denied that there are a good many – the transformation of the physique of the patients is often astounding: they look ten years younger, regain their vitality, and, among other functions, the sexual is improved. But – and this is important – the sexual improvement is only part of the general rejuvenation, and if the organism is either too exhausted to be improved, or if the general health of the man is still too good to need improvement, an effect of the operation on the sexual function alone cannot be expected. Moreover, of all partial improvements the sexual is the least reliable, inasmuch as even in otherwise successful cases the sexual function need not necessarily take part in the general rejuvenation. Consequently, every such operation is hardly more than an experiment with uncertain chances, and in no case should it be advised as a cure for sexual deficiency alone.

Thus psychological treatment remains the method of choice, and we find ourselves confronted with the familiar question what the psychological cause of this impotence may be. The answer is the same as in any other case of sexual difficulties: a deficient sense of virility. In a fairly large group of cases this is due to the above-mentioned tension between the gradually decreasing vitality and the still heavy demands on a man's energy. This difference produces a definite sense of growing inadequacy, and as sexuality is very sensitive to even a slight disturbance of our psychophysical budget, it is only to be expected that the sexual capacities of these men suffer first and most. A second reason is that sexuality more and more loses its importance as men grow older, and occupational worries take its place. But as sexuality is, apparently, very sensitive to such a loss of prestige, it withdraws if it is no longer wholeheartedly wanted. This motive is the cause why in many marriages sexual relations between husband and wife cease during these critical years. It is not that through habit and the familiarity of many years of married life the wife loses attraction for her husband; we know by now that these things do not exist. The real cause is that the marriage has ceased to be a living union, and that other interests, pleasant and unpleasant, have become dominant: not the physical potency of the man is dying, but the incentive to employ it.

Generally speaking, a man keeps his sexual capacity as long as proper sexuality occupies an essential part in his life. The emphasis lies on the word 'proper' because the basic laws of love and sex are operative in the late autumn of life as well as in the spring. There are men, for instance, who have enjoyed a perfectly normal sexuality all their lives, yet in later years were for some reason or another denied a proper relationship with an adequate partner; but as sexuality has always been an essential part of their lives they succumb to the many temptations that come their way – they may even be fond of one or other of their partners – yet it can never be the real relationship: thus they lose their potency because they have betrayed the essential nature of sex – and their own.

The third reason for a climacteric loss of potency has a slight element of the tragic in it. We remember the type of woman who, for want of anything better, has built up her whole life on her female attraction and tries in the later part of life to retain this small basis of her existence at all costs, and who breaks down if this illusion cannot be kept up any longer. She finds her counterpart in a type of man who has adopted the same policy, with the difference that he uses the chimera of authority as a tonic for his self-esteem. Yet this illusion cannot be maintained for ever: children grow up and outgrow the sphere of paternal influence, the so far tenaciously held hope of success which never came cannot be sustained any longer, a new generation of Josephs grows up, which knows nothing of the Pharaohs of the past, and gradually – sometimes quite suddenly – this illusion of power collapses. Or there are men who reach maturity rather late and laboriously climb the zenith of their lives, so that at this time many an idea on principle which, in earlier times, had been taken for right and final proves temporary or definitely wrong. Such disappointments and delusions often enough shake a not too stable faith in values and confidence in one's own judgement and leave such men in a shattered world of scepticism, cynicism, and despair.

Thus the period we are discussing appears as the last phase of the lifelong struggle of man against Time. Whatever philosophers may say about the nature of Time, from a psychological point of view, Time is the greatest power in man's life; it moves on relentlessly, completely indifferent to man's wishes and fears, and those who fall out of step are left on the roadside. The attitude of a person towards Time is an unfailing test of his mental, particularly his emotional, health. Health in this context means to be aware of and keep pace with the flow of Time and to adjust oneself to the changes which that flow entails. It is often difficult for parents to realize that their children have grown up, but it is equally, or more, difficult for many a young man and woman to realize that they are grown up, and being no longer subject to their parents' authority, can no longer rely on parental care and protection either. This is the time-problem of the young. The main characteristic of the state of maturity is to live firmly rooted in the present, to be able to forget past pleasures without wallowing in sentimental memories, as well as to forget past failures without lapsing into a gloomy sense of inferiority. And finally, when we grow old we must have learnt to accept this unpleasant fact, however young we may still feel, and preserve the poise and decorum befitting our age. The art of timing is an essential part of the art of living. The healthy adult knows the virtue of patience. He understands the symbolic meaning of the change of the seasons: he feels respect for the mystery of growing and ripening, and faces serenely the inevitable decay.

Immature and neurotic people cannot accept Time as the supreme ruling force of human life, but see in it a hostile power against which they battle incessantly and without hope. Some waste Time light-heartedly, oblivious to the irreparable loss, others grudge Time, and being over-anxious to fill every minute with something 'useful', are incapable of enjoying leisure. They try to defy the compulsion of Time by being deliberately – although often unconsciously – unpunctual, or they submit, in a cowardly fashion, as it were, by being always much earlier than they need be.

These are only minor troubles, ruffling the surface of everyday life, but there is a major problem going down to the roots of human existence. Among scientists the view is widely accepted that the basic difference between Man and the animals is that animals, as I mentioned previously, are particles of the stream of life, forming it and being swept along by its current: for instance, they feed when they are hungry and stop feeding when they are satiated, they sleep when they are tired, and die when their organism is worn out. Man, on the other hand, has been given the fateful capacity to step out of this stream, to make use of it and even to divert it if necessary – less metaphorically speaking, the capacity to make 'a beginning and an end'. This existential capacity is the real substance of such well-worn concepts as free will, making decisions, taking on responsibility, facing the consequences. In short, life happens to animals, but Man is the maker of his destiny. I wonder how many people are aware how often in their workaday lives they are compelled to make use of this Pandora's gift. Many a writer knows a slight trepidation before he writes down the first sentence of a new book, because he knows that, having once 'made a beginning', he will live under the spell of his own creation, enslaved to a world of his own making. Still more difficult is it, perhaps, to 'make an end', because hardly any book is really 'finished'; it is only cut short because end somewhere it must. And the same thing happens whenever we sign a contract, call off a deal, enter into a new relationship. And what a welter of responsibility is unleashed when a surgeon begins an operation with the first incision into the skin.

No wonder that this task – to master Time by ordering a fragment of Time to begin, as it were, or to end it when necessary – is an insuperable one for the neurotic. Ridden by fear, these people endeavour to divest themselves of their human prerogative and to revert to the demi-paradise of a subhuman existence. They want things to happen to them, and they prefer submissiveness to mastery. Nowhere is this attitude more visible than in matters of sex, and it is true to say that every sexual symptom is an attempt to avoid coping with Time: the sexual act represents a 'beginning' of tremendous magnitude – new life; marriage means to 'put an end' to the independent existence of youth, to begin a totally different kind of existence, togetherness with another person, and it is meant to last for ever, which means voluntarily deciding that there shall be no end – surely the most drastic solution to the problem of 'ending'.

The change of life is the climax of this struggle, and the climacteric symptoms are the last distant rumble of a battle lost. Also from this angle the gradual cessation of sex is understandable. The art of timing is also the art of loving: it is part of the charm of an affair that it is passing, part of the virtue of marriage that it is lasting, and part of the wisdom of ageing to realize that the pleasures of the past are no more. When we are getting old, Time seems to stand still because the prospects of a future shrink with the passing years. The spirit of conquest, such an important part of the sexual impetus, has almost gone; the relationship of husband and wife, established long ago, is now firm and secure, and many a tired heart settles down to the tranquillity of a peaceful evening.

Here we must recall for the last time the basic principle of human psychology: not the facts as such, that is to say not the circumstances, are responsible for our behaviour, but what matters decisively is our attitude towards them. An upright man will, at any stage of his life, meet in an upright manner increased demands on him – illness, disappointments, but also new insight into life and himself and the certainty of an approaching end. He will take them as material for the work, the piece of art, as which he has always shaped his life, and goes on shaping it to the end of his days. But if a neurotic man finds himself confronted with the same – in themselves rather trivial – adversities, a breakdown of his power to resist and of his confidence to cope with these facts is almost inevitable, simply because he 'interprets' them as warnings, as signals of an inevitable doom. As a matter of fact, a climacteric breakdown hardly ever comes as a surprise; it is, on a bigger scale perhaps, only a repetition of smaller similar experiences which such a man frequently passed through during his life. And this applies particularly to his sex life. It is perhaps not quite true in every case of climacteric impotence, but as a general rule it is safe to say that only a man who never was in full command of his sexual capacities is in danger of losing them during these critical years.

Although the 'climacteric' is only a passing phase in a man's life, and most of the symptoms disappear spontaneously after he has passed through it, the sexual trouble often establishes itself as a permanent impotence. But psychological treatment has a fair chance of success. As the trouble is based on an error of judgement, the psychologist, acting as a kind of chartered accountant, need only convince the patient that his assets still outweigh his debits, and that final bankruptcy is still far off. And he must persuade the patient to embrace philosophically the 'comfortable doctrine' of 'autumnal felicity' which Edward Gibbon propounds in the closing sentence of his autobiography: 'I will not suppose any premature decay of the mind or body, but I must reluctantly observe that two causes, the abbreviation of time and the failure of hope, will always tinge with a browner shade the evening of life.'

# INDEX

*(Words like 'sexuality', 'man', 'woman', which appear on almost every page, are not mentioned in the index. Italicized figures indicate important references.)*